Evolutionary and Genetic Biology of Primates

VOLUME I

Evolutionary and Genetic Biology
of Primates

A TREATISE IN TWO VOLUMES

Evolutionary and
Genetic Biology of
PRIMATES

Edited by JOHN BUETTNER-JANUSCH

Laboratory of Physical Anthropology, Department of Anthropology,
Yale University, New Haven, Connecticut

VOLUME I

1963

ACADEMIC PRESS
New York and London

ACADEMIC PRESS INC.
111 Fifth Avenue, New York 3, New York

United Kingdom Edition published by
ACADEMIC PRESS INC. (LONDON) LTD.
Berkeley Square House, London W.1

LIBRARY OF CONGRESS CATALOG CARD NUMBER: 63-16719

PRINTED IN THE UNITED STATES OF AMERICA

CONTRIBUTORS TO VOLUME I

M. A BENDER, *Biology Division, Oak Ridge National Laboratory, Oak Ridge, Tennessee*

JOHN BUETTNER-JANUSCH, *Laboratory of Physical Anthropology, Department of Anthropology, Yale University, New Haven, Connecticut*

E. H. Y. CHU, *Biology Division, Oak Ridge National Laboratory, Oak Ridge, Tennessee*

RICHARD A. ELLIS, *Arnold Biological Laboratory, Brown University, Providence, Rhode Island*

WILLIAM MONTAGNA,* *Arnold Biological Laboratory, Brown University, Providence, Rhode Island*

NORMAN MOSKOWITZ,† *Department of Anatomy, Columbia University, New York, New York*

CHARLES R. NOBACK, *Department of Anatomy, Columbia University, New York, New York*

ELWYN L. SIMONS, *Department of Geology and Peabody Museum, Yale University, New Haven, Connecticut*

R. K. WINKELMANN, *Section of Dermatology, Mayo Clinic and Mayo Foundation, Rochester, Minnesota*

---

* Present Address: Oregon Regional Primate Center, University of Oregon Medical School, Beaverton, Oregon.

† Present Address: Department of Anatomy, Jefferson Medical College, Philadelphia, Pennsylvania.

PREFACE

In this treatise we have attempted to present some landmarks of contemporary research on the Primates rather than an exhaustive treatment of the members of our own taxonomic order. Research on the Primates, *qua* Primates, is carried out in many different kinds of laboratories, field situations, and in several scientific disciplines. As a consequence of this diversity of interests it is necessary, at frequent intervals, to bring together people of different backgrounds and interests and those whose research goes in rather different directions. As physical anthropology, for example, becomes increasingly concerned with modern studies of the genetic and evolutionary biology of man, its interest has turned more and more to the genetic and evolutionary biology of other members of the order. We are presenting in these two volumes articles that cover some of the newer and developing research interests of contemporary students of the Primates. Physical anthropologists will be particularly interested in the diversity of research problems which bear upon the central question of primate and, of course, human evolution. However, the special interests of psychologists and sociologists are represented in some of the articles, and work of importance to histologists, anatomists, neurologists, geneticists, cytologists, and a host of other specialists are covered by the various authorities who have written the chapters.

We have included a number of articles which are oriented in a more classical direction to fill gaps in the existing literature and to show how closely the most modern work on Primates is connected to the vast work of the past. Because certain of the fields represented herein are so new to primatology and to such disciplines as physical anthropology and genetics, or are being rediscovered, some of the chapters are reports of work in progress, and others are prolegomena for research that is necessary to enhance our understanding of this order. We present a sample, and we believe it is a representative sample, of contemporary research on the Primates.

After the Editor read a number of the chapters, it was clear that an introduction to the entire order was required. Writing this introduction led to a serious consideration of the problems of primate classification. The first chapter is, thus, a preliminary to an eventual serious reorganization of the classification of the Primates. It is clear that some of the proposals made in that chapter are not, by any means, radical enough for a proper revision, and it is to be taken principally as a prologue to the complex and tangled problems of primate classification. The authors of the other chapters either take for granted the name list printed at the end of Chapter 1 or use Fiedler's very useful compilation. A number of problems in classification were evaded. It is clear that the genera *Macaca* and *Papio* are, in modern evolutionary terms, one genus. However, we decided to leave this problem for extensive treatment elsewhere. Some specific points were overlooked, such as the elimination of *Brachyteles* as a generic designation for *Ateles arachnoides;* where superseded terms have been used, a footnote has been inserted in the first instance and a cross reference provided in the index. The classification of fossil Primates with its problems is not discussed in the introductory chapter. The material is presented in detail by Dr. Simons in Chapter 2.

As we read the various chapters, we realized that some confusion over the use of the terms "Primates" and "primates" existed in many of the manuscripts. Lengthy discussions with certain authors, particularly Dr. Simons, and with the publisher led us to the following usage. When referring to the entire order or to animals as part of this order of mammals, we use "Primates," pronounced with three syllables. The more colloquial "primates," pronounced with two syllables, is used in all other contexts. Some of our British colleagues insist that primate (with no terminal *s*) must never be used as a noun, but only as an adjective, when referring to a member of the order Primates. We do not agree that any confusion is likely to occur. Contemporary usage, however, seems to be settling upon "primate" primarily as an adjective and "Primates" as the singular and plural form of the noun.

The extensive survey of contemporary research on the Primates in these two volumes includes much hitherto unpublished material and new work on fossils, biochemical genetics and cytogenetics, modern analyses of display and manipulative behavior, and the histochemistry and histology of the skin as well as studies of the anatomy and physiology of the Primates.

The Editor is grateful to each of the authors, whose patience, energy, and contributions to these two volumes are appreciated. In particular, we wish to acknowledge the most useful contribution of Mrs. Vera Deutsch who typed or retyped most of the manuscripts.

JOHN BUETTNER-JANUSCH

June, 1963

CONTENTS

1. An Introduction to the Primates

JOHN BUETTNER-JANUSCH

2. A Critical Reappraisal of Tertiary Primates

ELWYN L. SIMONS

7. The Chromosomes of Primates

M. A BENDER AND E. H. Y. CHU

CONTENTS OF VOLUME II

Chapter 1

An Introduction to the Primates

JOHN BUETTNER-JANUSCH

Laboratory of Physical Anthropology, Department of Anthropology, Yale University, New Haven, Connecticut

I. INTRODUCTION

The Order Primates groups together many different forms that live in a wide range of ecological provinces in Asia, Africa, Madagascar, Central America, and South America. The fossil remains of many kinds of Primates are found in Europe and North America as well as in the places where living forms occur. Only certain Pacific Islands, notably Australia, New Zealand, New Guinea, and the islands of Oceania, have not produced evidence of occupation by Primates before the arrival of the genus *Homo* on their shores. The present distribution of most Primates is primarily in tropical and subtropical regions. The genus *Homo* is an exception to this, as are the macaques of Japan, and certain monkeys of Asia whose ranges extend into the temperate latitudes of the northern part of India and the southern part of China.

There are many characteristics which set off the Primates from all other mammals. The most significant, in the adaptive and evolutionary sense, are unquestionably the opposable thumb and the grasping, manipulative extremities and the potentials that this ability implies. If the tree shrews are included among the Primates, such a simple distinguishing characteristic is not applicable. The Tupaiidae do not possess a fully developed grasping hand with an opposable thumb. Recent detailed studies of the hands of Primates by Napier (1960, 1961) and by Bishop (cf. Chapter 12 in Volume II), among others, show clearly that this grasping hand is a most complex trait. It is the basic adaptation which distinguishes the primate lineage from all others. Yet the multitude of variations on this fundamental trait strongly suggests that this is not a simple, primitive trait as has so often been thought. The plasticity of the hand in Primates, clearly demonstrated by Bishop's detailed analysis of prosimian manipulative behavior, argues against the view that the hand is a generalized structure. The impressive thing about the primate grasping organ is the variety of special anatomical forms in which it exists, yet its specialization does not seem to have led to an evolutionary dead end. The behavioral consequences of the basic grasping adaptation have apparently such a wide range of applications to varying ecological sites that specialization has not yet proved to be maladaptive.

The principal groups or taxa of Primates are listed next. This list is based on a recent discussion of primate taxonomy by Simpson (1962) as well as upon general consensus in recent literature devoted to the Primates. Each of these major taxa, which occupy different levels in the taxonomic system, are considered monophyletic in origin. The members of any one taxon are more closely related to one another than they are to members of the other taxa.

Tupaiidae—the tree shrews of Malaysia. The bulk of recent evidence supports their claim to close affiliation with the Primates. Whether they are "true" Primates, should be given ordinal status in their own right, belong to the Insectivora, or belong to another order are still interesting and important questions. The opinion that the Macroscelididae are closely related to the Tupaiidae is intriguing. Simpson, for one (1962), states that he considers the tupaiids as Primates and the macroscelidids as not.

Lemuroidea—prosimian primates all of whose living members are found only on the island of Madagascar.

Lorisiformes—nocturnal, arboreal prosimian primates of Africa and Asia.

Tarsiidae—island living animals consisting of only one genus, separate at quit a high level from the other taxa (Simpson, 1962).

Ceboidea—comprising all the living New World primates. Currently they are divided into two closely related families.

Cercopithecoidea—this group, next to *Homo*, has the widest distribution and greatest number of individuals of any of these taxa. Various subdivisions into more than one taxon have been suggested from time to time, yet this group of Old World monkeys seems clearly to be a single, natural unit.

Pongidae—the four great apes, chimpanzees, gorillas, orangutans, gibbons, including the siamang. Recent work in biochemical genetics and immunogenetics has suggested to some that this taxon should be split.

Hominidae—the most widely distributed, the largest in numbers, and probably the most successful of the Primates to exploit its evolutionary niche. This group comprises a single genus and a single species, with sufficient variation within the species for subdivision to be made. Present evidence supports the often implicitly made assumption that only a single genus, and probably only a single species, existed at any one time period.

Huxley, as early as 1863, recognized a unique feature of the Primates —that they exist as a series of successively more advanced forms (Huxley, 1876). There exist living representatives of many of the major forms developed in the long history of the order. This unique feature is illustrated in a diagrammatic view of their evolutionary course (Fig. 1, taken from Clark, 1960).

One must be cautious about using living forms to make deductions about the past history of the order. We are fortunate, as Simons points out (Chapter 2 in this volume), to have an extensive fossil record that can be related to many of the living groups. However, it is not at all clear whether any living primate populations can be taken to represent truly transitional forms or new forms which led to the next most advanced stages. An example will make this clear. There is no known living member of the order which represents the first erect, bipedal hominid. Nor does there exist any form which is transitional between the quadrupedal primates and the bipedal, i.e., a form which exhibits the bony and neuromuscular changes in the pelvic girdle which led to the first erect, bipedal type.

However, various living populations of Primates are often believed to be closely related to those groups out of which the more advanced forms developed. As an example of the difficulties in this kind of enquiry we can take the question of which living primates are most like the populations from which the hominids arose. At one time this was conceived as an attempt either to find man's closest relatives or, more crudely, to

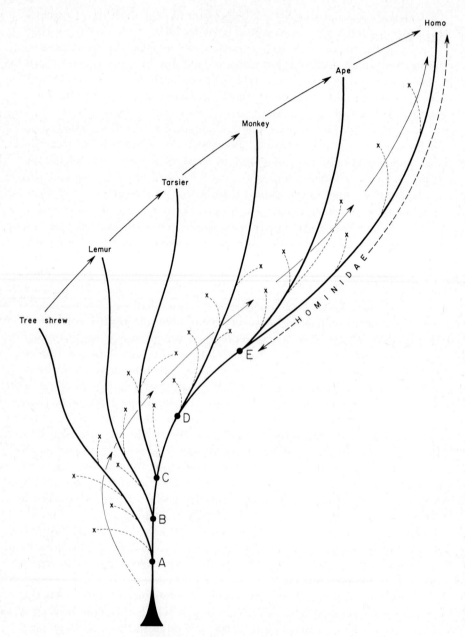

Fig. 1. Diagram of primate evolution. Living Primates form an evolutionary series which indicates a general trend of development (after Clark, 1960).

show from which apes man is descended. Modern evolutionary theory does not recognize these statements as meaningful. At the present time the discussion about the type of progenitor of the hominids has focused on two types of animals. One popular view is that an arboreal brachiator, from which the pongids probably also developed, was a transitional stage. Another view is that a social, terrestrial primate, such as the baboon or macaque, is the stage out of which the Hominidae developed. How then to decide between such alternative views? There is excellent anatomical evidence to show that *Homo* has the muscle-bone arrangements in the shoulder that imply a recent derivation from a brachiator. There is equally good evidence that the hand of man is that of a terrestrial primate (see Chapter 12 by Bishop in Volume II) and not that of a brachiator. Experimental studies might well provide part of the answer. Is it easier to rearrange the anatomy of a brachiating ape or a terrestrial monkey to make a bipedal hominid? Unfortunately such experiments have not yet been completed. We can only appeal, apparently, to the fossil record. And this is not complete or clear. Indeed, such gaps in the fossil record are one of the compelling reasons for examination of the living Primates.

There is more to be said about the nature of the evolutionary development which led to erect bipedalism. There are, as Simons among others notes, several forms which brachiate or, to pay respect to the heat which that term generates, incipiently brachiate, semibrachiate, or pseudobrachiate. There are indications in the fossil record that brachiation arose several times among the Primates. Straus (personal communication) points out that the entire question of brachiation in man's ancestry may be misinterpreted. He suggests that the long trunk of Primates, the way it must achieve balance by adjusting various bone-muscle systems, and the locomotor consequences such adjustments make possible are fundamental to understanding why brachiation or semibrachiation has appeared more than once in the phylogeny of these animals. An examination of living primates is illuminating in this regard. Among prosimian primates the Indriidae include two genera, *Indri* and *Propithecus*, which are diurnal, arboreal forms with long trunks and long limbs. *Indri* and *Propithecus* have been seen by the author to haul themselves along, in the very high tree tops of the Forest of Perinet, hand over hand in a fashion that resembles the brachiation of *Hylobates*. Several *Propithecus verreauxi coquereli* kept in captivity "brachiated," swinging hand over hand by grasping the heavy wire mesh of their cage tops. The point here is not whether any of the Indriidae are "true brachiators," but that large, agile primates with long trunks seem most naturally to include a type of incipient brachiation in their locomotor repertory.

There are brachiators or semi-bachiators among the Ceboidea and the Cercopithecoidea (the Colobinae) as well as among the Pongidae.

Figure 2 illustrates another aspect of the discussion of the origin of erect bipedalism among the Primates. It is a photograph of a full-grown *Propithecus verreauxi coquereli* walking in a bipedal manner along a shelf in her cage. This particular animal was quite able to take several

Fig. 2. *Propithecus verreauxi coquereli*, adult female, walking in a bipedal fashion.

steps in somewhat clumsy but true bipedal fashion. Indeed many *Propithecus* are able to do so. The author and several of his students have seen *Propithecus diadema* running along branches for short distances, in a bipedal manner similar to that of the illustrated animal. J.-J. Petter (personal communication) and the author have seen at least two *Lemur catta* in captivity who were able to take several true bipedal steps and who repeated this sort of locomotion on numerous occasions. There are observations of erect posture and skillful bipedalism among baboons, macaques, and other monkeys. The author has observed a number of baboons who could run fairly rapidly for 10 to 30 yards on their hind legs while they carried away melons and squash held in their arms. Again the point is that erect bipedalism is a potential of a number of primate forms. It is quite plausible that a tree-dwelling primate began the trend to erect bipedalism by first running successfully along heavy, thick branches. It is also plausible that a highly social, terrestrial primate began to emphasize erect posture and a bipedal gait. Such locomotion would free the hands for ever increasing skill at manipulation of objects and eventually would lead to the making of tools. The evidence that man has the hand of a terrestrial rather than an arboreal primate may give added support to the latter interpretation.

It is well to remember that each living group of Primates has behind it a long evolutionary development. The less advanced, such as the lemurs, have a longer history than the more advanced, in one sense. Each major population or form is separated from all others by as long a period of time as each has been separated from the common ancestor. Thus, one must always bear in mind that although a form such as *Lemur* can in one sense be viewed as a true Eocene primate, *Lemur* has had a very long span of time during which it has unquestionably diverged markedly from its Eocene progenitor. Living lemurs are "living fossils" only in a very general sense. Despite this cautionary statement, Simons (1962) has shown that much can be inferred about the behavior of Eocene fossil primates by watching and studying the behavior of the living lemurs.

A comprehensive list of the Primates is included at the end of this chapter in Section IV. It includes many of the colloquial names as well as the species and subspecies designata. The number of names is imposing and very likely misleading. It will be clear after reading a number of chapters that the list must, eventually, be subjected to a severe revision. The trend in taxonomy is away from the splitting tendencies which were the fashion when most of the names in this list were bestowed. Recently Simpson (1962) stated that the principal activity in primate taxonomy at present seems to be changing the status of this or that name. It may seem time that a new taxonomy of the Primates be proposed. Simpson declined an obvious opportunity recently (1962) because the vast amount of new information and new kinds of data about the Primates have not been assimilated. *All* currently used classifications are unsatisfactory (see Simpson's detailed comments on this problem— 1962). Before we indulge ourselves in revising the classification and even before we tinker with bits and pieces of the current ones, some comments about the uses of classification are in order.

The classification of the Primates provides us with a useful set of names for communication among students of this order. The hierarchy of species, genus, family, etc., has been built upon the work of many students and many years of experience with the Primates. Since it attempts to be, and indeed *is*, phylogenetic in character, despite obvious inadequacies, it still represents a very useful system for expressing one's ideas about primate evolution. Some of the discussions and arguments, over the adequacy of lumping or splitting certain animals into one family or into two, are most illuminating in the development of general theories about the evolution of the order.

Biochemical traits, new to taxonomy, and techniques for analyzing these traits have, in the view of some, undermined many of the divisions of the system. An example will illustrate this point. Proponents of the use of biochemical and immunochemical traits in revising the taxonomy of Primates, and other groups, have yet to show that these traits are more fundamental, in a taxonomic sense, than those of gross anatomy which have been the basis of the system. A particular example concerns a proposed division of the Pongidae into two groups. One would include *Pongo, Hylobates,* and *Symphalangus,* the other *Pan* and *Gorilla.* There are many reasons why this may be reasonable and useful. *Most* of the reasons have been known for a generation. Recent work by Goodman (1962), Zuckerkandl and his colleagues (1960), and R. L. Hill and the author has demonstrated some differences between the genetically controlled blood proteins of the southeast Asiatic apes and those of Africa. When studies of the albumins of the apes were reported (Goodman, 1962) it was clear there is a difference, immunochemically, between albumin of the orangutan and gibbon on the one hand and that of the gorilla and chimpanzee on the other. Goodman (1962 and personal communication) suggests that this clearly indicates that the Asiatic apes have diverged markedly from those of Africa and should be put into a separate family or superfamily, and that the African apes belong in the same family as does *Homo.*

Immunochemical studies of ceruloplasmin and transferrins, also by Goodman, seem to confirm the implications of the work on albumin. When other proteins such as α_2-macroglobulin and γ-globulin were tested, the results did not fall into the same clear-cut pattern of differences.

Detailed analysis of the hemoglobin of *Pan* and *Gorilla* have revealed that they differ very slightly from human hemoglobin while the hemoglobin of certain orangutans shows greater differences from human. At first glance this might imply that the African apes and man are genetically more closely linked with each other than they are with the Asiatic

apes. Further work by R. L. Hill and the author and by Zuckerkandl
(personal communication) reveals that the hemoglobin of the gibbon
is quite as similar to that of man as is that of the gorilla, while the
differences found among orangutans are not any greater than the differences found within the group of abnormal human hemoglobins. In other
words, the hemoglobin of some orangutans seems quite similar to that
of normal human hemoglobin, while that of others is different. But the
differences are no greater, and are apparently of the same type, as those
between one abnormal human hemoglobin and another.

This discussion returns us to the taxonomic point at issue. The two
most extreme views are that the study of variations in, and the evolution
of, genetically controlled proteins supersedes the data used hitherto, and
that the inconsistencies, which the data from these biochemical studies
show, demonstrate their lack of value in taxonomy. Both of these positions are, really, examples of extreme parochialism in scientific thought.
It is more instructive to consider the implications of supplementing the
standard taxonomy with these new data and new techniques. If differences are implied, are they ones of interpretation or are they actually
inconsistencies in the phylogenetic attribution which the new data demonstrate? It is certainly not clear at all whether the differences in the
immunochemistry of albumin of the African and the Asiatic apes is
symptomatic of a highly labile protein (in the evolutionary sense) or
whether it reflects fundamental evolutionary differences between the
two groups of Primates. What about other, perhaps more conservative,
proteins? How shall we weigh those that show little or no immunochemical change within the various primate genera? Or what are we
to make of the rather large genetic variation found among the transferrins of *all* the Primates (including man)? Despite the immunochemical similarities of chimpanzee and human transferrin, other analyses of
this protein imply rather large differences among the Pongidae and between the Pongidae and *Homo* (Buettner-Janusch, 1962). The fact that
a protein shows enormous genetic variation between members of the
same taxonomic *family* may have no more fundamental phylogenetic
significance than the variation which occurs in similar proteins within a
species.

However, tinkering with the system of classification in use may become necessary when gross inconsistencies between two lines of evidence
exist. It is generally believed that the best taxonomic system is evolutionary in basis and expresses genetic similarity and differences among
the animals classified. When two kinds of genetic or genetic and anatomical data apparently imply different classificatory conclusions, interesting problems in evolutionary biology arise. An excellent example of

this is provided by the data on lemur chromosomes presented in Chapter 7 by Bender and Chu in this volume and in the paper by Chu and Bender (1962). Several examples of lemurs considered to be members, as subspecies or races, of the same species *Lemur fulvus* have been found to have rather different chromosome numbers. Variation in the pelage color of animals that seem basically similar led a number of workers to propose a variety of subspecies. An ecological dimension was added to such a division when it seemed quite clear that each color variety of the *L. fulvus* types apparently inhabited separate forest areas. Such ecological separation and, indeed, isolation as the forests of Madagascar were reduced to noncontiguous remnants, lead one to suggest that many of the *L. fulvus* types may indeed be separable and given specific status. Recent work by Petter (1963) on the taxonomy of the Malagasy lemurs has produced a system of classifying the lemurs, particularly the *L. fulvus* types, which tends to extensive lumping of species. He finds a continuum of traits among all *L. fulvus* types with *L. macaco*. He prefers to lump all these as subspecies of *L. macaco*.

If we take Petter's list, based on the only recent study of the distribution of the lemurs on Madagascar and on the usual morphological traits, and add to it a consideration of only the chromosome numbers which Chu has discovered, certain fascinating problems arise. Whether they are problems of cytology or problems of lemur evolution, or both, remains to be seen. Only tentative remarks about the question of the effect of recent cytological discoveries can be made until Chu has published his karyotypes and karyological analyses (Table I).

Analysis of the chromosomes is, for primate studies, an activity new to taxonomic problems. How shall the data discovered be integrated with the material collected by more conventional techniques? If we maintain that the weight of all the evidence supports the conclusions reached by Petter, then we must pursue the fascinating question of how so much chromosome variation developed within what, on other grounds, is considered one population of animals. If they are one species with racial variation expressed in pelage color, etc., then barriers to breeding cannot, by definition, exist. On the other hand such variation in the chromosome complement may be interpreted as demonstrating genetic differentiation among the various subgroups leading to the barriers that define species. Such barriers to interfertility may be impossible to determine unless hybrids can be produced. A much simpler explanation may also be possible. The original classification of Lemuroidea may have been made on the basis of incomplete observations of the distribution and relationships of the various populations and subpopulations of the animals.

Bolwig (1960) has proposed a new genus of Lemuridae, *Odorlemur catta*, to supplant the older *Lemur catta*. His reasons are based upon analysis of the brachial glands, the antebrachial organs (or carpal glands), and the associated spurs of this fascinating animal. We believe this is a graphic, contemporary example of what Simpson meant when

TABLE I

CHROMOSOME NUMBERS IN LEMUROIDEA

Genus and species	Chromosome number (2N)
Microcebus murinus murinus	66
Microcebus murinus smithii	—
Microcebus coquereli	—
Cheirogaleus trichotis	—
Cheirogaleus major	66
Cheirogaleus medius	—
Phaner furcifer	—
Varecia varia (Lemur variegatus)	46
Varecia rubra	46
Hapalemur griseus griseus	54
Hapalemur griseus olivaceus	58
Hapalemur simus	—
Lepilemur mustelinus mustelinus	—
Lepilemur mustelinus microdon	—
Lepilemur mustelinus ruficaudatus	—
Lepilemur mustelinus leucopus	—
Lepilemur mustelinus dorsalis	—
Lemur macaco macaco	44
Lemur macaco flavifrons	—
Lemur macaco sanfordi	—
Lemur macaco albifrons	60
Lemur macaco fulvus	48 and 60
Lemur macaco collaris	48 and 54
Lemur macaco rufus	60
Lemur macaco mayottensis	—
Lemur mongoz mongoz	60
Lemur mongoz coronatus	—
Lemur catta	56
Lemur rubriventer	—
Avahi laniger occidentalis	—
Avahi laniger orientalis	—
Indri indri	—
Propithecus diadema	48
Propithecus verreauxi verreauxi	48
Propithecus verreauxi coquereli	48

he castigated most attempts at primate classification (see quotation page 37). Montagna and Yun (1962) published a detailed account of the histology, histochemistry, and anatomy of the various dermal and carpal glands and organs of *Lemur catta*. They found many startling resemblances to similar structures in *Hapalemur*. If it is appropriate to reclassify *L. catta* on the basis of this evidence, and we doubt that it is, it would seem more appropriate to join it in a taxon with *Hapalemur*. Genera should be named to lump related species, or species deemed related, and species should be named to account for meaningful, useful, real biological differences. We have here again, clearly, an example of what Simpson (1945) complained about in primate taxonomy. A more detailed discussion of this and some other problems occurs under the various sections below.

II. PROSIMII

A. TUPAIIDAE

There seems to be general agreement that the tree shrews (Tupaiidae) are to be classified with the Primates (Clark, 1960; Simpson, 1962; Straus, 1956). Grassé (1955) reaffirms the opinion that they belong to the Order Insectivora, an opinion that no longer arouses much agreement. One other major student of the Primates, Hill (1953), does not include them in the order. The tupaiids, at very least, represent an important link with the Insectivora, the group presumably most closely related, in a phylogenetic sense, to Primates. Certainly much can be learned by studying a group of animals that may be said to have a foot in more than one taxon, though whether this situation is due to the animal's truly transitional form or to our ignorance is yet to be determined. Much could undoubtedly be learned by study of *Galeopithecus*, the so-called flying lemur of Borneo. This strange animal impresses one very much as a second line of effort in the attempt to develop a primate type. However the taxonomic decision is finally made, students of the Primates are increasing the amount of attention that they pay to the tupaiids. The list of names given in this chapter is a long one. It is likely that many contemporary scholars would reduce the number of separate groups by a factor of two. However, it is well to remember that many of these tupaiids are island dwellers and that such mutual isolation will have emphasized tendencies toward divergence.

B. LEMUROIDEA

Were it not for the survival of the lemurs of Madagascar, it would be difficult indeed to argue that any prosimian fossils, now known in relative abundance, included diurnal populations. The Malagasy lemurs have been isolated, presumably from Eocene times, on the island of Madagascar, and have not been subject to the competitive pressure of the more intelligent, more cleverly manipulative monkeys. This remarkable group of survivals from the Eocene is gradually being given more attention by scholars interested in the Primates. They provide us with many interesting inferences about the course of development from primitive mammal to monkey.

Through geological and geophysical processes still obscure, the island of Madagascar separated from the mainland of Africa sometime during the Eocene. The native forests and the native flora of the island seem to be closely related to Eocene forms. The fact that lemurs, an Eocene primate development, are the only Primates on the island lends support to the view that the separation occurred before the development of the more advanced monkey-like forms now found in Africa. The other types of mammals on the island, rodents, insectivores, and the curious fossa (*Cryptoprocca ferox*), a carnivore that resembles both canids and felids, also lend support to the view that the development of arboreal diurnal monkeys provided competition too severe for the diurnal lemurs of the continents. The discovery of fossil tenrecs in Kenya may presage the discovery of fossil lemurs in the right time zones to document this fully. From the fact that no forms of Primates other than Lemuroidea developed on Madagascar it may be argued that the higher forms derived from a nonlemur-like population. Nevertheless, the fossil evidence, as Simons shows, implies a prosimian line leading directly to the monkeys. Similar evidence indicates that the fossil lemurs clearly belong to the same general prosimian group.

Contemporary lemurs have diverged, specialized, and developed a large variety of types adapted to many ecological niches on their island home. It is this specialization, diversity, and divergence which led to the belief of many that lemurs are a definite separate group of prosimians, to be separated at a high taxonomic level. It has also been the basis for a number of different, often conflicting, classifications of the lemurs. We agree with the position of Washburn (1951), for example, that there seems to be little essential difference between lemurs, lorises, and tarsiers. The fact that there are many different kinds of lemurs (see Figs. 3–10 for examples), most of them quite different from the nocturnal prosimians of the continents, has led to an emphasis of their differences. There are a number of diurnal and nocturnal lemur types. Nocturnal types include the tiny *Microcebus*, probably the smallest of living primates, *Cheirogaleus, Phaner, Lepilemur, Avahi* (sometimes designated as *Lichanotus*), and the very special *Daubentonia* (aye-aye). The diurnal and crepuscular types, with the nocturnal lemurs, belong to no less

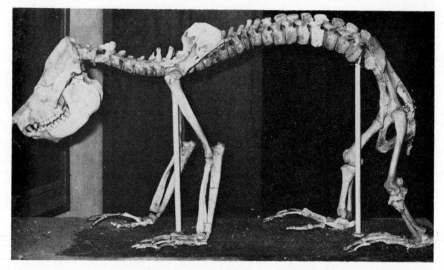

FIG. 3a. *Megaladapis,* a subfossil lemur, largest of the Lemuridae.

FIG. 3b. *Microcebus murinus,* the smallest of living Lemuridae, probably the smallest of living Primates.

FIG. 4a.   *Cheirogaleus medius,* male.

FIG. 4b.   *Lepilemur mustelinus ruficaudatus,* male.

Fɪɢ. 5a. *Lemur catta,* male. [Photograph by the author; from *Am. J. Phys. Anthropol.* **20**(2), 104 (1962).]

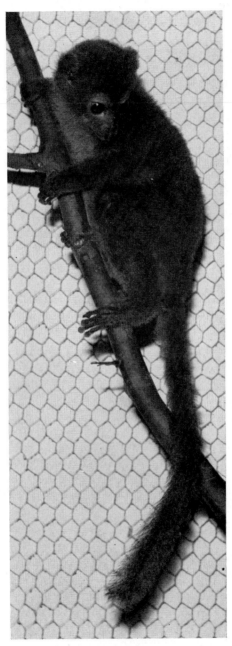

FIG. 5b. *Hapalemur griseus,* female.

FIG. 6a. *Lemur macaco*, female with male infant.

FIG. 6b. *Lemur macaco*, male, adult.

FIG. 7a. *Lemur variegatus* (*Varecia variegatus*).

FIG. 7b. *Lemur mongoz*, female.

Fig. 8a.　*Lemur fulvus fulvus*, female (*Lemur macaco fulvus*).

Fig. 8b.　*Lemur fulvus collaris* (*Lemur macaco collaris*), male, red-collared form.

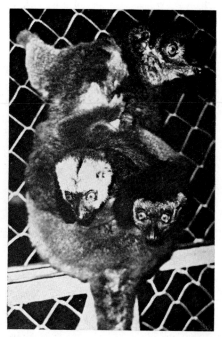

FIG. 9a. *Lemur fulvus albifrons* (*Lemur macaco albifrons*), adult female with twin offspring, male white-headed and white-fronted, female black-headed and black-fronted.

FIG. 9b. *Lemur fulvus rufus* (*Lemur macaco rufus*), male with typical red top-knot in center, female with typical rufous coat on right.

Fig. 10a. *Propithecus verreauxi verreauxi.*

FIG. 10b. *Indri indri.*

than three taxonomic families. The diurnal and crepuscular (it is some-times difficult to draw a line between these two types) range from the small brush-living types, *Hapalemur* and *Lemur*, to the large, gibbon-like forest dwellers, *Propithecus* and *Indri*.

The Malagasy lemurs provide one example of successful primate ex-ploitation of all, or most, ecological zones potentially open to the order. There are many remarkable convergences between lemurs and other primates. One of the most amazing is the gibbon-like *Indri*. This is an arboreal, diurnal form that lives in the tops of tall trees in the Eocene forests of Madagascar. The size of the social group is probably variable. During the breeding season it is likely that couples form into tightly knit "family" groups until the offspring is old enough to leave its mother. In January and February, 1962, *Indri* were seen by the author only in groups of three, two adults and one immature offspring clinging to its mother. Several such "family" groups may come together to form larger, loosely organized troops. Recordings of the hoots of *Indri* made in the Forest of Perinet by the author were analyzed on a sound spectrograph by Andrew. A remarkable convergence to the calls of *Hylobates* was found.

Lemur catta is a social animal with many similarities to baboons and macaques in the way it exploits a terrestrial niche. It occurs in moder-ately large troops and has many of the temperamental characteristics of an unintelligent baboon. The characterization of *L. catta* social be-havior in detail is apparently going to be a difficult task. A student of the author's spent several weeks in a small region in Madagascar which abounded in *Lemur catta*, in the rocky, bushy sections, and *Propithecus verreauxi coquereli*, in the *Didierea* trees. *Propithecus* could be observed and photographed at relatively close range (20–30 yards), but *L. catta* fled in concerted panic when the observer was within 100–200 yards of a group.

An inventory of the Lemuroidea would show that almost every type of primate has been developed, except an erect, bipedal, symbolling one. This is not to claim that a true, efficient brachiating ape-like lemur inhabits the high forests of Madagascar. Rather this situation can be interpreted as showing that given primate form and isolating it from the competition of more advanced members of the order, and given other favorable ecological factors, a large range of the potential of the entire order is realized. This is instructive in another sense. The fact that, given isolation and, presumably, an ancestral lemur, no forms more ad-vanced than lemurs developed, argues strongly that there was a wide divergence of the lemurs from any common ancestor before the monkeys developed. It is clear from the analyses of lemur manipulative abilities

(Bishop) and of primate behavior (Andrew, 1962, and Chapter 13 in Volume II) that lemurs are on a distinctly lower level than monkeys and that there is a distinct break between prosimians and higher Primates. It is reasonable to postulate that some lemur of prosimian, more advanced toward a monkey-like type than any which now exists, was the transitional form from Prosimii to Anthropoidea.

The attention devoted to the Malagasy lemurs has been increasing in recent years. Some special problems in classifying and identifying them must be discussed. Petter (1963), as noted earlier, has suggested a revision in the classification of the Malagasy lemurs. His revision is based upon his lengthy field studies and upon an exhaustive examination of lemur skins and skeletons in the museums of Europe, Africa, and the United States. He has taken a lumping *and* a splitting view of the usual classifications in an attempt to arrive at more natural and coherent groupings than are provided by the traditional lists. His is a more concise list than the comprehensive one included in the exhaustive primate iteration provided at the end of this chapter. Petter's list is presented in Table I. In the last column of this table are listed the chromosome numbers for many of the species. These numbers were taken from Bender and Chu (Chapter 7 in this volume) and from Chu and Bender (1962). Since karyological analyses have not been considered, the different numbers of chromosomes within what Petter considers a single species do not necessarily imply that there is genetic discontinuity within a species. After all, the famous shrews of Harwell (Ford *et al.*, 1957) are polymorphic within a single population with respect to chromosome numbers. However, the differences among these lemurs seem larger than the polymorphism reported for the Harwell shrews. The apparent chromosome diversity among lemurs deemed similar, or even identical, is rather astonishing. Yet we know so little of these animals that apparent phenotypic similarity may be more apparent than real. One line of investigation this suggests is the accurate determination of the range of each of the animals in question. There are many microdifferences in the phytogeographical zones of Madagascar. It does not seem unlikely that the isolation of various *L. fulvus* types (or *L. macaco* types) from each other in different forests has led to chromosomal variation as well as variation in pelage characteristics. A study of hybrids would be helpful. Unfortunately the identification of species and subspecies of lemurs is so unreliable that Gray's (1954) list, based on a study of published reports from zoos and similar institutions, cannot be used with safety. The difficulties in correctly identifying and labeling animals is apparent to anyone who visits one of the great zoological gardens in Europe or the United States. When a relatively little known and poorly photographed group such as the Lemuriformes is concerned, the reliability of identifications in zoos and in recent literature is extremely low.

An example of the problems one faces in using the literature on the lemurs occurs in a recent paper by Bolwig (1960). He illustrates his remarks on lemur behavior with some photographs labeled *Lemur mongoz*. These same animals were studied and photographed by us, later in the same year, and they are clearly *L. fulvus* types. Petter has examined our photographs of these animals and confirms our identification, although he suggests the name *L. macaco fulvus* in accord with his proposed revision of the Lemuridae. Some of the confusion in identifying Lemuridae results from using the superb illustrations in Milne-Edwards and Grandidier (1875, 1890–1896) as well as their names for the animals illustrated. Schwartz's contribution to the naming of Lemuridae further compounded the confusion.

The obvious thing to do is to obtain more specimens suitable for chromosome studies, from the lemurs not yet studied, as well as to pursue extensive field studies in an attempt to delineate actual population ranges. Unfortunately such studies are expensive of time, not to say of money. The laudable desire of the Malgache to protect vigorously the remaining lemurs is another factor that requires consideration in order to save all of these unique and rare animals and not destroy them in order to study them.

C. LORISIFORMES

The relationship of the more primitive prosimian primates to the more advanced monkeys and apes is not clear. The most carefully studied prosimians, until recently, were the wholly nocturnal Lorisiformes of Africa and Asia, and the nocturnal, intriguing, and to some extent puzzling, island form, *Tarsius*, of Borneo, Sumatra, Celebes, and the Philippine Islands. *Tarsius* has been discussed in great detail by Hill (1955), despite which its relationship to the other taxa of the order is still not at all clear.

The nocturnal, arboreal lorises (*Perodicticus, Galago, Arctocebus, Euoticus, Galagoides, Loris, Nycticebus*) are probably the remnants of a widespread, variable prosimian population from which the forms ancestral to the monkeys developed. The survival of some lorises is due, probably, to their occupation of a nocturnal, arboreal, ecozone which does not bring them into competition with the diurnal monkeys. It is now considered probable (Simpson, 1962; Simons, Chapter 2 in this volume) that at least two separate groups of prosimians gave rise to the two types of monkeys which exist today, the cebids of the New World and the cercopithecids of the Old World. The relationship of the New to the Old World monkeys has puzzled many. The similarities between the two groups are startling. But they are similarities that indicate separate developments from different members of a common prosimian ancestral group. The similarities are convergences due to the continuing exploitation by advancing groups of Primates of similar econiches. It is unfortunate that the fossil record has few examples that bear upon this problem.

The Lorisiformes present a number of problems in classification. It is not clear why *Arctocebus* and *Perodicticus* should be separated at the generic rather than the specific level. The fact that these are both relatively slow moving, arboreal, nocturnal forms that occur in a number of populations isolated from each other by intervening geographical barriers may have given impetus to extreme splitting tendencies by naturalists and others who reported finding these animals. The generic separation of the various galagos also seems extreme to us. *Galagoides*, *Galago*, and *Euoticus* would, if they were being investigated for the first time today, end up in a single genus. Despite our tendency toward extensive lumping today, Montagna informs me that histological and histochemical studies of the skin of *Galago senegalensis* and *G. crassicaudatus* reveal very great differences between the two which are of the sort usually found in animals more distantly related than are these two. The species *G. crassicaudatus* has been divided into a number of subspecies, some of which show pelage, skeletal, and size differences from *G. crassicaudatus crassicaudatus* that are at least as extreme as the differences between *Galago senegalensis* and *Galagoides demidovii*. Figures 11 and 12 are pictures of *G. crassicaudatus crassicaudatus* and *G. crassicaudatus argentatus* which were born and raised in the author's laboratory. The *argentatus* variety are not only radically different in pelage, but also are very much larger. Their ears are larger and they have bigger and broader skulls with rather large nasal bones. If these two are to be considered members of the same species, and there is no good reason to separate them yet, then the generic separation of some of the other African lorises is certainly unreasonable.

Recently, a number of color varieties of *G. crassicaudatus* have been examined, all from the same forest location in Kenya. Tentatively, this group of galagos, all from a single population, covers the entire range of differences which have been defined for all the subspecies of *G. crassicaudatus*. A number of investigators have held tenaciously to the view that *G. crassicaudatus kikuyuensis* is "different" from *G. crassicaudatus crassicaudatus*. Breeding experiments in the author's laboratory demonstrated that a female *G. crassicaudatus kikuyuensis*, positively identified

FIG. 11a. *Galago crassicaudatus crassicaudatus,* female infant, 3 weeks old.

FIG. 11b. *Galago crassicaudatus argentatus,* female infant 4 weeks old, one of triplets born in author's laboratory.

FIG. 12a. *Galago crassicaudatus crassicaudatus,* adult female with 10-day-old female infant. [From A. Bishop, *Ann. N.Y. Acad. Sci.* **102,** 329 (1962).]

FIG. 12b. *Galago crassicaudatus argentatus,* adult female with 10-day-old triplets, two males, one female.

by one of the partisans of that view, has produced several offspring, all of which are indistinguishable from the *crassicaudatus* subspecies. At best, most of the traits that have been used to differentiate the subspecies of *Galago crassicaudatus* should be treated as minor racial variations of a single major population.

The situation among the Asiatic lorises is made less complicated by the lack of excessive splitting. Only *Loris* and *Nycticebus* are recognized as generically different, and within each of the two genera, only a single species with racial variants is recognized. Many of these variants have been given the status of subspecies, but the variation has never been given any greater weight than that. And this relatively high degree of lumping includes island forms of *Loris* from Ceylon in the same species with mainland forms. Had these been examined by the students of the tupaiids, the list of species and subspecies might well have been as staggering as that of the tree shrews.

D. Tarsiidae

Very little modern work has been done on *Tarsius*. No data are available on its hematology, behavior, vocalizations, or biochemistry that are of comparable quality with the material assembled in this volume from studies on other primates. Yet *Tarsius* poses some of the greatest problems to students of primate evolution. Its evolutionary position is hard to assess. There are many fossils assignable to a tarsioid group, but it is not clear, even today, what the essential differences between tarsioid and lemuroid fossil assemblages are, if any (Simpson, 1940; Simons, Chapter 2 in this volume).

Tarsius has many features which argue for calling it the most primitive of the Primates. Despite the development of a number of specializations *Tarsius* retains many generalized traits that seem to be derived from the tupaiids (Hill, 1955). As many as thirty-two (Hill, 1955) fossil genera have been allied to *Tarsius*. But this was before serious attention was directed to the difficulty of detecting the differences between "lemuroid" and "tarsioid" fossil assemblages.

Tarsius has had a vogue as representing an ancestor of man. Jones (1929) considered that the Anthropoidea passed through a tarsioid stage. The difficulties in this view are discussed in detail by Simons in Chapter 2 of this volume. Suffice to say here that it would be of great interest to examine the plasma proteins by immunogenetic methods and also compare the structure of *Tarsius* hemoglobin with that of other Prosimii. It would be most interesting if its hemoglobin had an adult alkali-resistant component as does that of the lemurs and lorises (Buettner-Janusch and Twichell, 1961, and unpublished data).

III. ANTHROPOIDEA

A. CEBOIDEA

A rather large gap in our knowledge of the Primates occurs in the material available for assessing the relationship of the Prosimii to the South American Ceboidea. The fact that the South American Primates are considered to be of the monkey grade of organization, and are called monkeys, has stressed a probably spuriously close relationship between Old and New World forms. At present we can add nothing to the discussion of the Ceboidea provided by Hill's comprehensive work (1957, 1960, 1962). The cytogenetics of this group has been studied by Bender and Mettler (1958) and by Bender and Chu (Chapter 7 in this volume). However, the paucity of ecological and behavioral studies on this important group of primates, with the exception of the work of Carpenter and his students on the howler monkeys of Panama, makes it difficult to comment on the adequacy of the distinction made in the past among the various species and genera. It is also very difficult to consider the history of any contemporary cebid groups, for the fossil record is so poor. Indeed, it is almost nonexistent.

Contemporary thought generally concedes that the Ceboidea originated from a different group of Prosimii than that from which the Old World monkeys sprang. The similarities between the two groups are, as Simons points out, more apparent than real. It is, indeed, for this reason that the Ceboidea are potentially such an important group of monkeys for students of primate evolution. The independent development, in a second primate stock, of structures and functional adaptations that often exactly parallel functional adaptations of the Old World monkeys is a datum about primate evolution that has not received proper consideration.

The long list of primate names at the end of the chapter includes an exhaustive enumeration of names of cebids. This is based on Hill's exhaustive treatise on the New World monkeys. Simpson has a considerably simplified view of the taxonomy of the Ceboidea, and it is certainly more consistent with modern views of the uses of taxonomy than is Hill's (Simpson, 1945, 1962). Table II lists the genera, subfamilies, and families of the Ceboidea according to Simpson.

B. CERCOPITHECOIDEA

The Old World monkeys, the Cercopithecoidea, are probably the most numerous and variable group in the order. The majority of the genera of this superfamily occur in Africa. There is probably a close relationship between Asiatic macaques and African baboons. The similarities are detailed, and Gray (1954) reports reliable accounts of hybrids between these two genera. It may be reasonable to view them as a major group that has a continuous distribution from southern Africa to northeastern Asia. There are some difficulties with this view, however. The occurrence of fossil baboons in India (Simpson, 1945) and living populations in Arabia may imply that they were superseded by the macaques in Asia. There is also the presence of *Macaca sylvana*, the Barbary ape,

TABLE II

THE CEBOIDEA: GENERA, FAMILIES, AND SUBFAMILIES ACCORDING TO SIMPSON

Family CEBIDAE (Swainson 1835)
　　Subfamily AOTINAE (Elliot 1913)
　　　　Aotes (Humboldt 1911)
　　　　Callicebus (Thomas 1903)
　　Subfamily PITHECINAE (Mivart 1865)
　　　　Cacajao (Lesson 1840)
　　　　Chiropotes (Lesson 1840)
　　　　Pithecia (Desmarest 1804)
　　Subfamily ALOUATTINAE (Elliot 1904)
　　　　Alouatta (Lacépède 1799)
　　Subfamily CEBINAE (Mivart 1865)
　　　　Cebus (Erxleben 1777)
　　　　Saimiri (Voigt 1831)
　　Subfamily ATELINAE (Miller 1924)
　　　　Ateles (Geoffroy 1806)
　　　　Brachyteles (Spix 1823)
　　　　Lagothrix (Geoffroy 1812)
　　Subfamily CALLIMICONINAE (Thomas 1913)
　　　　Callimico (Ribeiro 1911)
Family CALLITHRICIDAE (Thomas 1903)
　　　　Callithrix (Erxleben 1777)
　　　　Leontocebus (Wagner 1839)

in North Africa to consider. Since fossil macaques occur in European Pleistocene deposits, it may be that *Macaca sylvanus* is the survivor of a population with a continuous distribution around the Mediterranean and into Asia (Tappen, 1960). If this is so, one implication is that *Macaca* and *Papio* were once living side by side. On the one hand this would imply a definite species and perhaps generic difference between the two; on the other, it might imply a relatively recent common ancestry —or both.

Among the other groups of monkeys only the leaf-eating monkeys, the Colobinae, are common to both continents. If one accepts the genus *Procolobus,* two genera of this family occur in Africa and five in Asia. Since these monkeys have a relatively special diet of leaves and consequently a fairly specific and restricted ecozone in which they can survive, the occurrence of members in both continents may be taken to imply a continuous forest corridor which connected the two continents at one time.

The tremendous detailed variations in the genus *Cercopithecus* have led to the definition of a very large number of species, subspecies, races, and local varieties. An extreme is reached, perhaps, by attempts to define species and subspecies of the *C. aethiops* group on the basis of variations in the shades of blue and blue-green of the male testicles. Booth (personal communication) has pointed out that in her field studies of this group, the color variation in male genitalia is conditioned by age and may be part of the apparent differences in mature and immature animals that are part of the repertory of sccial signals that facilitate troop life and troop cohesion. Differences among the various species so far defined are undoubtedly real, but their *meaning* for understanding the history of this genus has not yet been explored. Currently classifiers tend toward a lumping of species rather than splitting them. Such a trend has had very little effect on the classification of the monkeys of Africa. The list of species and subspecies is vast and only a very small part of the taxonomy has been based upon ecological and field studies. Almost no genetic investigations have been done. Both of these are essential in assessing the many debatable divisions made among these monkeys.

Tappen (1960) has summarized many of the problems that face anyone attempting to generalize about African monkeys. Most of his strictures apply equally well to study of the Asiatic monkeys.

Two problems in classifying various cercopithecid monkeys have been cleared up recently by Verheyen (1962). The genera *Allenopithecus* and *Erythrocebus* have been eliminated. He has shown, in his excellent study of the craniology of the genus *Cercopithecus*, that these two monkeys are to be included in that genus. *Allenopithecus* has always had, at best, a tenuous existence (Lang, 1923). It has really been an example of using characters on the specific level to define a genus. *Erythrocebus patas* presented a more difficult problem, since there are many specialized characteristics of the limbs and locomotor apparatus of this monkey that are rather different from those of most *Cercopithecus* monkeys. Verheyen's analysis of the craniology clearly implies that the patas monkey is a member of the genus *Cercopithecus* and he so considers it. The unique features of *C. patas* are probably best explained as modifications in a basically arboreal *Cercopithecus* monkey for a largely terrestrial way of life. To some extent *C. patas* resembles the highly terrestrial baboon in its locomotor behavior and mode of existence. Field studies of this interesting monkey, long a popular laboratory animal, should go far toward elucidating this problem.

A most interesting problem arises when one considers the African genus *Cercopithecus* and its relationships, historical and evolutionary, to its forest-dwelling companions, the colobus monkeys. The *Cercopithecus* group is extremely widespread in Africa. Although considered an arboreal animal, it can and does exploit the floor of the forest and such environments as sisal plantations and heavy scrub land that lies between open bush-savanna country and the taller forests along the banks of rivers. As Tappen (1960) notes, the same animal (species) occurs again and again throughout Africa. No good evidence that a cercopithecid ever existed in Asia has been found. One implication may be that the cercopithecid group is more recent as an evolutionary development than the colobid types. The known distributions of the African colobus monkeys may indicate they were once widespread and are now the remnant of an older population which has retreated to its special forest environments as the vegetation of Africa changed, the forests giving way to deserts, savannas, and scrub. The newer *Cercopithecus* genus, more versatile in exploiting the changing environment, grew in numbers and differentiated as extensively as it has because of the isolating effects of changes in the forest environment. This process was most certainly accelerated with the rise of agricultural populations in Africa that have destroyed many sections of forest land. This same evidence may also be interpreted, as it has by Tappen, to indicate that the cercopithecids are the more ancient inhabitants. The great number of types and the wide distribution testify to their older stratum in Africa. The colobus types then are viewed as a later incursion. If the colobus monkeys are a later invading group an extensive forest corridor existed between Asia and Africa in relatively recent times. Upon the disappearance of the forest the leaf-eating monkeys of Africa were isolated from their Asian relatives. It is unfortunate that there is no geographical, geological, or botanical evidence which can be used to bring this problem into better focus.

C. PONGIDAE

There are four distinct groups of pongids that have clearly differentiated sufficiently from each other to be given generic status. *Symphalangus* is clearly very closely related to *Hylobates,* but recent cytogenetic information tends to confirm the view that the former is distinct from the latter. Whether this distinction is worth generic status is a matter for some consideration when a thorough revision of the Primates is undertaken. The large number of species and subspecies that have been named in the genus *Hylobates* seems rather excessive. It is certainly extremely difficult to find any profound morphological differences in pelage or skeletons of a number of subspecies and species which the author has examined. The color differences, once thought to be profoundly important traits in defining species of gibbons, now appear to be another example of species polymorphism.

It might be legitimate to divide island forms of *Hylobates* into separate species, but, here too, more profound differences than have been demonstrated should be shown to exist. Earlier in this discussion we noted the desire of certain workers with immunogenetic tools to classify the Asiatic apes, *Pongo* and *Hylobates,* in some taxon which is distinct at the family level, at least, from *Pan* and *Gorilla* and to put the latter into a taxon with *Homo* at a level lower than the present one, that of the superfamily. We have indicated reasons why this strikes us as premature.

The differences between the mainland form and the two island forms of *Pongo* might be expected to be great enough to warrant division into species. However, these three populations are not distinct and apparently subspecific status is accorded them because of their island habitats. At the Basel zoo a male from Borneo has successfully mated with a female from the mainland. There are some minor genetic differences among the three strains, but they are clearly instances of, for example, hemoglobin polymorphism within distinct populations of the same species —a situation which is very like that of various human populations.

The African apes have been divided into a number of subspecies on various grounds. The evidence for the usefulness of these subdivisions is not particularly convincing. The amazing florescence of specific and subspecific categories throughout the primate order is unquestionably the result of the fascination our closest mammalian relatives have for hordes of variously trained explorers, naturalists, casual travelers, and overly enthusiastic zoologists. It seems quite reasonable that many of the classifiable differences suggested by the long lists of subspecific names are of no greater and generally of lesser magnitude than the traits which are used to make racial divisions in the species *Homo sapiens.* The African apes exist as small populations of two species that are nearing extinction. The geographical separateness of these populations and the probable development of traits that are not common to all the separate groups has been taken by many naturalists as indicating greater genetic separation than is the case.

D. HOMINIDAE

It is beyond the scope of this volume to do more than mention the most advanced of the Primates, the Hominidae. There has always been but a single species of the genus *Homo,* according to most contemporary paleontological and anthropological research. The modern species *Homo sapiens* includes the fossil and skeletal forms such as Neanderthal, the Rhodesian man, and many other prehistoric "races" such as Heidelberg man, Cro-magnon man, and Mount Carmel man.

IV. THE CLASSIFICATION OF THE PRIMATES

The list of names of Primates which follows has been prepared from a number of sources. The "secondary" publications listed were used rather more extensively than original papers for two reasons. First, the original papers are, in a majority of cases, reports of field observations, of museum specimens, or of specimens collected in the field. They demonstrate an enthusiasm that is difficult to understand and sympathize with—enthusiasm for defining as unique the specimen under examination and for honoring the author with the opportunity for naming a new subspecies, species, or genus. Second, the authors of the summary or secondary publications have the advantage of more information or a wider view of Primates than the average field worker. This statement should not be taken as conclusive support for the various views of taxonomy these authors exhibit. The major sources used were Allen, 1939; Booth, 1955; Ellerman and Morrison-Kott, 1951; Elliot, 1913; Fiedler, 1956; Hill, 1939, 1953, 1955, 1957, 1960, 1962; Lyon, 1913; Miller, 1933; Pocock, 1907, 1934; Regan, 1930; Remane, 1961; Schwarz, 1928; Simpson, 1945; Straus, 1949; Washburn, 1944.

The name list or classification of the Primates has been organized as closely as possible, given the fantastic number of names, in accordance with Simpson's 1945 classification. In certain cases, notably that of the cebids, the elegant simplicity of Simpson's classification would be marred if the comprehensive lists as given by Hill were to be rearranged to fit. Therefore, the longer and highly subdivided list is given here, and Simpson's is presented in Table II. Unfortunately the Rules could not be followed strictly in making up our list. We intended to attempt as exhaustive a compendium of the commonly used names as possible. Had we used the Rules in making this list, we would have ended with a thorough revision of the Primates. However, no revision should be attempted, as we said earlier, without taking account of modern work on primate karyology, biochemical genetics, immunogenetics, neurology, behavior, and anatomy. Furthermore, the Ceboidea require more intentive study before such a revision is made. Hill's list (1957, 1960, 1962), for example, apparently ignores the Rules, and he presents what is decidedly a "splitter's" view of classification. No one should use the list we present here as authority for classifying Primates. It is first a demonstration of the excessive classificatory importance that has been given extremely small differences between individuals and populations of Primates. Second, it will enable students to find in one place the entire list. We are certain that a large number of the names apply, in actuality, to the same group of animals; that is, there are fewer distinct primates than there are names on this list. In some cases, of course, greater distinctions than are made on the list will be made in the future. What this list demonstrates most of all is the necessity of attacking the taxonomy of the Primates with the contemporary view of species in mind and then revising the list completely. Following the detailed list we present a synoptic classification that follows Simpson very closely. In this list the fossils are included and names down to the level of the genus only are given.

There is no better way to introduce a classification of Primates than to take an extensive quotation from Simpson (1945, pp. 180–181):

"The primates are inevitably the most interesting of mammals to an egocentric species that belongs to this order. No other mammals have been studied in such detail, yet from a taxonomic point of view this cannot be considered the best-known order, and there is perhaps less agreement as to its classification than for most other orders. A major reason for this confusion is that much of the work on primates has been done by students who had no experience in taxonomy and who were completely incompetent to enter this field, however competent they may have been in other respects, and yet once their work is in print it becomes necessary to take cognizance of it. For this reason, if for no other, it is not surprising that most primates have alternative names and that hardly any two students use the same nomenclature for them. The importance of distinctions within the group has also been so exaggerated that almost every color phase, aberrant individual, or scrap of fossil bone or tooth has been given a separate name, almost every really distinct species has been called a genus, and a large proportion of the genera have been called families. The peculiar fascination of the primates and their publicity value have almost taken the order out of the hands of sober and conservative mammalogists and have kept, and do keep, its taxonomy in a turmoil. Moreover, even mammalogists who might be entirely conservative in dealing, say, with rats are likely to lose a sense of perspective when they come to the primates, and many studies of this order are covertly or overtly emotional."

A. Comprehensive List

Order PRIMATES (Linnaeus 1758)
  Suborder PROSIMII (Illiger 1811)
    Infraorder LEMURIFORMES (Gregory 1915)
      Superfamily TUPAIOIDEA (Dobson 1882)
        Family TUPAIIDAE (Mivart 1868)
          Subfamily TUPAIINAE (Lyon 1913)

Tupaia (Raffles 1822) .... Tree shrew
  anambae (Lyon 1913)
  belangeri (Wagner 1841)
  carimatae (Miller 1906) .... Carimata island tupaia
  castanea (Miller 1903)
  chinensis (Anderson 1879)
  chrysogaster (Miller 1903)
  chrysomalla (Miller 1900)
  concolor (Bonhote 1907)
  cuyonis (Miller 1910) .... Cuyo island tupaia
  demissa (Thomas 1904)
  discolor (Lyon 1906)
  dissimilis (Ellis 1860)
  glis (Diard 1820)
    glis (Diard 1820)
    batamana (Lyon 1907)
    ferruginea (Raffles 1822)
    pemangilis (Lyon 1911)
    pulonis (Miller 1903)
    sordida (Miller 1900)
  gracilis (Thomas 1893) .... Slender tupaia
    gracilis (Thomas 1893)
    edarta (Lyon 1913)
    inflata (Lyon 1906)
  hypochrysa (Thomas 1895)
  javanica (Horsfield 1821) .... Javanese tupaia
  lacernata (Thomas & Wroughton 1909)
    lacernata (Thomas & Wroughton 1909)
    longicauda (Kloss 1911)
    obscura (Kloss 1911)
    raviana (Lyon 1911)
    wilkinsoni (Robinson & Kloss 1911)
  longipes (Thomas 1893)
    longipes (Thomas 1893)
    salatana (Lyon 1913)
  lucida (Thomas & Hartert 1895)
  minor (Günther 1876) .... Lesser tupaia
    minor (Günther 1876)
    malaccana (Anderson 1879)
    sinicipis (Lyon 1911)

modesta (Allen 1906)
  annamensis (Robinson & Kloss 1922)
  assamensis (Wroughton 1921)
  brunetta (Thomas 1923)
  cambodiana (Kloss 1919)
  clarissa (Thomas 1917)
  cochinchinensis (Robinson & Kloss 1922)
  laotum (Thomas 1914)
  lepcha (Thomas 1922)
  olivacea (Kloss 1919)
  sinus (Kloss 1916)
  siaca (Thomas 1914)
  versurae (Thomas 1922)
möllendorffi (Matschie 1898) .... Möllendorf's tupaia
montana (Thomas 1892) .... Montane tupaia
  montana (Thomas 1892)
  baluensis (Lyon 1913)
  natunae (Lyon 1911)
nicobarica (Zelebor 1869) .... Nicobar tupaia
  nicobarica (Zelebor 1869)
  surda (Miller 1902)
palawanensis (Thomas 1894) .... Palawan Island tupaia
  phaeura (Miller 1902)
picta (Thomas 1892) .... Great painted tupaia
  riabus (Lyon 1913)
  siaca (Lyon 1908)
splendidula (Gray 1865) .... Little painted tupaia
  tephrura (Miller 1903)
Anathana (Lyon 1913) .... Indian tupaia
  ellioti (Waterhouse 1849) .... Madras tupaia
  pallida (Lyon 1913) .... Northeast Indian tupaia
  wroughtoni (Lyon 1913) .... Bombay tupaia
Dendrogale (Gray 1848) .... Mountain tupaia
  frenata (Gray 1860) .... Cambodian tupaia
  murina (Schlegel & Müller 1843) .... Pigmy tupaia
  melanura (Thomas 1892) .... Bornean tupaia
    melanura (Thomas 1892)
    baluensis (Lyon 1913)
Tana (Lyon 1913) .... Great tupaia
  tana (Raffles 1821) .... Common greater tupaia
    tana (Raffles 1821)
    besara (Lyon 1913) .... West Bornean tupaia
    bunoae (Miller 1900) .... Tambelan island tupaia
    sirhassenensis (Miller 1901) .... Natuna island tupaia
    tuancus (Lyon 1913) .... Banjok island tupaia
    utara (Lyon 1913)
  cervicalis (Miller 1903) .... Batu island tupaia
    cervicalis (Miller 1903)
    masae (Lyon 1913)
  chrysura (Günther 1876) .... Labuan tupaia

dorsalis (Schlegel 1857) .... Striped tupaia
lingae (Lyon 1913) .... Lingga island tupaia
paitana (Lyon 1913) .... North Bornean tupaia
Urogale (Mearns 1905) .... Philippine tupaia
everetti (Thomas 1892) .... Everett's tupaia
Subfamily PTILOCERCINAE (Lyon 1913)
  Ptilocercus (Gray 1848) .... Feather tails
    continentis (Thomas 1910)
    lowii (Gray 1848)
      lowii (Gray 1848)

Superfamily LEMUROIDEA (Mivart 1864)
  Family LEMURIDAE (Gray 1821)
    Subfamily LEMURINAE (Mivart 1864)
      Lemur (Linnaeus 1758)
        catta (Linnaeus 1758) .... Ring-tailed lemur
        fulvus (E. Geoffroy 1812) .... Brown lemur
          fulvus (E. Geoffroy 1812)
          albifrons (E. Geoffroy 1812) .... White-fronted lemur
          collaris (E. Geoffroy 1812) .... Yellow-whiskered lemur
          flavifrons (Gray 1867) .... Sclater's lemur
          mayottensis (Schlegel 1886) .... Mayotte lemur
          rufus (Audebert 1800) .... Red-fronted lemur
          sanfordi (Archbold 1932) .... Sanford's lemur
        macaco (Linnaeus 1766) .... Black lemur
        mongoz (Linnaeus 1766) .... Mongoose lemur
          mongoz (Linnaeus 1766)
          coronatus (Gray 1842) .... Crowned lemur
        rubriventer (I. Geoffroy 1850) ....Red-bellied lemur
        variegatus (Kerr 1792) .... Ruffed lemur
          variegatus (Kerr 1792)
          editorum (I. Geoffroy 1851)
          ruber (E. Geoffroy 1812) .... Red-ruffed lemur
          subcinctus (A. Smith 1833)
      Hapalemur (I. Geoffroy 1851) .... Gentle lemur
        griseus (Link 1795) .... Gray gentle lemur
          griseus (Link 1795)
          olivaceus (I. Geoffroy 1851) .... Olivaceus lemur
        simus (Gray 1870) .... Broad-nosed gentle lemur
      Lepilemur (I. Geoffroy 1851) .... Weasel, sportive lemur
        mustelinus (I. Geoffroy 1851) .... Weasel lemur
        ruficaudatus (A. Grandidier 1867) ...... Red-tailed sportive lemur
          ruficaudatus (A. Grandidier 1867)
          leucopus (Forsyth-Major 1894) .... White-footed sportive lemur
    Subfamily CHEIROGALEINAE (Gregory 1915)
      Cheirogaleus (E. Geoffroy 1812)
        major (E. Geoffroy 1812) .... Greater dwarf lemur
          major (E. Geoffroy 1812) .... Milius's dwarf lemur
          crossleyi (A. Grandidier 1870) .... Crossley's mouse lemur
          melanotis (Forsyth-Major 1894) ..... Black-eared mouse lemur
          sibreei (Forsyth-Major 1896) .... Sibree's mouse lemur

medius (E. Geoffroy 1812) .... Fat-tailed lemur
   medius (E. Geoffroy 1812) .... Eastern fat-tailed lemur
   samati (A. Grandidier 1868) .... Samat's fat-tailed lemur
  trichotis (Günther 1875) .... Hairy-eared dwarf lemur
Microcebus (I. Geoffroy 1828) .... Mouse lemur
  coquereli (A. Grandidier 1867) .... Coquerel's mouse lemur
  murinus (J. F. Miller 1777) .... Miller's lesser mouse lemur
   murinus (J. F. Miller 1777)
   myoxinus (Peters 1852) .... Peters', dormouse dwarf lemur
  smithii (Gray 1842) .... Smith's mouse lemur
Phaner (Gray 1870)
  furcifer (Blainville 1839) .... Fork-marked mouse lemur
Family INDRIIDAE (Burnett 1828)
  Indri (E. Geoffroy & Cuvier 1795) .... Indris, babakoto
   indri (Gmelin 1788)
  Avahi[1] (Jourdan 1834) .... Woolly indris
   laniger (Gmelin 1788)
   laniger (Gmelin 1788) .... Eastern woolly indris
   occidentalis (Lorenz 1898) .... Western woolly indris
  Propithecus (Bennett 1832) .... Sifaka, monkey lemur
   diadema (Bennett 1832) .... Diademed sifaka
    diadema (Bennett 1832)
    candidus (A. Grandidier 1871) ...... Grandidier's, silky sifaka
    edwardsi (A. Grandidier 1871) .... Milne-Edward's sifaka
    holomelas (Günther 1875) .... Black sifaka
    perrieri (Lavauden 1931) .... Perrier's sifaka
   verreauxi (A. Grandidier 1867) .... Verreaux's sifaka
    verreauxi (A. Grandidier 1867)
    coquereli (A. Milne-Edwards 1867) .... Coquerel's sifaka
    coronatus (A. Milne-Edwards 1871) .... Crowned sifaka
    deckeni (Peters 1870) .... Van der Decken's sifaka
    majori (Rothschild 1897) .... Forsyth-Major's sifaka
Superfamily DAUBENTONIOIDEA (Gill 1872)
  Family DAUBENTONIIDAE (Gray 1870)
   Daubentonia (E. Geoffroy 1795) .... Aye-Aye
    madagascariensis (Gmelin 1788)
Infraorder LORISIFORMES (Gregory 1915)
  Family LORISIDAE (Gregory 1915)
   Subfamily LORISINAE (Flower & Lydekker 1891)
    Loris (E. Geoffroy 1796) .... Slender loris
     tardigradus (Linnaeus 1758)
     tardigradus (Linnaeus 1758)
     grandis (Hill & Phillips 1932)
     lydekkerianus (Cabrera 1908)
     malabaricus (Wroughton 1917)

---

[1] The name *Avahi* (Jourdan 1834) is clearly superseded by *Lichanotus* (Illiger 1811) by the rule of priority. This is one case where priority, which Simpson followed in his 1945 classification, has been completely ignored by students of the Lemurinae. We note *Avahi* in the long list but use *Lichanotus* in the synoptic list.

    nordicus (Hill 1942)
    nycticeboides (Hill 1942)
Arctocebus (Gray 1863) .... Angwantibo
    calabarensis (J. A. Smith 1860)
        calabarensis (J. A. Smith 1860)
        aureus (de Winton 1902)
Nycticebus (E. Geoffroy 1812) ....Slow loris
    coucang (Boddaert 1785)
        coucang (Boddaert 1785)
        bancanus (Lyon 1906)
        bengalensis (Fischer 1804)
        borneanus (Lyon 1906)
        hilleri (Stone & Rehn 1902)
        insularis (Robinson 1917)
        javanicus (E. Geoffroy 1812)
        natunae (Stone & Rehn 1902)
        pygmaeus (Bonhote 1907) .... Lesser slow loris
        tenasserimensis (Elliot 1912)
Perodicticus (Bennett 1831) .... Potto
    potto (P. L. S. Müller 1766)
        potto (P. L. S. Müller 1766) .... Bosman's potto
        edwardsi (Bouvier 1879) .... Milne-Edward's potto
        faustus (Thomas 1910)
        ibeanus (Thomas 1910)
        ju-ju (Thomas 1910)
Subfamily GALAGINAE (Mivart 1864)
    Galago (E. Geoffroy 1796) .... Galago, bush baby
    alleni (Waterhouse 1837) .... Allen's galago
    crassicaudatus (E. Geoffroy 1812) ..... Grand, thick-tailed galago
        crassicaudatus (E. Geoffroy 1812)
        agisymbanus (Coquerel 1859) .... Komba, Coquerel's galago
        argentatus (Lönnberg 1913) .... Silvery galago
        garnetti (Ogilby 1838)
        kikuyuensis (Lönnberg 1912) .... Kikuyu galago
        lasiotis (Peters 1876) .... Woolly-eared galago
        lonnbergi (Schwarz 1930)
        monteiri (Gray 1863) .... Monteiro's galago
        panganiensis (Matschie 1906) .... Arusha galago
        umbrosus (Thomas 1917)
    senegalensis (E. Geoffroy 1796) .... Lesser galago
        senegalensis (E. Geoffroy 1796) .... Senegal galago
        albipes (Dollman 1909) .... White-footed galago
        braccatus (Elliot 1907) .... Yellow-thighed galago
        bradfieldi (Roberts 1931)
        dunni (Dollman 1910) .... Abyssinian galago
        gallarum (Thomas 1901) .... Galla galago
        granti (Thomas & Wroughton 1907) .... Grant's galago
        moholi (A. Smith 1839) .... Moholi galago
        sotikae (Hollister 1920) .... Sotik galago
        zanzibaricus (Matschie 1893) .... Zanzibar galago

Euoticus (Gray 1863)
    elegantulus (Le Conte 1857) .... Needle-clawed galago
        elegantulus (Le Conte 1857)
        pallidus (Gray 1863)
        inustus (Schwarz 1930)
Galagoides (A. Smith 1833) .... Dwarf galago
    demidovii (Fischer 1808)
        demidovii (Fischer 1808) .... Demidoff's galago
        anomurus (Pousargues 1894)
        murinus (Murray 1859) .... Murine galago
        orinus (Laurence & Washburn 1936)
        phasma (Cabrera & Ruxton 1926)
        poensis (Thomas 1904)
        thomasi (Elliot 1907)
Infraorder TARSIIFORMES (Gregory 1915)
  Family TARSIIDAE (Gill 1872)
    Tarsius (Starr 1780)
      bancanus (Horsfield 1821) .... Western tarsier
        bancanus (Horsfield 1821) .... Sumatran tarsier
        borneanus (Elliot 1910) .... Bornean tarsier
        natunensis (Chasen 1940) .... Sirhassen tarsier
        saltator (Elliot 1910) .... Billiton tarsier
      spectrum (Pallas 1778) .... Eastern tarsier
        spectrum (Pallas 1778) .... Celebesian tarsier
        dentatus (Miller & Hollister 1921)
        pelengensis (Sody 1949)
        pumilus (Miller & Hollister 1921)
        sangirensis (Meyer 1896) .... Sangir tarsier
      syrichta (Linnaeus 1758) .... Philippine tarsier
        syrichta (Linnaeus 1758) .... Larger Philippine tarsier
        carbonarius (Heude 1898) .... Mindanao tarsier
        fraterculus (Miller 1911) .... Lesser Philippine tarsier
Suborder ANTHROPOIDEA (Mivart 1864)
  Superfamily CEBOIDEA (Simpson 1931)
    Family HAPALIDAE (Wagner 1840)
      Subfamily CALLIMICONINAE (Thomas 1913)
        Callimico (Ribeiro 1911)
          goeldii (Thomas 1904) .... Goeldi's monkey
      Subfamily HAPALINAE (Wagner 1840)
        Hapale (Illiger 1811) .... Tufted-eared marmoset
        albicollis (Spix 1823) .... White-necked marmoset
        aurita (E. Geoffroy 1812) .... White-eared marmoset
        chrysoleucos (Wagner 1842) ...... Yellow-legged, silky marmoset
        flaviceps (Thomas 1903) .... Buff-headed marmoset
        humeralifer (E. Geoffroy 1812) ...... White-shouldered marmoset
        jacchus (Linnaeus 1758) .... Common marmoset, ouistiti
        leucocephala (E. Geoffroy 1812) White-fronted, Geoffroy's marmoset
        penicillata (E. Geoffroy 1812) .... Black-penciled marmoset
          penicillata (E. Geoffroy 1812)
          jordani (Thomas 1904)

petronius (Ribeiro 1924) .... Elegant marmoset
santaremensis (Matschie 1893) .... Santarem marmoset
Cebuella (Gray 1866) .... Pygmy marmoset
  pygmaea (Spix 1823)
    pygmaea (Spix 1823)
    niveiventris (Lönnberg 1940)
Leontocebus (Wagner 1839) .... Maned lion marmoset
  chrysomelas (Kuhl 1820)
                      Golden-headed, black and gold, Wied's tamarin
  chrysopygus (Mikan 1820) .. Golden-rumped, yellow-tailed tamarin
  rosalia (Linnaeus 1766) ..... Lion, gold marmoset, silky tamarin
Marikana (Lesson 1840) .... Bare-faced, bald tamarins
  bicolor (Spix 1823) .... Pied tamarin
  martinsi (Thomas 1912) .... Martin's tamarin
Mico (Lesson 1840) .... Naked-eared marmoset
  argentatus (Linnaeus 1771) .... Black-tailed, silvery marmoset
    argentatus (Linnaeus 1771) .... Silver marmoset
    emiliae (Thomas 1920)
    melanurus (E. Geoffroy 1812) .... Black-tailed marmoset
Oedipomidas (Reichenbach 1862) ..... Crested, bare-faced tamarin
  oedipus (Linnaeus 1758) .... Pinche, cotton-headed tamarin
  spixi (Reichenbach 1862) .... Geoffroy's tamarin
Tamarin (Gray 1870) .... Hairy-faced, black-faced tamarin
  tamarin (Link 1795) .... Negro tamarin
    tamarin (Link 1795)
    umbratus (Thomas 1922)
  inustus (Schwarz 1951)
  midas (Linnaeus 1758) .... Red-handed, Lacépède's tamarin
    midas (Linnaeus 1758)
    egens (Thomas 1912)
    rufimanus (E. Geoffroy 1812)
Tamarinus (Trouessart 1899) .... White-faced tamarin
  fusciollis (Spix 1823) .... Brown-headed tamarin
  graellsi (Espada 1870) .... Rio Napo tamarin
  illigeri (Pucheran 1845) .... Red-mantled tamarin
    illigeri (Pucheran 1845) .... Illiger's tamarin
    lagonotus (Espada 1870) .... Hare-lipped tamarin
  imperator (Goeldi 1907) .... Emperor tamarin
    imperator (Goeldi 1907)
    subgrisescens (Lönnberg 1940)
  labiatus (Humboldt 1812) ..... Red-bellied, white-lipped tamarin
    labiatus (Humboldt 1812)
    griseovertex (Goeldi 1907)
    thomasi (Goeldi 1907)
  leucopus (Günther 1876) .... White-footed tamarin
  melanoleucus (Miranda Ribeiro 1912) .... White tamarin
  mystax (Spix 1823) .... Moustached tamarin
  nigricollis (Spix 1823) .... Black and red tamarin
    devilli (I. Geoffroy 1848)
    leucogenys (Gray 1866)

micans (Thomas 1928)
pacator (Thomas 1914)
purillus (Thomas 1914)
rufoniger (I. Geoffroy & Deville 1848)
pileatus (I. Geoffroy & Deville 1848) Red-capped, bonneted tamarin
pluto (Lönnberg 1926) .... Lönnberg's tamarin
tripartitus (Milne-Edwards 1878) .... Golden-mantled tamarin
weddelli (Deville 1849) .... Weddell's or Deville's tamarin
Family CEBIDAE (Swainson 1835)
  Subfamily CEBINAE (Mivart 1865)
    Cebus (Erxleben 1777) .... Capuchin monkey
      albifrons (Humboldt 1812) .... White-fronted capuchin
        albifrons (Humboldt 1812)
        adustus (Hershkovits 1949) .... Brown-faced capuchin
        aequatorialis (Allen 1914) .. Ecuadorian white-fronted capuchin
        cesarae (Hershkovits 1949)
        cuscinus (Thomas 1901) .... Shock-headed capuchin
        hypoleucus (Humboldt 1812)
        leucocephalus (Gray 1865) .... White-headed capuchin
        malitiosus (Elliot 1909)
        pleei (Hershkovits 1949)
        trinitatis (Pusch 1942) .... Trinidadian capuchin
        unicolor (Spix 1823) .... Pale, slender capuchin
        versicolor (Pucheran 1845) .... Varied capuchin
        yuracus (Hershkovits 1949)
      apella (Linnaeus 1758) .... Brown, tufted capuchin
        apella (Linnaeus 1758) .... Guianan brown capuchin
        cay (Illiger 1815) .... Azara's capuchin
        fatuellus (Linnaeus 1766) .. Hooded, Colombian brown capuchin
        frontatus (Kuhl 1820) .... White-cheeked capuchin
        libidinosus (Spix 1823) .... Bearded, Spix's capuchin
        macrocephalus (Spix 1823) .... Large-headed capuchin
        magnus (Pusch 1942)
        margaritae (Hollister 1914) .... Margarita island capuchin
        nigritus (Goldfuss 1809) .... Black-horned capuchin
        pallidus (Gray 1865) .... Pale capuchin
        peruanus (Thomas 1901) .... Peruvian brown capuchin
        robustus (Kuhl 1820) .... Crested capuchin
        tocantinus (Lönnberg 1939)
        xanthosternos (Wied 1826) .... Smooth-headed capuchin
      capucinus (Linnaeus 1758) .... White-throated capuchin
        capucinus (Linnaeus 1758)
        curtus (Bangs 1905)
        imitator (Thomas 1903) ... Panamanian white-throated capuchin
        limitaneus (Hollister 1914)
        nigripectus (Elliot 1909) .... Black-chested capuchin
      griseus (F. Cuvier 1819) .... Cai weeper capuchin
        griseus (F. Cuvier 1819) .... Gray, olive weeper capuchin
        brunneus (Allen 1914) .... Brown, weeper capuchin
        castaneus (I. Geoffroy 1851) .... Chestnut capuchin
        leporinus (Pusch 1941) .... Brazilian weeper capuchin

Saimiri (Voigt 1831) .... Squirrel monkey
  boliviensis (d'Orbigny 1834) ...... Black-headed squirrel monkey
    boliviensis (d'Orbigny 1834)
    jaburuensis (Lönnberg 1940)
    nigriceps (Thomas 1902)
    pluvialis (Lönnberg 1940)
  madeirae (Thomas 1908)
    madeirae (Thomas 1908)
    juruanus (Lönnberg 1940)
  oerstedi (Reinhardt 1872) .... Red-backed squirrel monkey
    oerstedi (Reinhardt 1872) Panamanian red-backed squirrel monkey
    citrinellus (Thomas 1904) Costa Rican red-backed squirrel monkey
  sciurea (Linnaeus 1758) .... Common squirrel monkey
    sciurea (Linnaeus 1758)
    caquetensis (J. A. Allen 1916)
    cassiquiarensis (Humboldt 1812) .. Humboldt's squirrel monkey
    codajazensis (Lönnberg 1940) .... Codajaz squirrel monkey
    collinsi (Osgood 1916) .... Collins' squirrel monkey
    macrodon (Elliot 1907) .... Ecuadorian squirrel monkey
    petrina (Thomas 1927)
  usta (I. Geoffroy 1844) .... Short-tailed squirrel monkey
Subfamily ALOUATTINAE (Elliot 1904)
  Alouatta (Lacépède 1799) .... Howler monkey
    belzebul (Linnaeus 1766) .... Rufous-handed howler
      belzebul (Linnaeus 1766)
      discolor (Spix 1823)
      mexianae (Hogmann 1908)
      nigerrima (Lönnberg 1941)
      ululata (Elliot 1912)
    caraya (Humboldt 1812)
    guariba (Humboldt 1812) .... Brown, ursine howler
      guariba (Humboldt 1812)
      beniensis (Lönnberg 1941)
      clamitans (Cabrera 1940)
    palliata (Gray 1848) .... Mantled howler
      palliata (Gray 1848) .... Nicaraguan mantled howler
      aequatorialis (Festa 1903) .... Ecuadorian mantled howler
      coibensis (Thomas 1902) .... Coiba howler
      luctosa (Lawrence 1933) .... Honduran mantled howler
      mexicana (Merriam 1902) .... Mexican mantled howler
      pigra (Lawrence 1933) .... Guatemalan mantled howler
      trabeata (Lawrence 1933) .... Panamanian mantled howler
    seniculus (Linnaeus 1766) .... Red howler
      seniculus (Linnaeus 1766)
      amazonica (Lönnberg 1941)
      arctoidea (Cabrera 1940)
      insulanus (Elliot 1910)
      juara (Elliot 1910)
      macconnelli (Elliot 1910)
      puruensis (Lönnberg 1941)

sara (Elliot 1910)
stramineus (Humboldt 1812)
villosa (Gray 1845) .... Guatemalan howler
Subfamily AOTINAE (Elliot 1913)
Aotes (Humboldt 1811) .... Douroucouli, night monkey
trivirgatus (Humboldt 1811) .... Three-banded night monkey
trivirgatus (Humboldt 1811) .... Noisy douroucouli
azarae (Humboldt 1812) .... Azara's douroucouli
boliviensis (Elliot 1907) .... Bolivian douroucouli
griseimembra (Elliot 1912) .... Gray-legged douroucouli
infulatus (Olfers 1818) .... Feline douroucouli
lemurinus (I. Geoffroy 1843) .... Lemurine douroucouli
microdon (Dollman 1909) .... Dollman's douroucouli
nigriceps (Dollman 1909) .. Black-headed, Peruvian douroucouli
roberti (Dollman 1909) .... Robert's douroucouli
rufipes (Sclater 1872) .... Red-footed douroucouli
Subfamily ATELINAE (Miller 1924)
Ateles (E. Geoffroy 1806) .... Spider monkey
belzebuth (E. Geoffroy 1806) .... Long-haired spider monkey
belzebuth (E. Geoffroy 1806) .... Marimonda
hybridus (I. Geoffroy 1829) .... Variegated spider monkey
marginatus (E. Geoffroy 1809) . White-whiskered spider monkey
fusciceps (Gray 1866) .... Brown-headed spider monkey
fusciceps (Gray 1866)
dariensis (Goldman 1915)
robustus (J. A. Allen 1914) ... Colombian black spider monkey
geoffroyi (Kuhl 1820) .... Miriki
geoffroyi (Kuhl 1820) .... Nicaraguan spider monkey
azuerensis (Boles 1937) .... Azuero spider monkey
frontatus (Gray 1870) .... Black-browed spider monkey
grisescens (Gray 1866) .... Grizzled, hooded spider monkey
ornatus (Gray 1870) .... Ornate, Costa Rican spider monkey
pan (Schlegel 1876) ..... Guatemalan, Schlegel's spider monkey
panamensis (Kellogg & Goldman 1944) .... Red spider monkey
vellerosus (Gray 1866) .... Mexican spider monkey
yucatanensis (Kellogg & Goldman 1944) Yucatanian spider monkey
paniscus (Linnaeus 1758) .... Coaita, black spider monkey
paniscus (Linnaeus 1758) .... Guianan black spider monkey
chamek (Humboldt 1812) .... Black-faced spider monkey
longimembris (J. A. Allen 1914)
rufiventris (Sclater 1872) .... Red-bellied spider monkey
Brachyteles (Spix 1823) .... Woolly spider monkey
arachnoides (E. Geoffroy 1806)
Lagothrix (E. Geoffroy 1812) .... Woolly monkey
lagotricha (Humboldt 1811) .... Humboldt's woolly monkey
cana (E. Geoffroy 1812) .... Gray, smoky woolly monkey
cana (E. Geoffroy 1812)
hendeei (Thomas 1927)
lugens (Elliot 1907)
olivacea (Spix 1823)
poeppigi (Schinz 1844)

Subfamily CALLICEBINAE (Pocock 1925)
Callicebus (Thomas 1903) .... Titi monkey
    cinerascens (Spix 1823) .... Ashy titi
    cupreus (Spix 1823) .... Red titi
      cupreus (Spix 1823)
      acreanus (Vieira 1952) .... Acre titi
      brunneus (Wagner 1842) .... Brown titi
      caligatus (Wagner 1842) .... Chestnut-bellied titi
      egeria (Thomas 1908)
      leucometopus (Cabrera 1900) .... White-browed titi
      modestus (Lönnberg 1939)
      napoleon (Lönnberg 1922)
      ornatus (Gray 1866) .... Ornate titi
      paenulatus (Elliot 1909)
      rutteri (Thomas 1923) .... Rutter's titi
      subrufus (Elliot 1907)
      toppini (Thomas 1914) .... Toppin's titi
      ustofuscus (Elliot 1907) .... Dusky titi
    gigot (Spix 1823) .... Gray titi
      gigot (Spix 1823) .... Eastern gray titi
      donacophilus (d'Orbigny 1847) .... Reed titi
      oenanthe (Thomas 1924) .... Isabelline titi
      pallescens (Thomas 1907) .... Pale, Paraguayan gray titi
    moloch (Hoffmannsegg 1807) .... Orabassu titi
      moloch (Hoffmannsegg 1807)
      baptista (Lönnberg 1939)
      emiliae (Thomas 1911)
      hoffmannsi (Thomas 1908)
    ollalae (Lönnberg 1939) .... Ollala's titi
    personatus (E. Geoffroy 1812) .... Masked titi
      personatus (E. Geoffroy 1812) .... Northern masked titi
      brunello (Thomas 1913) .... Southern masked titi
      melanochir (Kuhl 1820) .... Black-handed titi
      nigrifrons (Spix 1823) .... Black-fronted titi
    torquatus (Hoffmannsegg 1807) ...... Collared, yellow-handed titi
      torquatus (Hoffmannsegg 1807) .... White-collared titi
      ignitus (Thomas 1927) .... Western collared titi
      lucifer (Thomas 1914)
      lugens (Humboldt 1812) .... White-chested titi
      purinus (Thomas 1927)
      regulus (Thomas 1927)
Subfamily PITHECIINAE (Mivart 1864)
Pithecia (Desmarest 1804) .... Saki
    pithecia (Linnaeus 1766) .... Pale-headed saki
      pithecia (Linnaeus 1766) .... White-headed saki
      chrysocephala (I. Geoffroy 1850) .... Golden-headed saki
    monachus (E. Geoffroy 1812) .... Hairy saki
      monachus (E. Geoffroy 1812)
      albicans (Gray 1860) .... Whitish saki
      capillamentosa (Spix 1823) .... Guianan hairy, Humboldt's saki
      milleri (J. A. Allen 1914) .... Miller's saki

Cacajao (Lesson 1840) .... Uakari
   calvus (I. Geoffroy 1847) .... Bald uakari
   melanocephalus (Humboldt 1811) .... Black-headed uakari
   roosevelti (J. A. Allen 1914) .... Black uakari
   rubicundus (I. Geoffroy & Deville 1848) .... Red uakari
      rubicundus (I. Geoffroy & Deville 1848)
      ucayali (Thomas 1928)
Chiropotes (Lesson 1840) .... Cuxius, bearded saki
   chiropotes (Humboldt 1811) .... Red-backed saki
   albinasa (I. Geoffroy & Deville 1848) .... White-nosed saki
   satanas (Hoffmannsegg 1807) .... Black saki
Superfamily CERCOPITHECOIDEA (Simpson 1931)
  Family CERCOPITHECIDAE (Gray 1821)
    Subfamily CERCOPITHECINAE (Blanford 1888)
      Cercopithecus (Brünnich 1772) .... Guenon
        aethiops (Linnaeus 1758) .... Green, grivet, vervet monkey
          aethiops (Linnaeus 1758)
          arenarius (Heller 1913)
          callida (Hollister 1912)
          callitrichus (I. Geoffroy 1851)
          centralis (Neumann 1900)
          cloetei (Roberts 1931)
          cynosuros (Scopoli 1786)
          excubitor (Schwarz 1923)
          griseoviridis (Desmarest 1820)
          griseus (Cuvier 1824)
          hilgerti (Neumann 1902)
          johnstoni (Pocock 1907)
          majoriae (Bradfield 1936)
          marrensis (Thomas & Hinton 1923)
          matschiei (Neumann 1902)
          nesiotes (Schwarz 1923)
          ngamiensis (Roberts 1932)
          pygerythra (Hollister 1912)
          rufoviridis (I. Geoffroy 1842)
          sabaea (Linnaeus 1766)
          tantalus (Ogilby 1841)
          toldti (Wettstein 1916)
          viridis (Schultze 1910)
        cephus (Linnaeus 1758) .... Moustached, red-eared guenon
          cephus (Linnaeus 1758)
          buccalis (Leconte 1857)
          erythrotis (Waterhouse 1838)
          pulcher (Lorenz 1915)
        diana (Linnaeus 1758) .... Diana monkey
          diana (Linnaeus 1758)
          dryas (Schwarz 1932)
          faunus (Linnaeus 1766)
          roloway (Schreber 1774)
        hamlyni (Pocock 1907) .... Owl-faced guenon

l'hoesti (Sclater 1899) .... L'Hoest's guenon
   l'hoesti (Sclater 1899)
   preussi (Matschie 1898)
   thomasi (Matschie 1905)
mitis (Wolf 1822) .... Diadem guenon, Sykes' monkey
   mitis (Wolf 1822)
   albogularis (Sykes 1831)
   albotorquates (Pousargues 1896)
   boutourlinii (Giglioli 1887)
   diadematus (I. Geoffroy 1834)
   doggetti (Pocock 1907)
   erythrarchus (Peters 1852)
   kandti (Matschie 1905)
   kibonotensis (Lönnberg 1905) .... Blue monkey
   kolbi (Neumann 1902)
   labiatus (I. Geoffroy 1842)
   leucampyx (Fischer 1829)
   maesi (Lönnberg 1919)
   moloneyi (Sclater 1893)
   pluto (Gray 1848)
   schwarzi (Roberts 1931)
   stairsi (Sclater 1892)
   stuhlmanni (Matschie 1893)
mona (Schreber 1775) .... Mona guenon
   mona (Schreber 1775)
   campbelli (Waterhouse 1838)
   denti (Thomas 1907)
   elegans (Dubois & Matschie 1912)
   grayi (Fraser 1850)
   lowei (Thomas 1923)
   monacha (Schreber 1804)
   nigripes (Du Chaillu 1860)
   pogonias (Bennet 1833)
   pyrogaster (Lönnberg 1919)
   wolfi (Meyer 1891)
neglectus (Schlegel 1876) .... De Brazza's guenon
nictitans (Linnaeus 1766) ...... White-nosed, spot-nosed guenon
   nictitans (Linnaeus 1766)
   albinasus (Reichenbach 1863)
   ascanius (Audebert 1799)
   buttikoferi (Jentink 1886)
   erythrogaster (Gray 1866)
   katangae (Lönnberg 1919)
   martini (Waterhouse 1838)
   montanus (Lorenz 1914)
   mpangae (Matschie 1913)
   petaurista (Schreber 1774)
   schmidti (Matschie 1892)
   signatus (Jentink 1886)
   stricticeps (Elliot 1909)
   whitesidei (Thomas 1909)

patas (Schreber 1774) .... Patas, red Hussar monkey, nisnas
    patas (Schreber 1774)
    albo-fasciatus (Kerr 1792)
    baumstarki (Matschie 1905)
    nigro-fasciatus (Kerr 1792)
    pyrrhonotus (Hemprich & Ehrenberg 1832)
    rubra (Gmelin 1788)
talapoin (Schreber 1774) .... Talapoin
    talapoin (Schreber 1774)
    pileatus (E. Geoffroy 1812)
    nigroviridis (Pocock 1907)
Cercocebus (E. Geoffroy 1812) .... Mangabey
    albigena (Gray 1850) .... Gray-cheeked, black mangabey
        albigena (Gray 1850)
        johnstoni (Lydekker 1900)
        zenkeri (Schwarz 1910)
    aterrimus (Oudemans 1890) .... Black, peaked mangabey
    atys (Booth 1956) .... Sooty, white-crowned mangabey
    galeritus (Peters 1879) .... Agile mangabey
        galeritus (Peters 1879)
        agilis (Milne-Edwards 1886)
        chrysogaster (Lydekker 1900)
        fumosus (Matschie 1914)
    torquatus (Kerr 1792) .... White-collared, red-headed mangabey
        torquatus (Kerr 1792) .... Red-headed mangabey
        collaris (Gray 1843)
        fulginosus (E. Geoffroy 1812)
        lumulatus (Temminck 1853)
Cynopithecus (I. Geoffroy 1835) .... Black ape
    niger (Desmarest 1820)
Macaca (Lacépède 1799) .... Macaque
    assamensis (M'Clelland 1839) .... Assamese macaque
        assamensis (M'Clelland 1839)
        pelops (Hodgson 1840)
        problematicus (Gray 1870)
        rhesosimilis (Sclater 1872)
    cyclopis (Swinhoe 1862) .... Formosan macaque
    fuscata (Blyth 1875) .... Japanese macaque
        fuscata (Blyth 1875)
        yakui (Kuroda 1941)
    irus (Cuvier 1818) .... Crab-eating, cynomolgous macaque
        irus (Cuvier 1818)
        alacer (Elliot 1909)
        atriceps (Kloss 1919)
        aureus (I. Geoffroy 1834)
        bintangensis (Elliot 1909)
        carbonarius (Cuvier 1825)
        cynomolgous (Schreber 1775)
        fascicularis (Raffles 1821) .... Sumatran macaque
        kra (Lesson 1830)
        mandibularis (Elliot 1909)

umbrosus (Miller 1902) .... Nicobar island macaque
   validus (Elliot 1909)
maura (Cuvier 1823) .... Celebes macaque
   maura (Cuvier 1823)
   brunescens (Matschie 1901)
   cuvieri (Fischer 1829)
   fuscoater (Schinz 1844)
   inornatus (Gray 1866)
   ochreatus (Ogilby 1840)
   tonkeanus (Meyer 1899) .... Tonkean black baboon
   tonsus (Matschie 1901)
mulatta (Zimmerman 1780) .... Rhesus macaque
   mulatta (Zimmerman 1780)
   brevicaudatus (Elliot 1913) .... Island of Hainan macaque
   erythraea (Shaw 1800)
   lasiotus (Gray 1868) .... Hairy-eared macaque
   littoralis (Elliot 1909)
   momahoni (Pocock 1932)
   oinops (Hodgson 1840)
   vestitus (Milne-Edwards 1892)
   villosus (True 1894)
nemestrina (Linnaeus 1766) .... Pig-tailed macaque
   nemestrina (Linnaeus 1766)
   adusta (Miller 1906) .... Sunburned macaque
   andamanensis (Bartlett 1869) ...... Burmese pig-tailed macaque
   blythi (Pocock 1931)
   brachyurus (Smith 1842)
   carpolegus (Raffles 1821)
   insulana (Miller 1906)
   leoninus (Blyth 1863)
   pagensis (Miller 1903)
radiata (E. Geoffroy 1812) .... Bonnet monkey
   radiata (E. Geoffroy 1812)
   diluta (Pocock 1931)
silenus (Linnaeus 1758) .... Lion-tailed macaque
sinica (Linnaeus 1771) .... Toque monkey
   sinica (Linnaeus 1771)
   aurifrons (Pocock 1931)
   opisthomelas (Hill 1942)
speciosa (Cuvier 1825) .... Stump-tailed, brown macaque
   speciosa (Cuvier 1825)
   arctoides (I. Geoffroy 1831)
   melanotus (Ogilby 1839)
   thibetanus (Milne-Edwards 1870)   Short-tailed, Tibetan macaque
   ursinus (Gervais 1854)
sylvana (Linnaeus 1758) .... Barbary ape
Papio (Müller 1773) .... Baboon
papio (Desmarest 1820) .... Guinea, western baboon
comatus (E. Geoffroy 1812) .... Chacma baboon
   comatus (E. Geoffroy 1812)

    chobiensis (Roberts 1932)
    griseipes (Pocock 1911)
    ngamiensis (Roberts 1932)
    porcaria (Boddaert 1787)
    ursinus (Wagner 1840)
  cynocephalus (Linnaeus 1766) .... Yellow baboon
    cynocephalus (Linnaeus 1766)
    babouin (Desmarest 1820)
    kindae (Lönnberg 1919)
    langheldi (Matschie 1892)
    ochreaceus (Peters 1853)
    rhodesiae (Haagner 1918)
    sphinx (Erxleben 1777)
    strepitus (Elliot 1907)
    toth (Ogilby 1843)
  doguera (Pucheran 1856) .... Anubis, dog-faced baboon
    doguera (Pucheran 1856)
    anubis (Fischer 1829)
    furax (Elliot 1909)
    graueri (Lorenz 1917)
    heuglini (Matschie 1898) .... Heuglin's baboon
    ibeanus (Thomas 1893)
    neumanni (Matschie 1897) .... Neumann's baboon
    olivaceus (De Winton 1902)
    tessellatus (Elliot 1909)
  hamadryas (Linnaeus 1758) .... Hamadryas baboon
    hamadryas (Linnaeus 1758)
    arabicus (Thomas 1900) .... Arabian hamadryas baboon
    brockmanni (Elliot 1909)
    choeropithecus (Lesson 1840)
  leucophaeus (Cuvier 1807) .... Drill
  sphinx (Linnaeus 1758) .... Mandrill
    sphinx (Linnaeus 1758)
    burlacei (W. Rothschild 1922)
    escherichi (Matschie & Zukowsky 1917)
    maimon (Linnaeus 1766)
    planirostris (Elliot 1909)
    poensis (Zukowsky 1922)
    tessmanni (Matschie & Zukowsky 1917)
    zenkeri (Matschie & Zukowsky 1917)
Theropithecus (I. Geoffroy 1843) .... Gelada baboon
  gelada (Rüppell 1835)
Subfamily COLOBINAE (Elliot 1913)
  Colobus (Illiger 1811) .... Guereza
  badius (Kerr 1792) .... Red colobus
    badius (Kerr 1792)
    bouvieri (Rochebrune 1887)
    ellioti (Dollman 1909)
    ferruginea (Shaw 1800)
    foai (Pousargues 1899)

fuliginosus (Ogilby 1835)
gordonorum (Matschie 1900)
graueri (Dollman 1909)
gudoviusi (Matschie 1914)
kirkii (Gray 1868)
langi (J. A. Allen 1925)
nigrimanus (Trouessart 1906)
oustaleti (Trouessart 1906)
pennantii (Waterhouse 1838)
powelli (Matschie 1912)
preussi (Matschie 1900)
rufomitratus (Peters 1879)
temminckii (Kuhl 1820)
tephrosceles (Elliot 1907)
tholloni (Milne-Edwards 1886)
waldroni (Hayman 1935)
polykomos (Zimmerman 1780)
  polykomos (Zimmerman 1780)
  abyssinicus (Oken 1816) .... Abyssinian guereza
  adolfi-friederici (Matschie 1914)
  angolensis (Sclater 1860)
  caudatus (Thomas 1885) .... Mbega
  cottoni (Lydekker 1905)
  dodingae (Matschie 1913)
  dollmani (Schwarz 1926)
  gallarum (Neumann 1902)
  kikuyuensis (Lönnberg 1912)
  matschiei (Neumann 1899)
  occidentalis (Rochebrune 1886) .... Western colobus
  palliatus (Peters 1868)
  percivali (Heller 1913)
  regalis (Kerr 1792)
  ruwenzori (Thomas 1901)
  satanas (Waterhouse 1838) .... Black colobus
  sharpei (Thomas 1902)
  uellensis (Matschie 1913)
  ursinus (Ogilby 1835)
  vellerosus (I. Geoffroy 1834)
verus (Van Beneden 1838) .... Van Beneden's olive guereza
Nasalis (E. Geoffroy 1812)
  larvatus (Würm 1781) .... Proboscis monkey
Presbytis (Eschscholz 1821) .... Leaf monkey
  aygula (Linnaeus 1758) .... Sunda Island leaf monkey
    aygula (Linnaeus 1758)
    canicrus (Miller 1934)
    hosei (Thomas 1889)
    sabanus (Thomas 1893)
    thomasi (Collett 1892)
  carimatae (Miller 1906)
  cristatus (Raffles 1821) .... Silvered leaf monkey
    cristatus (Raffles 1821)

atrior (Pocock 1928)
auratus (E. Geoffroy 1812)
germaini (Milne-Edwards 1876)
pyrrhus (Horsfield 1823)
entellus (Dufresne 1797) .... Entellus monkey
  entellus (Dufresne 1797)
  achates (Pocock 1928)
  achilles (Pocock 1928)
  aeneas (Pocock 1928)
  ajax (Pocock 1928)
  anchises (Blyth 1844)
  dussumieri (I. Geoffroy 1843)
  elissa (Pocock 1928)
  hypoleucos (Blyth 1841)
  iulus (Pocock 1928)
  lania (Elliot 1909)
  priam (Blyth 1844)
  priamellus (Pocock 1928)
  schistaceus (Hodgson 1840)
  thersites (Blyth 1847)
francoisi (Pousargues 1898) .... François' leaf monkey
  francoisi (Pousargues 1898)
  delacouri (Osgood 1932)
  laotum (Thomas 1921)
  poliocephalus (Trouessart 1911)
frontatus (Müller 1838) .... White-fronted leaf monkey
johni (Fischer 1829)
melalophos (Raffles 1821) .... Banded leaf monkey
  melalophos (Raffles 1821)
  cruciger (Thomas 1892)
  chrysomelas (Müller 1838)
  femoralis (Martin 1838)
  natunae (Thomas & Hartert 1894)
  robinsoni (Thomas 1910)
  siamensis (Müller & Schlegel 1841)
obscurus (Reid 1837) ...... Dusky leaf monkey, spectacled langur
  obscurus (Reid 1837)
  flavicaudada (Elliot 1910)
  sanctorum (Elliot 1910)
phayrei (Blyth 1847)
  phayrei (Blyth 1847)
  crepusculus (Elliot 1909)
  ruhei (Knottnerus-Meyer 1933)
  shanicus (Wroughton 1917)
pileatus (Blyth 1843) .... Capped langur
  pileatus (Blyth 1843)
  brahma (Wroughton 1916)
  durga (Wroughton 1916)
  shortridgei (Wroughton 1915)
  tenebricus (Hinton 1923)
potenziani (Bonaparte 1856) .... Mentawi leaf monkey

rubicunda (Müller 1838) .... Maroon leaf monkey
senex (Erxleben 1777) .... Purple-faced langur, Wanderou
   senex (Erxleben 1777)
   kephalopterus (Zimmerman 1780)
   leucopyrmnus (Otto 1825)
   monticola (Kelaart 1850)
   nestor (Bennett 1833)
   ursinus (Blyth 1844)
   vetulus (Erxleben 1777)
Pygathrix (E. Geoffroy 1812)
   nemaeus (Linnaeus 1771)
   nigripes (Milne-Edwards 1871)
Rhinopithecus (Milne-Edwards 1872)
   avunculus (Dollman 1912) .... Tonkin snub-nosed monkey
   roxellanae (Milne-Edwards 1870)
               Snub-nosed monkey, Tibetan langur
   roxellanae (Milne-Edwards 1870)
   bieti (Milne-Edwards 1897)
   brelichi (Thomas 1903)
Simias (Miller 1903)
   concolor (Miller 1903) .... Pagi, pig-tailed, island langur
Superfamily HOMINOIDEA (Simpson 1931)
  Family PONGIDAE (Elliot 1913)
    Subfamily PONGINAE (Allen 1925)
    Pongo (Lacépède 1799)
     pygmaeus (Linnaeus 1760) .... Orangutan
     pygmaeus (Linnaeus 1760) .... Borneo orangutan
     abelii (Lesson 1826) .... Sumatra orangutan
    Pan (Oken 1816) .... Chimpanzee
     paniscus (Schwarz 1929) .... Lesser chimpanzee
     troglodytes (Blumenbach 1799) .... Chimpanzee
      troglodytes (Blumenbach 1799)
      africanus (Oken 1816)
      calvus (Du Chaillu 1860)
      graeri (Matschie 1914)
      ituricus (Matschie 1912)
      kooloo-kamba (Du Chaillu 1860)
      leucoprymnus (Lesson 1831)
      marungensis (Noak 1887)
      niger (E. Geoffroy 1812)
      schweinfurthii (Giglioni 1872) ...... Long-haired chimpanzee
      tschego (Duvernoy 1855)
      vellerosus (Gray 1862)
      verus (Schwarz 1934) .... Western chimpanzee
    Gorilla (I. Geoffroy 1852)
     gorilla (Savage & Wyman 1847)
      gorilla (Savage & Wyman 1847) .... Coast gorilla
      beringei (Matschie 1903) .... Mountain gorilla
      castaneiceps (Slack 1862)
      gina (I. Geoffroy 1855)

matschiei (Rothschild 1905)
mayéma (Alix & Bouvier 1877)
savagei (Owen 1848)
Subfamily HYLOBATINAE (Gill 1872)
Hylobates (Illiger 1811) .... Gibbon
 agilis (Cuvier 1821) .... Dark-handed gibbon
  agilis (Cuvier 1821)
  unko (Lesson 1829)
 concolor (Harlan 1826) .... Black gibbon
  concolor (Harlan 1826)
  gabriellae (Thomas 1909)
  hainanus (Thomas 1892)
  leucogenys (Ogilby 1840)
  nasutus (Kunkel d'Herculais 1884)
  niger (Ogilby 1840)
 hoolock (Harlan 1834)
  hoolock (Harlan 1834)
  fuscus (Lewis 1834)
 klossii (Miller 1903) .... Kloss's gibbon
 lar (Linnaeus 1771)
  lar (Linnaeus 1771) .... White-handed gibbon
  albimana (Vigors & Horsfield 1828)
  entelloides (I. Geoffroy 1842)
  longimana (Schreber 1774)
  pileatus (Gray 1861)
  variegatus (E. Geoffroy 1812)
 moloch (Audebert 1797) .... Sunda island gibbon
  moloch (Audebert 1797)
  funereus (I. Geoffroy 1850)
  leuciscus (E. Geoffroy 1812)
  mülleri (Martin 1841)
Symphalangus (Gloger 1841) .... Siamang
 syndactylus (Raffles 1821)
  syndactylus (Raffles 1821)
  continentis (Thomas 1908)
Family HOMINIDAE (Gray 1825)
Homo (Linnaeus 1758) .... Man
 sapiens (Linnaeus 1758)

B. Synoptic List

Order PRIMATES (Linnaeus 1758)
 Suborder PROSIMII (Illiger 1811)
  Infraorder LEMURIFORMES (Gregory 1915)
   Superfamily TUPAIOIDEA (Dobson 1882)
    Family TUPAIIDAE (Mivart 1868)
     Subfamily TUPAIINAE (Lyon 1913)
      Tupaia (Raffles 1822)
      Anathana (Lyon 1913)
      Dendrogale (Gray 1848)

  Tana (Lyon 1913)
  Urogale (Mearns 1905)
  Subfamily PTILOCERCINAE (Lyon 1913)
   Ptilocercus (Gray 1848)
 Family ANAGALIDAE* (Simpson 1931)
  *Anagale** (Simpson 1931)
Superfamily LEMUROIDEA (Mivart 1864)
 Family LEMURIDAE (Gray 1821)
  Subfamily LEMURINAE (Mivart 1864)
   Lemur (Linnaeus 1758)
   Hapalemur (I. Geoffroy 1851)
   Lepilemur (I. Geoffroy 1851)
  Subfamily CHEIROGALEINAE (Gregory 1915)
   Cheirogaleus (E. Geoffroy 1812)
   Microcebus (I. Geoffroy 1828)
   Phaner (Gray 1870)
  Subfamily ARCHAEOLEMURINAE* (Standing 1908)
   *Archaeolemur** (Filhol 1895)
  Subfamily HADROPITHECINAE* (Abel 1931)
   *Hadropithecus** (Lorenz 1900)
  Subfamily MEGALADAPINAE* (Flower and Lydekker 1891)
   *Megaladapis** (Forsyth-Major 1893)
   *Megalindris** (Standing 1908)
 Family INDRIIDAE (Burnett 1828)
  Indri (E. Geoffroy 1796)
  Lichanotus[1] (Illiger 1811)
  Propithecus (Bennett 1832)
  *Mesopropithecus** (Standing 1908)
  *Neopropithecus** (Lambert 1939)
  *Paleopropithecus** (Grandidier 1899)
 Family ADAPIDAE* (Trouessart 1879)
  Subfamily ADAPINAE* (Trouessart 1879)
   *Adapis** (Cuvier 1821)
   *Anchomomys** (Stehlin 1916)
   *Pronycticebus** (Grandidier 1904)
  Subfamily NOTHARCTINAE* (Trouessart 1879)
   *Notharctus** (Leidy 1870)
   *Pelycodus** (Cope 1875)
   *Protoadapis** (Lemoine 1878)
 ADAPIDAE incertae sedis:
  *Aphanolemur** (Granger & Gregory 1917)
  *Amphilemur** (Heller 1935)
  *Caenopithecus** (Rütimeyer 1862)
 Family PLESIADAPIDAE* (Trouessart 1897)
  *Plesiadapis** (Gervais 1877)
  *Chiromyoides** (Stehlin 1916)
  *Megachiromyoides** (Weigelt 1933)
  *Platychoerops** (Charlesworth 1854)

---

* Indicates fossil form.
[1] See page 41.

*Pronothodectes** (Gidley 1923)
Superfamily DAUBENTONIOIDEA (Gill 1872)
    Family DUABENTONIIDAE (Gray 1870)
        Daubentonia (E. Geoffroy 1795)
Infraorder LORISIFORMES (Gregory 1915)
    Family LORISIDAE (Gregory 1915)
        Subfamily LORISINAE (Flower & Lydekker 1891)
            Loris (E. Geoffroy 1796)
            Arctocebus (Gray 1863)
            Nycticebus (E. Geoffroy 1812)
            Perodicticus (Bennett 1831)
            *Indraloris** (Lewis 1933)
        Subfamily GALAGINAE (Mivart 1864)
            Galago (E. Geoffroy 1796)
            Euoticus (Gray 1863)
Infraorder TARSIIFORMES (Gregory 1915)
    Family TARSIIDAE (Gill 1872)
        Tarsius (Starr 1780)
    Family ANAPTOMORPHIDAE** (Cope 1883)
        Subfamily ANAPTOMORPHINAE** (Simpson 1940)
            *Absarokius** (Matthew 1915)
            *Anaptomorphus** (Cope 1872)
            *Euryacodon** (Marsh 1872)
            *Paratetonius** (Seton 1940)
            *Tetonius** (Matthew 1915)
            *Uintanius** (Matthew 1915)
        Subfamily NECROLEMURINAE** (Simpson 1940)
            *Microchoerus** (Wood 1846)
            *Necrolemur** (Filhol 1873)
        Subfamily OMOMYINAE** (Wortman 1904)
            *Chumashius** (Stock 1933)
            *Dyseolemur** (Stock 1934)
            *Hemiacodon** (Marsh 1872)
            *Loveina** (Simpson 1940)
            *Macrotarsius** (Clark 1941)
            *Navajovius** (Matthew & Granger 1921)
            *Omomys** (Leidy 1869)
            *Shoshonius** (Granger 1910)
            *Teilhardina** (Simpson 1940)
            *Washakius** (Leidy 1873)
        Subfamily PAROMOMYINAE** (Simpson 1940)
            *Palaechthon** (Gidley 1923)
            *Palenochtha** (Simpson 1935)
            *Paromomys** (Gidley 1923)
            *Plesiolestes** (Jepsen 1930)
        Subfamily PSEUDOLORISINAE** (Simpson 1940)
            *Pseudoloris** (Stehlin 1916)
    ANAPTOMORPHIDAE incertae sedis:
        *Nannopithex** (Stehlin 1916)

---

* Indicates fossil form.

*Periconodon** (Stehlin 1916)
*Yumanius** (Stock 1938)
PROSIMII infraorder uncertain
  Family APATEMYIDAE* (Matthew 1909)
    *Apatemys** (Marsh 1872)
    *Eochiromys** (Teilhard de Chardin 1927)
    *Heterohyus** (Gervais 1848-52)
    *Jepsenella** (Simpson 1940)
    *Labidolemur** (Matthew & Granger 1921)
    *Sinclairella** (Jepsen 1934)
    *Stehlinella** (Matthew 1929)
    *Teilhardella** (Jepsen 1930)
  Family CARPOLESTIDAE* (Simpson 1935)
    *Carpolestes** (Simpson 1928)
    *Carpodaptes** (Matthew & Granger 1921)
    *Elphidotarsius** (Gidley 1923)
PROSIMII infraorder or family uncertain
    *Adapidium** (Young 1937)
    *Ceciliolemur** (Weigelt 1933)
    *Europolemur** (Weigelt 1933)
    *Hoanghonius** (Zdansky 1930)
    *Megatarsius** (Weigelt 1933)
    *Microtarsioides** (Weigelt 1933)
    *Phenacolemur** (Matthew 1915)
    *Trogolemur** (Matthew 1909)
    *Uintasorex** (Matthew 1909)
Suborder ANTHROPOIDEA (Mivart 1864)
  Superfamily CEBOIDEA (Simpson 1931)
    Family CEBIDAE (Swainson 1835)
      Subfamily CEBINAE (Mivart 1865)
        Cebus (Erxleben 1777)
        Saimiri (Voigt 1831)
      Subfamily ALOUATTINAE (Elliot 1904)
        Alouatta (Lacépède 1799)
      Subfamily AOTINAE (Elliot 1913)
        Aotes (Humboldt 1811)
        Callicebus (Thomas 1903)
        *Homunculus** (Ameghino 1891)
      Subfamily ATELINAE (Miller 1924)
        Ateles (E. Geoffroy 1806)
        Brachyteles (Spix 1823)
        Lagothrix (E. Geoffroy 1812)
      Subfamily CALLIMICONINAE (Thomas 1913)
        Callimico (Ribeiro 1911)
      Subfamily PITHECIINAE (Mivart 1865)
        Cacajao (Lesson 1840)
        Chiropotes (Lesson 1840)
        Pithecia (Desmarest 1804)
    Family CALLITHRICIDAE (Thomas 1903)

---

* Indicates fossil form.

    Callithrix (Erxleben 1777)
    Leontocebus (Wagner 1839)
Superfamily CERCOPITHECOIDEA (Simpson 1931)
  Family CERCOPITHECIDAE (Gray 1821)
    Subfamily CERCOPITHECINAE (Blanford 1888)
      Cercopithecus (Brünnich 1772)
      Cercocebus (E. Geoffroy 1812)
      Comopithecus (Allen 1925)
      Cynopithecus (I. Geoffroy 1835)
      Macaca (Lacépède 1799)
      Mandrillus[2] (Ritgen 1824)
      Papio (Müller 1773)
      Theropithecus[3] (I. Geoffroy 1843)
      *Dinopithecus** (Broom 1936)
      *Lybipithecus** (Stromer 1913)
      *Parapapio** (Jones 1937)
      *Simopithecus** (Andrews 1916)
    Subfamily COLOBINAE (Elliot 1913)
      Colobus (Illiger 1811)
      Nasalis (E. Geoffroy 1812)
      Presbytis (Eschscholtz 1821)
      Pygathrix (E. Geoffroy 1812)
      Rhinopithecus (Milne-Edwards 1872)
      Simias (Miller 1903)
      *Dolichopithecus** (Depéret 1889)
      *Mesopithecus** (Wagner 1839)
    CERCOPITHECIDAE subfamily uncertain
      *Apidium** (Osborn 1918)
      *Moeripithecus** (Schlosser 1911)
      *Oreopithecus** (Gervais 1872)
Superfamily HOMINOIDEA (Simpson 1931)
  Family PARAPITHECIDAE* (Schlosser 1911)
    *Parapithecus** (Schlosser 1911)
  Family PONGIDAE (Elliot 1913)
    Subfamily PONGINAE (Allen 1925)
      Pongo (Lacépède 1799)
      Gorilla (I. Geoffroy 1852)
      Pan (Oken 1816)
      *Gigantopithecus** (von Koenigswald 1939)
    Subfamily HYLOBATINAE (Gill 1872)
      Hylobates (Illiger 1811)
      Symphalangus (Gloger 1841)

---

* Indicates fossil form.

[2] *Mandrillus* is considered insufficiently distinct from *Papio* by Fiedler (1956), and *Papio sphinx* is given by this authority as the most reasonable name. We can only applaud this further sign of a tendency to examine the excessive number of primate genera with a "lumper's" eye. This trend, however, may also become exaggerated. Simpson's discussion of the art of classification is pertinent to this.

[3] *Theropithecus* might well be reexamined with a view to determining the validity (or usefulness) of continuing to put this animal in a genus distinct from *Papio*.

*Limnopithecus** (Hopwood 1933)
*Paidopithex** (Pohlig 1895)
*Pliopithecus** (Gervais 1849)
*Propliopithecus** (Schlosser 1911)
Subfamily AUSTRALOPITHECINAE* (Gregory & Hellman 1939)
    *Australopithecus***[4] (Dart 1925)
Subfamily DRYOPITHECINAE* (Gregory & Hellman 1939)
    *Bramapithecus** (Lewis 1934)
    *Dryopithecus** (Lartet 1856)
    *Hylopithecus** (Pilgrim 1927)
    *Palaeosimia** (Pilgrim 1915)
    *Proconsul** (Hopwood 1933)
    *Ramapithecus** (Lewis 1934)
    *Sivapithecus** (Pilgrim 1927)
    *Sugrivapithecus** (Lewis 1934)
Pongid-like fossils of uncertain affinities
    *Amphipithecus** (Colbert 1937)
    *Pondaungia** (Pilgrim 1927)
    *Xenopithecus** (Hopwood 1933)
Family HOMINIDAE (Gray 1825)
    Homo (Linnaeus 1758)

REFERENCES

ALLEN, G. M. (1939). A Checklist of African mammals. *Bull. Museum Comp. Zool. Harvard* **83**.

ANDREW, R. J. (1962). Evolution of intelligence and vocal mimicking. *Science* **137**, 585-589.

BENDER, M., AND METTLER, L. E. (1958). Chromosome studies of the Primates. *Science* **128**, 186-190.

BOLWIG, N. (1960). A comparative study of the behaviour of various lemurs. *Mém. inst. sci. Madagascar Sér. A:* Biologie Animale **14**, 205-217.

BOOTH, A. H. (1955). Speciation in the mona monkeys. *J. Mamm.* **36**, 434-438.

BUETTNER-JANUSCH, J. (1962). Biochemical genetics of the Primates—hemoglobins and transferrins. *Ann. N.Y. Acad. Sci.* **102**, 235-248.

BUETTNER-JANUSCH, J., AND TWICHELL, J. B. (1961). Alkali-resistant haemoglobins in prosimian Primates. *Nature* **192**, 699.

CHU, E. H. Y., AND BENDER, M. (1962). Cytogenetics of the Primates and primate evolution. *Ann. N.Y. Acad. Sci.* **102**, 253-266.

CLARK, W. E. LeGROS (1960). "The Antecedents of Man." Chicago, Illinois, Quadrangle Press.

ELLERMAN, J. R., AND MORRISON-KOTT, T. S. (1951). "Checklist of Palearctic and Indian Mammals, 1758-1946." London, Brit. Museum (Nat. Hist.).

ELLIOT, D. G. (1913). A review of the Primates. *Bull. Am. Museum Nat. Hist.* **1-3**.

---

* Indicates fossil form.

[4] The trend of much contemporary theorizing about these South African man apes can be taken to imply that they should be a genus of the family Hominidae. A forthcoming publication by the Wenner-Gren Foundation will apparently deal with this problem. The classification of fossils relevant to the hominids is fraught with the emotional fervor of which Simpson remarks in the quotation on page 37.

FIEDLER, W. (1956). Übersicht über das System der Primaten. *In* "Primatologia" (H. Hofer, A. H. Schultz, and D. Stark, eds.), Vol. I, pp. 1-266. Basel, Switzerland, Karger.

FORD, C. E., HAMERTON, J. L., AND SHARMAN, G. B. (1957). Chromosome polymorphism in the common shrew. *Nature* **180**, 392-393.

GOODMAN, M. (1962). Immunochemistry of the Primates and primate evolution. *Ann. N. Y. Acad. Sci.* **102**, 219-234.

GRASSÉ, P.-P. (1955). "Traité de Zoologie," Vol. 17, Part II. Paris, Masson.

GRAY, A. P. (1954). Mammalian hybrids. A checklist with bibliography. Tech. Commun. No. 10, Commonwealth Agricultural Bureau, Farnham, Royal, England.

HILL, W. C. O. (1939). An annotated systematic list of the leaf-monkeys. *Ceylon J. Sci.* **B21**.

HILL, W. C. O. (1953). "Primates," I: Strepsirhini. New York, Wiley (Interscience).

HILL, W. C. O. (1955). "Primates," II: Haplorhini: Tarsioidea. New York, Wiley (Interscience).

HILL, W. C. O. (1957). "Primates," III: Pithecoidea, Platyrrhini. New York, Wiley (Interscience).

HILL, W. C. O. (1960). "Primates," IV: Cebidae, Part A. New York, Wiley (Interscience).

HILL, W. C. O. (1962). "Primates," V: Cebidae, Part B. New York, Wiley (Interscience).

HUXLEY, T. H. (1876). "Man's Place in Nature." New York, Appleton.

JONES, F. W. (1929). Some landmarks in the phylogeny of Primates. *Human Biol.* **1**, 219-228.

LANG, H. (1923). A new genus of African monkey, *Allenopithecus*. *Am. Museum Novitiates* **87**, 1-5.

LYON, M. W. (1913). Treeshrews: An account of the mammalian family Tupaiidae. *Proc. U. S. Natl. Museum* **45**, 1-188.

MILLER, G. S. (1933). The classification of the gibbons. *J. Mamm.* **14**, 158-159.

MILNE-EDWARDS, A., AND GRANDIDIER, A. (1875, 1890-1896). Histoire naturelle des Mammifères. *In* "Histoire physique, naturelle et politique de Madagascar," Vols. 6, 9 and 10. Paris.

MONTAGNA, W., AND YUN, J. S. (1962). The skin of primates. X. The skin of the ring-tailed lemur (*Lemur catta*). *Am. J. Phys. Anthropol.* **20**, 95-118.

NAPIER, J. R. (1960). Studies of the hands of living primates. *Proc. Zool. Soc. London* **134**, 647-657.

NAPIER, J. R. (1961). Prehensility and opposability in the hands of primates. *In* "Vertebrate Locomotion" (J. E. Harris, ed.), pp. 115-132. Symposium 5, Zool. Soc., London.

PETTER, J.-J. (1963). Apports de l'écologie et de l'étude du comportement à le systématique des Lémuriens malgaches. In press, Wenner-Gren.

POCOCK, R. I. (1907). A monographic revision of the monkeys of the genus *Cercopithecus*. *Proc. Zool. Soc. London* pp. 677-746.

POCOCK, R. I. (1934). Monkeys of the genera *Pithecus* (or *Presbytis*) and *Pygathrix* found to the east of the Bay of Bengal. *Proc. Zool. Soc. London* pp. 895-961.

REGAN, C. T. (1930). The classification of the Primates. *Nature* **125**, 125-126.

REMANE, A. (1961). Probleme der systemtik der Primaten. *Z. wiss. Zool.* **165**, 1-34.

SCHWARZ, E. L. (1928). The species of the genus *Cercocebus*. *Ann. Mag. Nat. Hist.* [10]1, 644-670.

SIMONS, E. (1962). Fossil evidence relating to the early evolution of primate behavior. *Ann. N. Y. Acad. Sci.* **102**, 282-294.

SIMPSON, G. G. (1940). Studies on the earliest Primate. *Bull. Am. Museum Nat. Hist.* **77**, 185-212.

SIMPSON, G. G. (1945). The principles of classification and a classification of the mammals. *Bull. Am. Museum Nat. Hist.* **85**, 1-350.

SIMPSON, G. G. (1962). Primate taxonomy and recent studies of nonhuman primates. *Ann. N. Y. Acad. Sci.* **102**, 497-514.

STRAUS, W. L. S., JR. (1949). The riddle of man's ancestry. *Quart. Rev. Biol.* **24**, 200-223.

STRAUS, W. L. S., JR. (1956). Review of "Primates I & II" by W. C. O. Hill. *Am. J. Phys. Anthropol.* **14**, 1-5.

TAPPEN, N. C. (1960). Problems of distribution and adaptation of the African monkeys. *Current Anthropol.* **1**, 91-120.

VERHEYEN, W. N. (1962). Contribution à la craniologie comparée des Primates. *Musée Roy. Afrique Centrale-Tervuren, Belgique, Sér. 8—Sci. Zool.* **105**.

WASHBURN, S. L. (1944). The genera of Malaysian langurs. *J. Mamm.* **25**, 289-294.

WASHBURN, S. L. (1951). The analysis of primate evolution with particular reference to the origin of man. *Cold Spring Harbor Symposia Quant. Biol.* **16**, 67-78.

ZUCKERKANDL, E., JONES, R., AND PAULING, L. (1960). A comparison of animal hemoglobins by tryptic peptide pattern analysis. *Proc. Natl. Acad. Sci.* **46**, 1349-1354.

Chapter 2

A Critical Reappraisal of Tertiary Primates

Elwyn L. Simons

Department of Geology and Peabody Museum,
Yale University, New Haven, Connecticut

I. Introduction

A. General

The intense interest of mankind in the study of Primates has produced an extensive and complex literature on the fossil record of this
group. However, the paleontology of this fourth most anciently documented order of living mammals consists largely of analyses based on
quite fragmentary materials. This situation combined with the fact that
a rather limited number of specialists have actually studied and described fossil forms of the order directly, makes it difficult to set forth
what is known of the past history of this group of vertebrates in a brief
and lucid manner. This does not mean, of course, that the story is not
worth the telling. There is only one direct way to approach the evolution
of the Primates—from the fossil record. Phylogeny of the Primates based
on analysis of modern forms alone is at best metaphorical and at worst
irrelevant.

Contrary to a popular impression that primates are rare and seldom
recovered in fossil mammalian faunas, only half a dozen or so of the
thirty-three orders of Mammalia recognized by Simpson (1945) contain
a greater number of fossil genera. To date, over one hundred and twenty
genera of extinct primates have been proposed. This means that of
known primate groups which are considered to be of generic significance
by at least some taxonomists, nearly two-thirds do not survive today.
However, the very inadequate representation of primate fossil forms in
some continents, and particularly in early Tertiary deposits, leaves much
to be desired in the interpretation of interrelationships within the order.
Knowledge of early primates in two continents, Europe and North
America, is rather complete. As a result the rate of identification and
description of new genera from holarctic deposits has leveled off in
recent years—presumably as the number of described groups approaches
the total of forms then existing in these two continents, at least in the
areas where fossil-bearing Paleocene and Eocene rocks are known. At
present no Paleocene-Eocene primates have been recovered in the continents of South America and Africa.

The evolutionary history of the Prosimii or lower primates is of particular interest to students of mammalian evolution for a variety of rather special reasons. Unlike many groups of placental mammals, these small creatures are known not only from an extensive and diversified series of species from the early Cenozoic (particularly from the Paleocene and Eocene epochs) but also from at least four separate stocks of these "sub-monkeys" which persist today in tropical and subtropical regions of the Old World. To varying degrees, these surviving groups all retain primitive morphological features which enable paleontologists or primatologists to supplement knowledge of the historical development of the order, based on the fossil actualities, in the areas of behavior, biochemistry, and soft anatomy.

The occurrence of an approximate scale of successively more advanced living types among the Primates, corresponding in miniature to the *scala naturae* of pre-Darwinian naturalists was early noted by Thomas Henry Huxley in an essay included in "Man's Place in Nature" (1876) when he remarked:

> "Perhaps no order of mammals presents us with so extraordinary a series of gradation as this—leading us insensibly from the crown and summit of the animal creation down to creatures, from which there is but a step, as it seems, to the lowest, smallest, and least intelligent of the placental mammals."

Two additional and perhaps unexpected factors add an element of challenge to the process of accurate interpretation of interrelationships within this order. First, an unusually high frequency of parallel development of similar structures was reached between the various prosimian stocks—misleading similarities which are further masked by the considerable disparity between the phyletic connections of lower primates deducible from their comparative morphology, and the actual record of fossil prosimian radiation (Simons, 1962c). At least some known fossil prosimians must be on, or near, the ancestral lines of surviving varieties, but in their osteology most early forms do not appear to exhibit the expected prerequisites for ancestors of present-day species. Second, a major break in the fossil record of prosimians during the Oligocene epoch which covered perhaps 10 million years makes it difficult to tie together known pre- and post-Oligocene lineages. This situation led G. G. Simpson to write (1955, p. 439) that the Primates appears:

> "to have split into a large number of divergent, progressing, lineages, symbolizable especially as families or subfamilies, among which some five or six survived and separately gave rise

to the later Cenozoic (Oligocene to Recent) Primates. Not a
single one of those ancestral lineages has been surely identified
in the Paleocene or Eocene."

Clearly, such problems affecting as they do interpretation of the evolutionary record of these early Tertiary prosimians also hold considerable
interest in the quest for documentation of the lengthy history of our
own derivation from more primitive organisms.

In addition to the significance for primate history there are several
practical applications of investigations on early primates, not all of
which can be outlined briefly. However, it does seem advisable here
to mention some geological applications of the study of prosimian evolution as well as some misconceptions inherent in this pursuit. One important application is to faunal (and thereby stratigraphic) correlation,
for which a single example will illustrate the process. One primate
species, belonging to the genus *Plesiadapis* from the French Paleocene
locality of Cernay, near Reims, resembles specimens of American Clark-
forkian provincial age, thereby providing a faunal element indicating the
possibility of an age correlation between these two areas. Such occurrences are of considerable significance in the question of intercontinental faunal exchange. Since early primates were primarily arboreal, it is
necessary to assume that the requisite continuous forest cover, through
which they would have extended species ranges, stretched across some,
at least, of the intervening intercontinental corridors. Primates are also
useful to faunal correlation among continental vertebrates because it
seems apparent that this is an order exhibiting comparatively rapid
evolutionary rates. Therefore, it is unlikely that the time duration for
unchanged persistence of a given species was very great. When species
existing in different continents cannot easily be distinguished, it may be
supposed that they are roughly synchronous. Such correlations are of
particular value in determining the stratigraphic and temporal position
of beds which cannot be traced laterally into marine equivalents, or
which cannot be dated geochemically.

In the first half of the Eocene, European and North American primates
show close similarities so that, although the two continents have but one
Eocene primate genus in common, there are many pairs of closely
similar genera (one European, one American) which agree well with
affinities seen in other members of the faunas of the two continents.
After the early Eocene such similarities decrease in frequency of occurrence. With land bridges gone and these continents separated by water,
divergence proceeded independently.

Another significant use of fossil primates lies in the interpretation of climate and ecology of the past. Unlike members of most other orders of mammals, the primitive primates, in particular, are good indicators of warm-temperate to tropical conditions. At least nearly their whole distribution today lies in such areas. Of course some primates do range into colder environments. Today, certain anthropoid apes, macaques, and langurs exist under essentially temperate or even colder conditions, for example, the Japanese macaque and the mountain gorilla. However, all these forms, including man, represent late or specialized end branches in the primate family tree. It would appear that primitive forms have always been restricted to the warmer climates while more plastic forms of later differentiation range more widely. Perhaps a primary reason why many of these prosimian primates yet survive is that their early ecological background exists today largely unchanged in the tropical forest canopy. As Clark (1960, p. 321) has put it "the trees of African and Asiatic forests still retain in rough outline a stratified population of Primates which represent the successive grades of the evolutionary tree of this order." Each successive grade has developed a new ecological domain within the over-all context of the tropical forest environment.

The supposition that early primates were restricted to warm climates gains some reinforcement, on negative grounds, through consideration of their frequency of occurrence in the early Cenozoic of western North America. Evidently cooling of climate in this continent, based primarily on paleobotanical evidence, appears to have proceeded from about the late Eocene up to the onset of continental glaciation in the early Pleistocene. A rapid check indicates the following decrease in abundance of primates (omitting apatemyids).

Epoch	Primate genera
Miocene	?1 (undescribed)
Middle and late Oligocene	0
Early Oligocene	1
Late Eocene	5
Middle Eocene	10
Early Eocene	12

Sampling error might affect such a tabulation. It should be pointed out, nonetheless, that in the early Tertiary beds of North America, as well as in Europe, specimens assignable to the same few genera are found over and over again at different localities and in rocks which indicate differing sedimentary conditions of deposition. Undoubtedly species so far undiscovered did exist on these continents, but it is clear by now that they were quite rare. In contrast to this some real imponderables in tracing primate history derive from the paucity of early Cenozoic small mammal faunas in Africa, Central America, and Central Asia—all regions where major advances in primate evolution may have been accomplished. When, and if, Paleocene sediments yielding small mammals are located in these areas, primates may be expected to be of fairly common occurrence in them.

One widespread misconception is that the early prosimians being tropical forest animals, are rare as fossils. This theory seems to be based on the observation that vertebrate skeletons do not long survive the vicissitudes of existence on the tropical forest floor. Nevertheless, there are a great many known Paleocene, and later, localities where primates make up a significant proportion of the specimens recovered and, at some sites nearly a majority. The nature of many of the sediments from which these animals have been collected suggests that their occurrence is as a thanatocoenose, or "death assemblage," of individuals transported to the spot of deposition by water and dropped in sediments of riparian, deltaic, or lacustrine type. Whatever the life environment, even arboreal mammals by falling into streams or rivers can be, and often are, assembled in such water-laid sediments.

In spite of recent additions to our knowledge, geographic distribution of fossil primates is quite uneven. In the Old World the only localities which have provided Paleocene primates are in Europe. On the other hand, unquestioned Oligocene primates of the eastern hemisphere are unknown outside of Africa. In the Old World Eocene faunas, the situation is slightly better in that a variety of species of this order have been recovered in Europe and Asia. Nevertheless, the African Eocene primate fauna, which must have existed, is completely undiscovered, as is also the case with the entirety of forms that may then have occurred in what are now the tropical regions of southeast Asia. The single definite exception is *Amphipithecus* of Burma.[1] In the New World the fossil record of nonhominid primates appears to end abruptly in North America in the early Oligocene. In South America on the other hand, nothing whatever is known of primates before the latest Oligocene, so that neither temporal nor areal overlap occurs between the primates of the New World continents before the Pleistocene. In the later Tertiary of the Old World an increasing number of finds of Miocene apes and

---

[1] Another form, *Pondaungia* described by Pilgrim, and based on a single jaw from the same area as *Amphipithecus*, may not be a primate. On the other hand, in size and in general proportions of M_{2-3} *Pondaungia* somewhat resembles *Propliopithecus*. The type specimen, now in Calcutta, should be restudied.

monkeys from widespread localities in Eurasia and Africa are providing new information as to the extensive areal distribution of a rather limited number of genera of these higher primates, but in contrast to this, with the exception of a few species from the Miocene beds of Kenya, practically no Miocene-Pleistocene prosimian or "lower" primate fossils have been found in the Old World.

Although it is of the greatest value to have knowledge of the skull and skeleton in order to interpret relationships and ecology in these fossil forms, it is not true that little accurate knowledge of affinities and ecology can be derived from the teeth alone. In fact, during the past 20 years, nearly all early Cenozoic primates have been reasonably well assorted, mainly on the basis of dental analysis, into ten groups of subfamily or family status while a few similar categories have been removed from the order. Moreover, the recovery of new and better cranial and postcranial remains acquired during the same period for a number of forms has provided material for the demonstration that taxonomic assignments made earlier on the basis of teeth alone were correct.

A rather fallacious practice which seems to have been growing in recent years is the indiscriminate elimination of various early forms from this order. In general it is easier to assign a given species to the order Primates than it is to show that it definitely does not belong there. This is because in order to show why a particular species belongs with some other major taxon of Mammalia a greater knowledge of early Cenozoic mammals is required than is possessed by most primatologists. Such removals seem to me to be more motivated by a desire to sweep under the carpet particular bones of contention than to delineate what is clearly an extremely complex and poorly understood radiation. Removal of such species makes for a simpler and more tidy story of primate evolution, but not necessarily a more truthful one. It would be tedious and perhaps somewhat embarrassing to certain colleagues to cite the cases which come to mind in this regard, but it should suffice to point out that during the last decade one or more authors have questioned in print the primate status of such forms as *Amphipithecus, Parapithecus, Apidium, Moeripithecus,* and *Oreopithecus.* To date, I cannot discover any adequate evidence on which any such removals could be based.

B. THE TARSIOID PROBLEM

One of the greatest sources of confusion on relationships among fossil primates of Paleocene and Eocene age has been caused by the fact that many researchers assign given species or higher taxa either to an ancient "lemuroid" or to a "tarsioid" assemblage, without giving sufficient attention to the difficulties of distinguishing and defining these two categories. Simpson (1940, 1955) has pointed out and justly criticized this practice and has reached the conclusion (Simpson, 1955, p. 439) that meaningful distinction between tarsier-like and lemur-like early Tertiary primates probably cannot be found. One or two examples of this sort of taxonomic transferal will show how difficult it can be to find any consistency in the literature. In describing the late Eocene prosimian species *Pronycticebus guadryi,* from the Quercy phosphorites, Grandidier (1904), both in the name he coined for it and in other statements implied a relationship to the lorises, but Gregory (1920) and Abel (1931) placed this form in the Tarsioidea. Clark (1934) demonstrated that the species was much more lemuriform than tarsiiform. Simons (1962a) has discussed the possibility that its relationships may be with such lorisoids as *Progalago* from the Miocene of Kenya. Thus the pendulum has now swung back to the suggestion of closest affinity between *Pronycticebus* and a member of the Lorisiformes, which is essentially the view of Grandidier. Placement of the genus *Necrolemur* from the Eocene of France, together with allied forms *Microchoerus* and *Pseudoloris,* has followed a similarly tortuous course. Abel, Clark, Gregory, Simpson, and others early placed this group, variously called Microchoeridae (Simpson, 1962) or Necrolemurinae (Simpson, 1940) with the Tarsioidea, and in fact Simpson (1940, p. 198), remarks with reference to the genus *Pseudoloris,* which he, however, placed in a separate subfamily: "So far as the dental evidence goes, this genus stands considerably closer to *Tarsius* than does any other known from the Paleocene or Eocene and should perhaps be placed definitely in the Tarsiidae." Simons (1961a, p. 54) has assigned *Necrolemur* and *Pseudoloris* to the same subfamily Necrolemurinae. However, in a comprehensive study of necrolemurids published in 1948, Hürzeler came to the conclusion that these creatures have no meaningful resemblance to *Tarsius* and suggested that the group should rank as a distinct superfamily of lemuroids. Later studies of *Necrolemur* (Simons, 1961a) have returned the group to the tarsioids, specifically as a subfamily of Tarsiidae. Obviously, general discussion of the rise and dispersal of the order Primates has its validity affected by this sort of wholesale taxonomic relocation of genera and even families. The significance of mentioning this matter here, however, is mainly to point out that the relationships of many of the categories of early primates are settling into more stable positions as sufficient documentation of degree of similarity or differences is made available in the newer literature.

As Patterson (1954, p. 203) has stressed, part of the difficulty in relating early primates with Miocene-Recent groups of the order derives from a deficiency of knowledge of Oligocene forms. Research is now being carried out in the only Old World area that has yielded Oligocene primates—the Fayum beds of Egypt, but the additional knowledge provided by new finds from these deposits has not yet resolved such important questions as whether or not the ancestry of man and other Old World Anthropoidea ever passed through a "tarsioid" stage. Although the extreme views summarized by Wood Jones (1929) placed the idea of a close relationship between Hominoidea and Tarsioidea in a very bad light, there are, of course, sufficient resemblances between Anthropoidea and *Tarsius* to indicate some sort of relationship in original differentiation. Nevertheless, the split between the two lineages seems to have come at the prosimian grade, unless one follows Hill (1953) in regarding Tarsioidea as higher primates. In any event, the newly discovered species, *Oligopithecus savagei* (Simons, 1962b), which possesses the most generalized dental pattern of any known Catarrhine does not appear to be particularly closer in dental morphology to the tarsier-like Eocene prosimians, such as *Necrolemur* or *Microchoerus*, than it is to forms which cannot be described as having advanced beyond the lemuroid grade, such as *Pelycodus* or *Pronycticebus*.

Separate from, but related to, the question of whether or not Anthropoidea passed through a grade that could be termed tarsioid is the obvious necessity of demonstrating a complex of similarities to *Tarsius* before a given early Cenozoic form could correctly be called tarsioid. Actually, such affinities have not been demonstrated for most Paleocene-Eocene primates that have been said to belong in Tarsioidea. This is for two principal reasons: (1) The living *Tarsius* obviously has acquired some *sui generis* specializations during its unknown derivation from some Eocene form such as *Pseudoloris parvulus* which would not have been present in its Eocene forerunners and which therefore cannot be taken to characterize any taxonomic concept bracketing species distributed throughout this whole time period. (2) Most species of Paleocene-Eocene primates are not well enough known anatomically to make it possible to demonstrate their similarity to, or difference from, the living tarsier. For instance, Abel (1931) lists twenty-three genera of early Cenozoic "tarsioids" and Hill (1955) includes here thirty-two fossil genera—the group having been enlarged in part by the description of new forms. In the writer's opinion, it is possible to show that *Necrolemur antiquus* is rather closely related to *Tarsius*. This demonstration is possible because over a dozen skulls of this small primate are known and detailed craniological comparisons between the two

can be made (Simons and Russell, 1960; Simons, 1961a). Of the remaining thirty-one genera listed as tarsioids by Hill (1955), the greater
part of the skull is known only in two species: in *Tetonius homunculus*
from the early Eocene and in an undescribed specimen of the middle
Paleocene genus *Palaechthon*, both North American forms. In one
further "tarsioid" species, *Hemiacodon gracilis*, also from the North
American Eocene, a considerable part of the postcranial skeleton and
most of the face (but not the brain case) is known. According to
Simpson (1940), there does not appear to be any taxonomically significant resemblance between comparable postcranial parts in *Tarsius*
and *Hemiacodon*.[2] Consequently, if a distinction is to be made between
Tarsius-allied and more primitive groups in the early Cenozoic, it
must be detectable dentally or craniologically. Cranial anatomy in
Tetonius and *Necrolemur* can be compared with that of *Tarsius* and,
as Gregory (1920) and others since have stressed, there are numerous
craniological similarities to the living form in these two Eocene primates.
On the basis of close taxonomic alliance to species of these two genera,
the other genera of the families to which they belong can presumably
be considered tarsioid. Such a list would, today, include species of
the genera:

Genera of the European Eocene:
Necrolemur
Nannopithex
Pseudoloris
Microchoerus

Genera of the North American Eocene:
Tetonius
Anaptomorphus
Anemorhysis
Absarokius

Perhaps also the following:
Uintalacus
Uintasorex
Uintanius
Trogolemur

---

[2] Nevertheless it should be pointed out that in a well preserved frontal of
Hemiacodon gracilis recently figured by Gazin (1958, pl. 4) the orbits are seen to
be unusually large for an Eocene prosimian and to exhibit a raised circumorbital
flange somewhat suggesting a condition antecedent to their extraordinary development in the living *Tarsius*.

No other early primate can be shown, at the present time, to have any special relationship to *Tarsius* whatever.

II. PALEOCENE PRIMATES

A. ORIGIN AND INTERRELATIONSHIPS

Primates of this epoch are of outstanding interest for they are the earliest known members of our own order of Mammalia. What can be determined about the nature of initial differentiation of this diversified series of human relatives should be of fundamental significance in determining the nature of our own ancestral and underlying behavioral commitments.

Unfortunately, no up-to-date assessment of these earliest primates is yet available, and it is even difficult to review systematically the major groups of Paleocene primates, for there has not been general agreement as to how these groups should be constituted. Most of the original discussion regarding interrelationships of higher categories of Paleocene primates has been provided by Simpson (1937, 1940, 1955).

The fossil record of the Primates, as it is now understood, begins in the middle Paleocene with several essentially contemporaneous species of the six genera *Paromomys, Palaechthon, Palenochtha, Plesiolestes, Elphidotarsius, Pronothodectes*. These are all North American forms which have been recovered in beds of Torrejonian provincial age in New Mexico, Wyoming, Colorado, and Montana. The differences between species of these genera are considerable but most of them could be placed in a single family or superfamily, if one did not have their relationship to later forms to take into account. Since some differentiation had already taken place by the middle Paleocene, the order itself must have had its origin in or before the early Paleocene but, to date, little or no evidence of earlier primates, or primate-like forms, has come to light. Because of the then close similarity to contemporary Insectivora, any future discrimination of such a basal stock would almost be drawing a distinction without a difference.

In general, the known Paleocene primates do not serve as good ancestral candidates for any of the major Eocene-Recent stocks of the order. In the middle and late Paleocene, before the appearance and expansion of the true rodents, a number of primate and insectivore groups appear to have specialized in the direction of the rodent habitus for which no ecological niches had then been occupied except, perhaps partly, by multituberculates. The majority of Paleocene primates are of this sort, exhibiting enlarged, procumbent, anterior teeth. It is mainly through determination of close similarities in the cheek teeth with later, undoubted primates that their assignment to the order can be defended. In addition to this the earliest primates are exceedingly primitive mammals lacking many of the cranial characters used by early taxonomists as common defining characters of the order. For instance, *all* Eocene-Recent primate species in which skulls are known show a continuous postorbital bar, while neither of the two known skulls of Paleocene primates (one, at present, undescribed) exhibit this feature (Fig. 1).

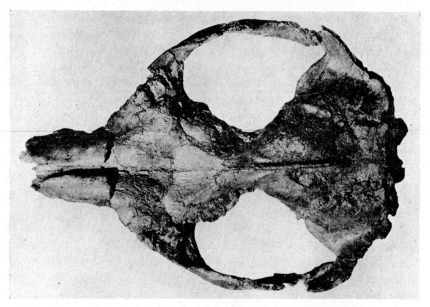

FIG. 1.   Dorsal view of the skull of *Plesiadapis* sp. from late Paleocene deposits in France; the oldest described skull of a primate. (From Russell, 1959.) Magnification: 1.33.

The possession of at least some flattened nails on the fingers or toes of all known primate species (except the generalized tupaioids) also has an exception here in that in the one Paleocene form in which feet have been found, *Plesiadapis*, large laterally compressed claws occur. Although conceivably, flattened nails could have been present on hallux and/or pollex. Of course, primitive features are to be expected in early forms, but the inclusion of such Paleocene species makes it impossible to define the order in terms of osteological characters shared in common by all its members. Consequently, Primates is not a higher category grouped together by possession of features shared throughout its range. The ordinal grouping more nearly resembles a series of stages each of which is bracketed by slight but significant common similarities to adjacent grades or stages. Consequently (when earlier placentals are better known) the most primitive primates will be seen to bracket in this manner with nonprimates. There would be no entirely satisfactory method for dividing such a continuum, and, as Simpson (1955, p. 436) remarked, the one place in this order where there is a fairly "definite shift of structural and adaptive level" lies between Prosimii and Anthropoidea. The order could be cut off at this point, excluding Prosimii, were it not for the fact that recent finds of Oligocene primates are rapidly closing this morphological gap between higher and lower primates. Moreover such a change would render all previous primate taxonomy quite obsolete—to no good purpose. All serious future students would still have to learn the classification of the order as it stood before the change in order to understand earlier literature.

In addition to the six middle Paleocene primate genera listed on page 75, species of at least seven additional genera, *Carpodaptes, Carpolestes, Chiromyoides, Navajovius, Phenacolemur,* and *Plesiadapis* appear in late Paleocene sediments of North America and Europe. Of these *Plesiadapis* is found in both continents, *Chiromyoides* in Europe only and the remainder have been recovered in western North America. A few species of *Carpolestes, Phenacolemur,* and *Plesiadapis* survive into the North American early Eocene, while in Europe members of *Plesiadapis* and a descendant genus *Platychaerops* cross into the latter epoch; but, in general, the affinities and/or actual date of most of these species lie in the Paleocene. As they are all of a distinctly archaic and aberrant aspect, it seems advisable to discuss them as taxa of mainly Paleocene orientation. Members of these thirteen genera may be grouped taxonomically into three higher categories, all of which appear to be of valid family status. These are:

Carpolestidae
>   *Elphidotarsius* (Gidley 1923), middle Paleocene, North America
>   *Carpodaptes* (Matthew and Granger 1921), late Paleocene, North America
>   *Carpolestes* (Simpson 1928), late Paleocene to early Eocene, North America

Plesiadapidae
>   *Chiromyoides* (Stehlin 1916), late Paleocene, Europe
>   *Platychaerops* (Charlesworth 1854), early Eocene, Europe
>   *Plesiadapis* (Gervais 1877), late Paleocene-early Eocene, North America, Europe
>   *Pronothodectes* (Gidley 1917), Middle Paleocene, North America

Phenacolemuridae
Phenacolemurinae
  Phenacolemur (Matthew 1915), late Paleocene, early Eocene, North America
Paromomyinae
  Paromomys (Gidley 1923), middle to late? Paleocene, North America
  Palaechthon (Gidley 1923), middle Paleocene, North America
  Palenochtha (Simpson 1935), middle Paleocene, North America
  Plesiolestes (Jepsen 1930), middle Paleocene, North America
  Navajovius (Matthew and Granger 1921), late Paleocene, North America

B. CARPOLESTIDAE

This family name, meaning "fruit stealers," has reference to the possibility that the peculiar dentition characterizing included species was adapted to opening seeds, fruits, or similar edible materials. The last lower premolar of members of this family is greatly enlarged and serrate, and this as well as the upper premolars have considerable convergent resemblance to members of the mainly Mesozoic order of allotherian mammals, Multituberculata. These resemblances together with instances of equally convergent dentitions of this type among two main groups of the marsupials were discussed by Simpson (1933) as varieties of the "plagiaulacoid" type of dentition, and he very tentatively concluded that the enlarged serrate lower tooth, opposing a large multicusped crown above, in all such forms does indicate convergent evolution toward a similar function. What this function was is uncertain, but, judging from the living Australian rat kangaroos, *Bettongia* and allied forms, this kind of dentition is adapted, according to Simpson (1933, p. 105)—

> "to an exclusively vegetable diet, and to one in which woody or other coarse fibers, bark, roots, grass and the like predominate. The food is first secured by the incisors, not strictly by gnawing but rather by simple seizing, cut by the shearing teeth and ground or crushed by the molars."

Species of the genera now included in Carpolestidae seem to represent but a single ancestor-dependant phylum, *Elphidotarsius, Carpodaptes, Carpolestes,* exclusively of North American occurrence, as far as is known, which apparently became extinct in the early Eocene. Judging from the size of the jaws, species of this family would have ranged in body size from approximately that of the house mouse to that of the hamster. No portions of the skeleton other than mandibles and maxillae are known for any carpolestid and so little can be said of their osteology. Reference of them to this order has also been questioned more than once, see Saban (1961, p. 638). However, Simpson (1935) has clearly pointed out the very great resemblance of the lower second and third molars of *Elphidotarsius* to those of the plesiadapid *Pronothodectes* and to those of species of several Eocene primate genera, such as *Pelycodus*. He concludes (1935, p. 162):

> "I do of course recognize that a really definitive determination in such cases is practically impossible from teeth alone, but since teeth are, in fact, all we have I see no useful alternative to classifying them at least tentatively as belonging to the group they most resemble, that is, to the Primates."

As Primates, the most aberrant dental features of carpolestids are undoubtedly their enlarged and polycuspidate posterior premolars, but since large fourth premolars characterize several other types of early members of the order, particularly species of the genera *Tetonius*, *Navajovius*, *Nannopithex*, a latency for this sort of development seems to have existed in early primates.

C. PLESIADAPIDAE

Species currently assigned to this primitive family are the best known osteologically of any taxon of the order occurring prior to the middle Eocene. Judging mainly from two partial skeletons of *Plesiadapis*, one from Colorado, the other from near Cernay, France, and from an entire skull from the latter locality (Fig. 1) the outward appearance must have been rather rat-like, as is also the case for the most primitive living primates, the tupaias. Like tupaias, the unguals of *Plesiadapis* take the form of claws flattened from side to side. There is no indication, to date, for possession of flattened nails on hallux or pollex. Members of this family appear to have ranged in body size from about that of the field mouse (*Microtus*) to that of the South American agouti (*Dasyprocta*). *Plesiadapis*, at least, had fore and hind limbs of nearly equal length and seems likely to have been exclusively arboreal, with an adaptation loosely similar to that of some of the larger tropical squirrels of the present day. As in the other mainly Paleocene primate families the anterior teeth of plesiadapids were enlarged and procumbent. This feature of resemblance led a number of early students, Stehlin (1916), Abel (1931), and others, to conclude that the family bore a direct ancestral relationship to the living Malagasy prosimian *Daubentonia* (aye-aye). Simpson (1935) has shown the improbability of such a conclusion on both morphological and zoogeographical grounds.

Phyletically, relationships of plesiadapids like those of carpolestids are rather simple, with the mid-Paleocene *Pronothodectes* a suspected ancestor of *Plesiadapis* of the late Paleocene. *Chiromyoides* of the late Paleocene of France is surely close to *Plesiadapis* in ancestry, while *Platychaerops* of the European Early Eocene may be immediately descended from some species of *Plesiadapis*. Although rodent-like in overall appearance, plesiadapids seem best ranked taxonomically as Primates in view of virtual identity of cheek-tooth morphology with the undoubted primate *Pelycodus* and to a lesser extent with many other early prosimians.

McKenna (1960) has pointed out dental resemblances between plesiadapids and microsyopids. The latter family, now placed in this order by McKenna, comprises a previously little known group, of rather common occurrence in the Eocene beds of western North America. The possibility of remote affinities between Plesiadapidae and the modern colugos (Dermoptera) has also been noted by a number of students, but requires further confirmation. Although rejecting *Plesiadapis* as being too late in time to occupy an ancestral position for the order, Wood (1962) has suggested that this family may also stand in some rather close phyletic relationship to the earliest Rodentia.

D. PHENACOLEMURIDAE

This family name, meaning roughly "the deceptive ghosts," is, perhaps, a good term for a group which includes most of the earliest and least understood basal members of our own order. Relationships among possible members of this ancient prosimian family are left somewhat in doubt by its describer Simpson (1955), and he is not responsible for the arrangement of genera in this family given in the introduction to Section II above, which, although based on Simpson's conclusions (1935, 1940, 1955) has not been proposed before and may be somewhat more open to doubt as a natural unit than are most of the other higher categories discussed in this article.

Of the genera here included in Phenacolemuridae, *Phenacolemur* (Fig. 2) is by far the most distinctive and long ranging type and it seems quite consistent with taxonomic practice to consider it as belonging to a distinct subfamily. Some doubts have been raised by McKenna (1960, p. 70) as to whether this family should not more properly be called Paromomyidae since it includes *Paromomys*, made the type of a subfamily by Simpson (1940). However, if the group is understood to contain two subfamilies Phenacolemurinae and Paromomyinae which seems to have been the intention of Simpson (1955) although not explicitly so stated by him, then according to conservative practice in nomenclature the family group may be named for the subfamily Phenacolemurinae, even though Paromomyinae (Simpson 1940) has in effect priority. Figure 3 compares upper cheek dentitions of species of two genera, *Paromomys* and *Palaechthon*, tentatively placed in this family by Simpson (1955) with the earliest known plesiadapid *Pronothodectes*, from which they do not differ greatly. Species of three other genera from the North American Paleocene, *Plesiolestes*, *Palenochtha*, and *Navajovius*, show various degrees of resemblance to each other and particularly

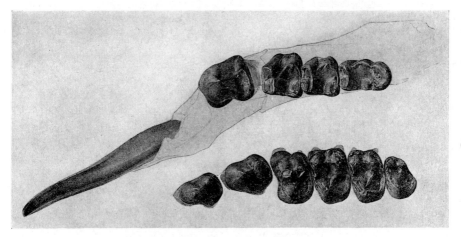

FIG. 2. *Phenacolemur pagei*, late Paleocene of Wyoming, upper left and lower right dentitions. (From Simpson, 1955.) Magnification: 4.4.

to *Paromomys* and *Palaechthon*, and probably should be ranked in the same family. Both *Palenochtha* and *Navajovius* have been indicated also as showing affinities with certain Eocene primates, such as species of *Omomys*, *Tetonius*, and *Absarokius*, but in the present rather deficient state of knowledge regarding them I see no reason to associate taxonomically these much earlier forms with their possible Eocene derivatives, although acquisition of new or better fossil materials of intervening age might make this possible, even desirable.

Either *Plesiolestes problematicus* or *Palaechthon alticuspis* could be close to the ancestry of Eocene Omomyidae and, if so, through the latter family they could stand near the common base of Ceboidea and Cercopithecoidea (Simons, 1961c, p. 13, 1962a, p. 27). Such an hypothesis, would, however, require the assumption that the enlarged lower incisors of these small Paleocene forms subsequently became reduced in size and more vertically implanted, a trend for which there is some evidence among omomyids (Simons, 1961c, p. 5).

Perhaps the most divergent of the primate genera here included in the Phenacolemuridae is *Navajovius* from the late Paleocene of Colorado

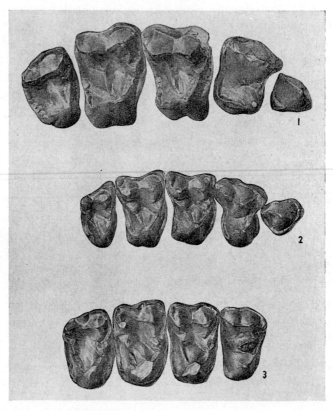

Fig. 3. Three middle Paleocene primates from Montana; upper right cheek teeth. (1) *Paromomys maturus* Gidley; (2) *Palaechthon alticuspus* Gidley; (3) *Pronothodectes matthewi* Gidley. (From Simpson, 1955.) Magnification: 9.0.

(Fig. 4). Although closely similar to the other members of this family in molar crown patterns the fourth premolars are enlarged and there is apparently reduction in the number of premolars, both features of resemblance to the Eocene anaptomorphids of North America and to the Necrolemurinae of Europe. This resemblance led Gazin (1958, p. 11) to refer this species tentatively to the otherwise Eocene family Anaptomorphidae, where it may eventually be shown to belong. Further investigation of this possibility should be carried out.

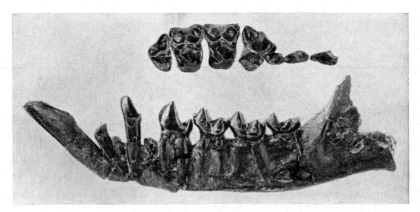

FIG. 4. *Navajovius kohlhasae* from the Paleocene of Colorado—right upper and left lower dentitions. (Courtesy American Museum of Natural History.) Magnification: 6.33.

III. EOCENE PRIMATES

A. NATURE AND RELATIONSHIPS

At the beginning of the Eocene epoch came the appearance of groups of species of more modern aspect within the order and, indeed, it is in part through the presence of species of such genera as *Tetonius* and *Pelcycodus* that the onset of early Eocene times is determined faunally in North America. While the major taxa of Paleocene primates were dying out, the latest of these, *Phenacolemur jepseni*, is last known from the middle early Eocene Lysite beds of Wyoming, other varieties of the order were definitely becoming established as the largest-brained mammals of their times, if estimates of brain volume be compared to those of body bulk.

Known skulls of species of *Tetonius* and *Smilodectes* from North America and of *Nannopithex* in Europe indicate that, before the end of the middle Eocene, active, large-brained prosimians had arisen among which substantial enlargement and forward rotation of the orbits had already taken place. This establishes the important point that the extraordinary capacities to be seen in modern Anthropoidea must be taken as the culmination of advances which have been more than 50 million years in the making. Figure 5 presents a comparison of ventral aspects of the cranium in two Eocene prosimians, species of *Tetonius* and *Necrolemur* respectively, with that of the modern Bornean tarsier showing several similarities of interest between the ancient and modern forms. Prime among these are the foreshortening of the face and shifting of the *foramen magnum* in *Necrolemur* (at least) forward onto the ventral face of the skull. These features, taken together with broad dental similarities, demonstrate that by early or middle Eocene times the process of dominance of the visual sense over the olfactory was already far advanced. In some of these lineages, it had reached almost the level of development to be seen in the modern tarsier. The position of spinal attachment, moreover, suggests that *Necrolemur* and *Tetonius* were hopping animals which held the body more or less erect, in the manner of living tarsiers and galagos. This point is of some importance for, although modern higher primates are not known definitely to be descended from the specific primates discussed here, these Eocene materials do serve to show that the body was often, if not habitually, held erect during locomotion. These early trends away from quadrupedality seem neglected in numerous current discussions of primate evolution. Several recent authors have tended to overstress "primitive" features in drawing contrasts between early prosimians and the advances taken as characterizing Hominidae.

Some Eocene prosimians were larger brained than are most modern mammals of equivalent size. The best estimate of the brain:body ratio in a progressive Eocene primate that can be made at present is for the species *Necrolemur antiquus* from the late Eocene Quercy phosphorites of France. In this small primate the brain may well have constituted 1/35 of the bulk of the whole animal which is certainly in marked contrast to the estimated brain:body ratio for most of its contemporaries. In the Eocene uintatheres, for instance, this ratio has been estimated as standing at 1:2000. Apparently, the remainder of Eocene Mammalia fell somewhere between these extremes in this particular ratio.

Present fossil evidence suggests that during the Eocene epoch prosimians may have reached their high point of abundance and diversity. In Europe, for instance, fifteen genera and twenty-eight contained species of this period have been proposed, while in North America the figures are in excess of thirty-one genera and forty-one species. The record for Asia in this epoch is poor, being no more than three genera and species of primates, but this is undoubtedly due to the limited recovery, to date, of micromammalian faunas in this continent. Moreover, collections from the tropical regions of the Old World Eocene, where Prosimii may be supposed to have been abundant, are virtually unknown and no undoubted prosimian fossils have yet been described from anywhere within this vast area. Nevertheless, the warmer world climate of the Eocene allowed prosimian species to range into what are now temperate areas of western United States, England, Europe, and western China, but from zoogeographical considerations alone we cannot suppose that there were not species of most of these same genera distributed nearer the equator.

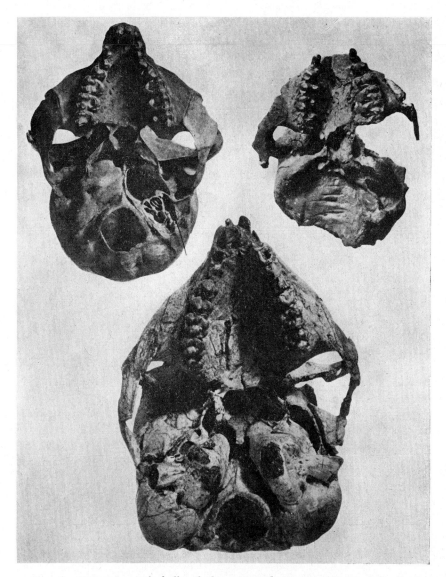

FIG. 5. Comparison of skulls of three tarsioid primates. Upper left, *Tarsius*, Recent. Upper right, *Tetonius homunculus*, early Eocene, Wyoming. Bottom, *Necrolemur*, late Eocene of France. Not to same scale. (From Gregory, 1920.)

There is a high probability that at least at the generic level we already know some of the taxa of the Eocene tropics.

It is from deposits of this epoch that the first, almost complete, prosimian skeletons have been recovered. These are principally from the North American middle Eocene Bridger beds and belong to species of the related lemur-like genera *Notharctus* and *Smilodectes*. Perhaps the best preserved single individual of these, shown here in Fig. 6, of *Notharctus* sp., is now under study in our laboratories at Yale. It should provide data for a fuller anatomical comparison between the notharctids and the modern lemurids of Madagascar which it closely resembles in several particulars.

Fig. 6. Skeleton of *Notharctus* sp. Position in rock as found. (Courtesy Yale Peabody Museum.) Magnification: 0.33.

Omitting the late surviving members of Paleocene taxa discussed in Section II above, the forty-five probably valid genera of Eocene Primates, described to date, may tentatively be grouped into six families in the following manner (a few genera which cannot definitely be maintained as belonging to the order are omitted here):

1. Adapidae
    Adapinae
        Adapis (Cuvier 1822), middle to late Eocene, Europe
        Anchomomys (Stehlin 1916), middle to late Eocene, Europe
        Caenopithecus (Rütimeyer 1862), middle Eocene, Europe
        Gesneropithex (Hürzeler 1946), late Eocene, Europe
        Pronycticebus (Grandidier 1904), late Eocene, Europe
        Protoadapis (Lemoine 1891), middle to late Eocene, Europe

Notharctinae
Notharctus (Leidy 1870), early to middle Eocene, North America
Pelycodus (Cope 1875), early Eocene, North America
Smilodectes (Wortman 1903), middle Eocene, North America
2. Anaptomorphidae
Absarokius (Matthew 1915), early Eocene, North America
Anaptomorphus (Cope 1872), middle Eocene, North America
Anemorhysis (Gazin 1958), early Eocene, North America
Tetonius (Matthew 1915), early Eocene, North America
Tetonoides (Gazin 1962), early Eocene, North America
Trogolemur (Matthew 1909), middle Eocene, North America
Uintalacus (Gazin 1958), early Eocene, North America
Uintanius (Matthew 1915), middle Eocene, North America
Uintasorex (Matthew 1909), middle Eocene, North America
3. Microsyopidae
Alsaticopithecus (Hürzeler 1947), middle Eocene, Europe
Cynodontomys (Cope 1882), early Eocene, North America
Microsyops (Leidy 1872), middle Eocene, North America
Craeseops (Stock 1934), late Eocene, North America
4. Omomyidae
Cantius (Simons 1962), early Eocene, Europe
Chlororhysis (Gazin 1958), early Eocene, North America
Chumashius (Stock 1933), late Eocene, North America
Dyseolemur (Stock 1934), late Eocene, North America
Hemiacodon (Marsh 1872), middle Eocene, North America
Hoanghonius (Zdansky 1930), late? Eocene, China
Loveina (Simpson 1940), early Eocene, North America
Lushius (Chow 1961), middle Eocene, China
*[*Macrotarsius* (Clark 1941), early Oligocene, North America]
Niptomomys (McKenna 1960), early Eocene, North America
Omomys (Leidy 1869), early? to middle Eocene, North America
Ourayia (Gazin 1958), late Eocene, North America
Periconodon (Stehlin 1916), middle Eocene, Europe
Shoshonius (Granger 1910), early Eocene, North America
Stockia (Gazin 1958), late Eocene, North America
Teilhardina (Simpson 1940), middle Eocene, North America
Utahia (Gazin 1958), middle Eocene, North America
Washakius (Leidy 1873), middle to late Eocene, North America
5. Pongidae?
Amphipithecus (Colbert 1937), late Eocene, Burma
Pondaungia (Pilgrim 1927), late Eocene, Burma
6. Tarsiidae
Necrolemurinae
Microchoerus (Wood 1846), late Eocene, Europe
Nannopithex (Stehlin 1916), middle Eocene, Europe
Necrolemur (Filhol 1873), middle to late Eocene, Europe
Pseudoloris (Stehlin 1916), late Eocene, Europe

---

* Brackets indicate post-Eocene occurrence of this omomyid.

B. Adapidae

As classified here, *Notharctus* and its North American allies are included as a subfamily of Adapidae, for essentially the reasons outlined by Simpson (1940, p. 200). The skeletal anatomy of *Notharctus* was described in detail by Gregory (1920) in what is clearly the most comprehensive report on any Tertiary primate. Similarly, Stehlin (1916) outlined what is known osteologically of the European species belonging to the genus *Adapis*. In spite of the completeness of these reports there

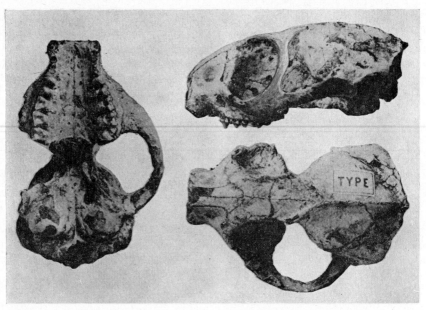

Fig. 7. *Pronycticebus gaudryi*. Late Eocene loris-like adapid from France. Postorbital bar restored hypothetically. (From Simpson, 1940.) Magnification: 0.90.

has long been divided opinion as to whether or not the European adapines and North American notharctines should be placed in the same family. Although inclusion of both groups in one family is opposed by Gazin (1958, p. 31), and I have followed his separation elsewhere (Simons, 1962a), it now seems more advisable to rank the two groups as of only subfamily distinction. The European adapines are quite variable and if more than one family is actually involved it may be among these forms that a division should be made. For instance the writer has reported (1962a, pp. 14-23) a number of lorisoid features to be seen in the European Eocene species of *Anchomomys* and *Pronycticebus* (Fig. 7). If these truly indicate the differentiation of Lorisiformes from the adapid stock they could be removed and classified vertically with the lorises. Moreover, species of *Pelycodus, Protoadapis, Caenopithecus,* and *Pronycticebus* all exhibit interrelationships in dental morphology which would make discrimination of two families difficult. Nevertheless, new or largely unstudied postcranial material of species of *Notharctus, Smilodectes,* and *Adapis* does exist, and further analysis of this, now being carried out at Yale, should produce additional data as to interrelationships of Eocene lemuroids.

Although probably not on the direct line to the modern lorises or Malagasy lemurs, adapines do seem closer to these modern Old World taxa than do *Notharctus* and its allies, while postcranially, at least, all are closely comparable. Like Malagasy lemurs, *Adapis* and *Notharctus* show no tarsal elongation, have a free tympanic ring within the middle ear, possess opposable hallux and pollex together with a generalized limb structure, elongate snout, comparable degrees of orbital frontality and many other features which tend to associate these three types of primates. The possibility that the ancestry of higher primates lies somewhere in this family is not completely out of the question but for reasons outlined below, omomyids seem to be considerably more plausible for this role. Nevertheless, cranially, Adapidae and Omomyidae are not known to be greatly different, and except for the primitive retention of four premolars above and below in most Adapidae, a character already lost in all other known Eocene and even Paleocene prosimians, they are close dentally as well. Presumably, these similarities indicate a rather recent common ancestry of these two families, perhaps in the middle or late Paleocene.

C. ANAPTOMORPHIDAE

As recently diagnosed and restricted by Gazin (1958, p. 73) this appears to be a valid family of the Primates, although the dental variability of contained species remains considerable. The group is restricted to the early and middle Eocene of North America, and is characterized by a tendency toward reduction of the anterior dentition, presumably in correlation with special dietary alterations and facial foreshortening. Fourth premolars, as in the possible Paleocene forerunner of the group, *Navajovius,* are large (Fig. 8, *Absarokius*) compared to other prosimians and there is always an enlarged and procumbent chisel-like pair of incisors below. Gazin (1958) supposes the dental formula in this group typically to have been

$$\frac{3.1. \quad 2 \text{ or } 3. \quad 3.}{2.1. \quad\quad 2. \quad\; 3.}$$

which of itself excludes the group from the ancestry of the New World monkeys. Evidently, the Anaptomorphidae were entirely a New World group in origin and radiation. The large brain and other features of the one known skull of a member of this family, *Tetonius homunculus*, suggest relationships with *Tarsius*. Nevertheless, it is debatable whether anything is gained by ranking this group with the "tarsioids," in the

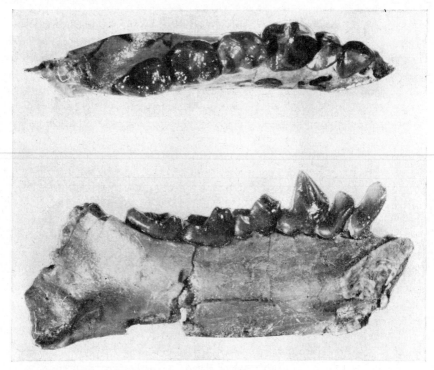

Fig. 8.   *Absarokius noctivegus*. Early Eocene anaptomorph primate. Left, lower jaw with partial dentition. Above, crown view. Below, internal view. (Courtesy American Museum of Natural History.) Magnification: 7.0.

absence of sufficient cranial or postcranial remains in this family upon which comparisons could be based. Dentally, the presence of a *Nannopithex*-fold and over-all molar morphology indicates relationship with the European Eocene Tarsiidae of the subfamily Necrolemurinae. These similarities are sufficient to suggest a community of original derivation with the Tarsiidae, but to call these early forms tarsioids perhaps suggests a greater resemblance to the living form than ever existed, and certainly more than can be demonstrated from available osteological materials. No members of this family have been identified as surviving after middle Eocene times.

D. MICROSYOPIDAE

This family has recently been diagnosed by McKenna (1960, p. 76) and discriminated by him from another early group of probable insectivore status, the Mixodectidae. Previously, the two families had not clearly been distinguished, which prevented recognition of the primate status of the taxa now regarded by McKenna as microsyopids. Nevertheless, Wortmann (1903, p. 202) did consider some members of the group to belong to the Primates and discussed species of the genus *Microsyops* at considerable length. In North America species of this family succeed each other in a fairly simple lineage running from species of the early Eocene genus *Microsyops* through those of the middle Eocene *Cynodontomys* to that of the late Eocene *Craeseops*. Throughout its history dental evolution in this phylum is characterized by increasing molarization of the premolars. Judging from mandibular and cranial remains, members of this group ranged in size from about that of species of the living Malagasy genus *Lichanotus* (often referred to as *Avahi* by modern students despite priority of *Lichanotus*) to that of *Indri*. Eocene distribution of microsyopids, like that of omomyids, could have been holarctic, for McKenna has referred *Alsaticopithecus leemanni* (Hürzeler, 1947) from the late Eocene of Alsace to this taxon.

Affinities of the family are strongest, perhaps, with the Paleocene Plesiadapidae and Eocene Adapidae, but analysis of much new and undescribed cranial and postcranial material of *Cynodontomys* and *Microsyops*, now under study by McKenna at the American Museum of Natural History, could significantly alter present understanding of microsyopid relationships.

E. OMOMYIDAE

As knowledge of this family now stands, omomyids appear to have been the most diversified and widely distributed family of early Cenozoic primates. The eighteen genera of the group described to date imply approximately twice as extensive a radiation for this group, at a minimum, as that of the Malagasy Prosimii. With the exception of *Macrotarsius montanus* of the North American early Oligocene, all known members of this family are of Eocene occurrence. They have been recovered to date in the North American, European, and Asian continents. Moreover, the lower molar morphology of a primitive African member of the Anthropoidea, *Oligopithecus savagei* (Simons, 1962b; see Section IV of this chapter), from the Fayum early Oligocene of the United Arab Republic is strongly reminiscent of the omomyid dental pattern. This suggests that Old World Anthropoidea could have differentiated from earlier, and unknown, African omomyids.

Possession of large incisors, in comparison to canine teeth above and below, in those omomyids in which the anterior dentition is preserved might be taken as weakening the possibility of the group's standing in an ancestral position to Anthropoidea; but there are few if any other known specializations to be seen in omomyids which would definitely eliminate such a possibility. The writer (1961c) has pointed out trends in omomyid species, occurring in successive substages of the American Eocene, that appear to eliminate most objections to their being in or near ceboid ancestry, and much the same observation could apply to cercopithecoid and hominoid derivation from this group as well. He remarks (1961c, p. 13):

> "that *Omomys*, or one or more forms allied to it, was smaller than any known ceboids, had suitably unspecialized molar crown patterns together with small third molars, shared with some ceboids the otherwise nearly unique possession of a pericone cusp, and belongs to a group showing trends away from the primitive prosimian condition toward foreshortening of the rostrum, orbital enlargement, and vertical incisor emplacement. Moreover, Omomyidae are the only known family of ancient and undoubted Primates now known which possessed exactly the same dental formula as do the living Cebidae. Nevertheless, only in earliest omomyids are relative sizes of respective tooth types reasonably satisfactory for derivation of the tooth morphology characteristic of Oligocene-Recent South American Monkeys."

Although no complete crania of any Omomyidae are known, parts of the facial region and skeleton are preserved in the North American middle Eocene species *Hemiacodon gracilis* (Fig. 9). These materials have been reported on by Simpson (1940, p. 190) and Gazin (1958, p. 55).

Simpson was not able to find any particularly "advanced" or "tarsioid" features in the skeletal remains of *Hemiacodon* studied by him (1940). The known postcranial remains of *H. gracilis* show it to have been lemur-like and comparatively generalized, so that, should Omomyidae be in or near the ancestry of Anthropoidea, no evidence that either group had passed through a "tarsioid" grade is provided by these postcranial remains. Gazin's frontal fragment of *H. gracilis* shows that considerable forward rotation of the orbits had taken place in at least one member of this group, and the interorbital septum is constricted, suggesting a foreshortened muzzle in this small primate, which incidentally is about the size of the living tarsier. Nevertheless, the dental patterns of *Hemiacodon* seem too complex to allow for its being in or near the ancestry of later forms. Knowledge of other omomyids is restricted almost entirely to dentitions. Consequently, allocation of all these forms to one family must therefore be regarded as provisional. Typically, on the other hand, omomyids are linked by a series of dental features which give the taxon

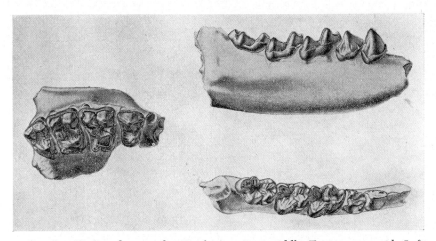

Fig. 9. *Hemiacodon gracilis*. North American middle Eocene omomyid. Left, upper right dentition. Right, lower right dentition. (From Gazin, 1958.) Magnification: 2.66.

a certain substance of validity. Although size is hardly a defining character all omomyids are rather small Prosimii ranging from forms evidently smaller than the deer mouse *Peromyscus*, such as *Niptomomys*, to about the size of the Malagasy species *Lichanotus* (or *Avahi*) *laniger*, in *Ourayia* and *Macrotarsius*. Typically omomyids display the following characters: a rather generalized dental formula

$$\left(\frac{2.1.3.3.}{2.1.3.3.} \right);$$

absence of the enlarged P_4 of necrolemurines, some paromomyines and anaptomorphids; presence of a large and rounded M_2 following a more rectangular M_1; occurrence of relatively smaller incisors than in most early Prosimii which in some cases (*Macrotarsius, Ourayia*) are not very procumbent; and fairly simple molar crown patterns often showing a tendency to exhibit an accessory cusp (pericone) anterolingual to the protocone, as in *Periconodon* (Fig. 10). Frequently the paraconid is reduced to a simple crest on M_{2-3}, while present on M_1.

Perhaps the closest relationships of this family are to the notharctines, by way of dental resemblances between the early Eocene English species *Cantius eppsi* and North American *Pelycodus* species, but there are also dental features of similarity to the European necrolemurines and to the Anaptomorphidae. Probably if members of these four taxa were better known osteologically it would be possible to demonstrate that they derive from a common middle or late Paleocene ancestry. Nevertheless assignment of some of the genera and species here placed in Omomyidae

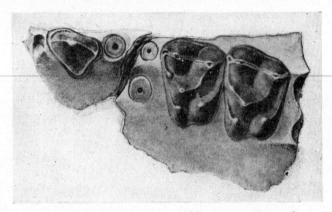

Fig. 10. *Periconodon helveticus.* Swiss middle Eocene omomyid primate. (From Stehlin, 1916.) Magnification: 7.33.

remains difficult. Documentation of the point would be tedious but a survey of the literature leaves the distinct impression that one or another species of each of the ten Paleocene-Eocene families of the Primates here accepted, has been urged at least once as being closely similar to a given species which is here (and by others) placed within a different family. The complex nexus of morphological similarities and presumed phyletic interrelationship which such comparisons imply has reached a level of ambiguity that can never be adequately resolved without discovery of much new postcranial material for members of all of these proposed families. The demand for such knowledge will require much additional paleontological field research in relevant localities.

Recent confirmation of placement of certain Old World Eocene prosimians among the Omomyidae and assignment of newly described forms to this group, by Hürzeler (1948) for *Teilhardina*, by Simons (1962a) for *Periconodon, Cantius, Hoanghonius,* and *Lushius,* leaves no doubt that it was more widely distributed than any of the other major taxa of early Cenozoic primates.

Cantius eppsi known from early Eocene deposits in Abbey Wood, Kent, has been shown by Simons (1962a) to have differed markedly from members of the genus *Protoadapis* to which it had previously been assigned and to more nearly resemble such undoubted omomyids as *Teilhardina* from the Belgian early Eocene and *Omomys* and *Hemiacodon*

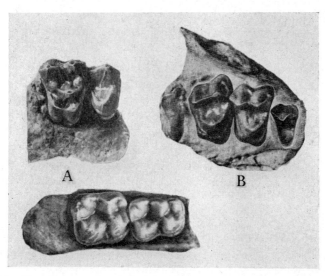

Fig. 11. Two Eocene omomyids from China. (a) *Hoanghonius stehlini.* Upper right P_4-M_1. Lower right M_1-M_2. (Courtesy Chow, 1961.) Magnification: 5.0. (b) *Lushius quilinensis.* Upper right P_4-M_2. (From Chow, 1961.) Magnification: 4.0.

from the North American middle Eocene. *Periconodon helveticus* is known only from a maxillary fragment with teeth from middle Eocene deposits near Egerkingen, Switzerland. This species exhibits the characteristic pericone cusp, made the basis of its generic name by Stehlin, and in size and in several morphological details closely resembles *Omomys.* These similarities of *Periconodon* to omomyids could be parallelistic, but I see no good reason to assume so, since four other Old World Eocene genera, *Teilhardina, Cantius, Hoanghonius,* and *Lushius* are most conveniently placed with omomyids and they seem to irrefutably establish the presence of this family in all three northern continents in Eocene times.

In 1957, Woo and Chow described new materials of the Eocene species *Hoanghonius stehlini* (Fig. 11) from localities on the banks of the Hoangho, near Mienchi, Honan, China which are sufficiently complete to show that the upper molars have the characteristic pericone cusp of omomyids. It is interesting that *Hoanghonius* also shows some broad features of resemblance to *Apidium* of the Egyptian Oligocene. More recently Chow (1961) has described a second Chinese Eocene primate, which appears to me to be an omomyid. This form, which comes from late Eocene rocks in the Lushi district of Honan, he has called *Lushius quilinensis* (Fig. 11). This species differs from *Hoanghonius* somewhat, more nearly resembling the North American omomyids than does the latter.

As a consequence of the relationships discussed above it would appear that omomyids are in the right places and have the most nearly proper morphology, insofar as it is known, to qualify as the prosimian stock from which ceboid, cercopithecoid, and hominoid primates arose. Unfortunately the very inadequate present state of knowledge of cranial and postcranial anatomy in this group prevents more certain demonstration of this possibility. On dental grounds alone, the case for their being in or near the direct ancestry of higher primates seems significant to me.

F. ?PONGIDAE

In 1938 Colbert tentatively assigned *Amphipithecus mogaungensis* from the late Eocene Pondaung formation of Burma to the Simiidae (= Pongidae). I agree that this allocation seems reasonable, or, that at the very least, the form does belong with the Hominoidea. Some students have even questioned the assignment of this species to the order Primates, but its close similarities to the newly discovered *Oligopithecus* now render such a possibility much more remote. In view of this resemblance of *Amphipithecus* to some of the Egyptian Oligocene primates, for the purposes of discussion, it will be considered further in Section IV below. Another little-known primate, *Pondaungia*, from the Eocene of Burma, may possibly belong here. The possibility that the Pondaung formation of Burma and the Quatrani formation of Egypt are more synchronous temporally than published ages indicate, late Eocene—early Oligocene respectively, should be considered in view of similarities in their faunas.

G. NECROLEMURINAE

A species of this subfamily of Tarsiidae, *Necrolemur antiquus* is one of the best known craniologically of early Cenzoic primates, as more than a dozen skulls of it have been found in the middle and late Eocene Quercy phosphorite deposits of south central France. A partial skeleton of another member of the subfamily *Nannopithex raabi* has been recovered from middle Eocene brown coal deposits near Halle am Saal, Germany. Simons (1961a, p. 57) ranked this subfamily in the Tarsiidae. This was done in view of a long series of characters which resembled the living tarsier and which are also to be seen in species of two other Eocene necrolemurine genera *Microchoerus* and *Necrolemur*. Nor is it particularly unusual that a surviving family of Mammalia could be distinguished as far back as the Eocene. The common qualities of tarsiines and necrolemurines could be attributed to parallel evolution as was implied by Hürzeler (1948). However, if common characters of the level of frequency seen between these two groups be interpreted as parallelisms then it would probably be impossible ever to sort out the difference between parallelistic and common heritage characters and the study of phylogenetic trees would wither at the root.

Although none of the necrolemurines, with the possible exception of *Pseudoloris parvulus* could be ancestral to species of the living *Tarsius,* because of crossing specializations in the teeth, their presence in the European Eocene does document the beginning of one of the surviving major types of primates. Necrolemurines have not been found outside Europe.

IV. OLIGOCENE PRIMATES

A. NATURE AND GEOGRAPHIC DISTRIBUTION

a. Asia. A consensus among recent workers indicates that *Anagale,* originally described as a tupaioid prosimian from the Oligocene of Mongolia, may not belong within this order, as is the case also for its supposed ally *Anagalopsis* (Bohlin, 1951), recently placed in the Insectivora by Saban (1958). With these forms removed from the order there remains only "*Kansupithecus*" another supposed primate from the Asian Taban-buluk badlands of Oligocene age. This generic name is technically invalid, since the describer, Bohlin (1946), failed to designate a type species for the genus—a form known only from one-half of a lower molar with associated jaw fragments. These scant remains are sufficient to indicate only a probability that this is a primitive pongid somewhat similar to *Amphipithecus*. Recently, Thenius (1958) has suggested that the age of "*Kansupithecus*" may be as late as middle Miocene.

b. Europe. The European Oligocene faunas lack all trace of primate species.

c. Africa. Earliest Oligocene deposits of the "Fluviomarine" or Quatrani formation of North Africa (Egypt) have, to date, provided almost the entirety of our knowledge of the earliest Old World Anthropoidea. None of these forms are prosimian, nor are any Prosimii whatever known from the Old World Oligocene, if *Anagale* be excluded from the order, so that, as far as the Old World is concerned, the subject matter of fossil primate studies of necessity changes subordinal grade abruptly in the mid-Tertiary.

Primate fossils so far recovered from the Fayum depression, 60 miles southwest of Cairo, show that Anthropoidea or near-Anthropoidea were already considerably varied at that remote period, approximately 35 million years ago. As a result of a recent comprehensive study by Kälin (1961), together with new finds secured by the 1961-1962 Yale Expedition to the Fayum, it is now possible to add considerably to our knowledge of these early forms.

B. PARAPITHECUS

Parapithecus fraasi (Fig. 12) is known from one specimen consisting of both mandibular rami with the entire lower dentition on one side or the other. Judging from the size of this jaw the animal it represents could not have been much larger than a squirrel—about the size of *Tarsius spectrum.* Almost from its discovery this small primate has been variously placed and assessed taxonomically. One of the most unusual statements about *Parapithecus fraasi* was made in connection with its original description by Schlosser (1910, p. 508):

> "Sie verbindet die eocänen Anaptomorphiden mit den Simiiden und vielleicht auch mit den Cercopitheciden. Die zweizahl der I and P is bei dieser beiden Familien möglicherweise dadurch zustande gekommen dass sich der C von Parapithecus in einen I_2, und P_2 in einen neuen C verwandelt hat."

The writer, on one occasion, had also arrived at this interesting but improbable conclusion—which does explain away the differences in dental formula separating all Eocene "tarsioids" from *Parapithecus.* On mentioning the possibility of this interpretation to a leading authority in the field, his only reply was that a proponent of such a view had better secure employment with tenure before publishing the idea. It was a relief to learn that Schlosser had previously done so. *Parapithecus* does have some resemblance to *Tarsius* in the high angle of posterior divergence of the mandibular rami and in shallowness of vertical depth of the mandibles, but it is difficult to see what this means in terms of relationship, in view of clear-cut similarities in the molars to its Fayum contemporary *Propliopithecus haeckeli.* Their degree of morphological resemblance is to be noted particularly in the third lower molars. *Propliopithecus,* although primitive, is clearly a member of the Anthropoidea, and by its degree of similarity so should be *Parapithecus.* On

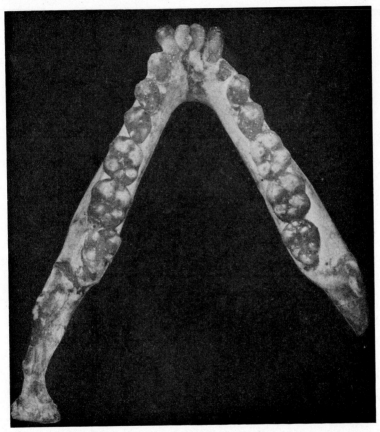

Fig. 12.   *Parapithecus fraasi.* From the Fayum early Oligocene of Egypt. (From Kälin, 1961.) Magnification: 3.0.

the other hand if *Parapithecus* is truly a *form de passage,* as some have thought, should it be regarded as simian or prosimian? In view of molar similarities with *Propliopithecus,* Kälin (1961, p. 29) suggests this genus as representing a family and superfamily of primates partly revealing the nature of the transition from prosimians to "Hominoidea and Pongoidea" as well as some degree of parallel differentiation of its own.

The probability that *Parapithecus* does represent a very primitive catarrhine type is strengthened, not only by its resemblance to *Propliopithecus*, but by its similarity to newly discovered materials of *Apidium* as well. However, both *Parapithecus* and *Apidium* may eventually prove to possess lower dental formulas (1.1.3.3. and 2.1.3.3.) different from nearly all other catarrhines. Interpretation of the exact lower dental formula of *Parapithecus* has always presented considerable difficulties in spite of the fact that all the lower teeth are known. The three posterior teeth are clearly the molars and anterior to these are two undoubted premolars (Fig. 12). In front of these is a tooth intermediate in morphology between a premolar and canine, before this a large caniniform tooth and most anteriorly a single incisor. If the second tooth, large and caniniform, be an incisor then the dental formula would be 2.1.2.3 as Schlosser eventually concluded. Nevertheless such incisor heteromorphy is most unusual since the second (more posterior) pair of incisors are typically smaller in the Primates than the most anterior pair—not the other way around, as in *Parapithecus*. Even if both these teeth are incisors it is almost impossible to derive any undoubted Anthropoidea from a form with such an incisor pattern. If the second large caniniform tooth is a canine then the dental formula would be 1.1.3.3 as Schlosser originally suggested, the same as in *Tarsius* and a few other prosimians, but not as in typical Anthropoidea. This is, of course not particularly surprising for there is no reason why all species assigned to Anthropoidea should have possessed a dental formula of 2.1.2.3., as is the case for Miocene-Recent members of this suborder, it being the exception rather than the rule that all members of a given mammalian suborder should possess the same dental formula.

C. Apidium

Apidium phiomense, described by Osborn in 1908, was largely overlooked in early discussions of Fayum Oligocene primates perhaps because its status as a member of this order was in doubt for some time and originally Osborn did not suggest an ordinal designation for it. The type specimen of this species was discovered in the upper fossiliferous horizon of the Quatrani formation, Egyptian Oligocene and therefore occurred considerably higher stratigraphically than the presumed level of Schlosser's *Parapithecus* type.[3]

---

[3] Exact localities are not known for the types of *Propliopithecus, Parapithecus,* and *Moeripithecus,* but since early collecting activities were almost entirely restricted to the lower fossil wood zone, Quatrani formation, it is most likely that Schlosser's collector, Richard Markgraf, secured these types there.

A new species, *Apidium moustafai*, described by Simons (1962b) comes from a level stratigraphically intermediate between the upper and lower fossil wood zones. This form is slightly smaller and more primitive than *A. phiomense*. Little resemblance between the latter species and *Parapithecus fraasi* is to be noted, for Osborn's *Apidium* type possesses highly multicuspidate molars, a character which led Hürzeler (1958) to suggest that *Apidium* was a condylarth related to *Phenacodus*, and Simons (1960a) to discuss the possibility of a special relationship between it and *Oreopithecus*—a primate which exhibits strikingly similar accessory molar cuspules as *Phenacodus* does *not*. The newly described species *A. moustafai* has a smaller M_3 and somewhat less pronounced molar cuspidation than has *A. phiomense*, slight distinctions which render more noticeable some strong similarities to *Parapithecus*, similarities which are particularly pronounced in the nature of cusp patterns and outline of the premolars and first lower molar. Although no anterior teeth are preserved in *A. moustafai*, there is also the possibility, judging from alveoli, that the dental formula in species of these two genera was the same.

D. MOERIPITHECUS

Moeripithecus markgrafi, the largest Egyptian Oligocene primate in which teeth have been preserved, has recently been well illustrated by Kälin (Fig. 13). This specimen consists of a jaw fragment carrying two

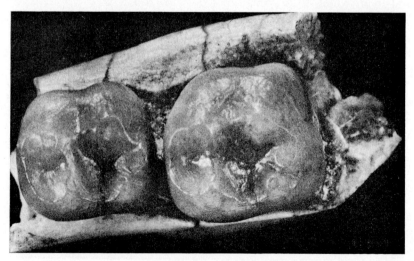

FIG. 13.   *Moeripithecus markgrafi.* From the Fayum early Oligocene of Egypt. (From Kälin, 1961.) Magnification: 8.0.

molars which has been said by Abel (1931) and others to reflect a suitable molar morphology from which to derive that of the cerco- pithecoid monkeys. Kälin does not favor this possibility, but does stress, following Schlosser, that there is a distinct resemblance to the same molars of *Parapithecus* and *Propliopithecus*, and mentions also a close similarity to the *Apidium* lower molar crown pattern save for the absence here of the molar centroconid present in *Apidium* and *Oreopithecus*. Agreeing that *Moeripithecus* does resemble most closely its Fayum contemporaries, the writer is more reluctant to question the primate status of this form than is Kälin (1961, p. 47). Molars of this sort can be seen elsewhere among the Primates, as for instance the M_{1-2} patterns of the Miocene ceboid *Homunculus* or the omomyid prosimian *Hoanghonius* from the Eocene of China. If not primates what sort of archaic mammals are such forms supposed to be? They certainly have no significant, or even passing, resemblance to any described taxon of non-Primates.

An unnamed and enigmatic mandible from the upper horizons of the Fayum Oligocene was illustrated and discussed by Simons (1961b). This specimen, which long remained undescribed in the Egyptian collections of the American Museum of Natural History in New York, represents the largest primate species so far discovered in the African Oligocene. Most of the teeth are broken away in this specimen, but the crown of lower P_3 is partly preserved and it shows a sectorial conformation for this tooth as in cercopithecids and pongids. The occurrence of P_3 sectoriality in a tooth which is also three-rooted (a condition seen elsewhere only in members of the genus *Hylobates*), together with reduced third molar size (alveolus), possession of a constricted ramus beneath M_3, and deep symphyseal region, all combine to suggest that this mandible indicates the presence of true hylobatines in the African Oligocene. In any case, the form the species represents is much more specialized in their direc- tion than is the only slightly earlier *Propliopithecus* which on rather uncertain grounds has been suggested by some students to have gibbon affinities.

E. Propliopithecus

Propliopithecus haeckeli (Fig. 14) was originally supposed by Schlosser (1911) to have been in or near the ancestry of *Pliopithecus* and through this connection the gibbons, a view followed by Gregory (1916) and by many others since. Later, Clark and Thomas (1952) outlined similarities between this Fayum species and *Limnopithecus macinnesi*, from the Kenya Miocene. This similarity is not at all sur- prising since *Limnopithecus* and *Pliopithecus* are virtually indistinguishable and both could be derived from an almost immediately precedent common species. Nevertheless Hürzeler (1945) questioned that *Propliopithecus* and *Pliopithecus* are in the same line of descent. Now that a much more gibbon-like mandible (discussed above) is known from the Egyptian Oligocene it does appear that *Propliopithecus* may be too generalized at too late a date to serve well in an ancestral position for the Hylobatinae. Actually it fits equally well as an exact morphological forerunner for all Hominoidea since, although it possesses rather pongid-

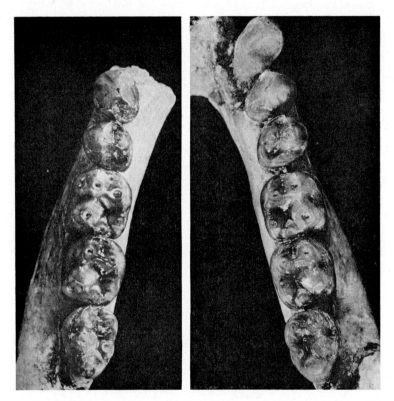

Fig. 14. *Propliopithecus haeckeli.* From the Fayum early Oligocene of Egypt. (From Kälin, 1961.) Magnification: 3.66.

like lower molars, this might merely be the primitive hominoid pattern. Moreover, premolars in this species resemble those of hominoids in that there is no heteromorphy between P_3 and P_4 as there is in Pongidae, both living and fossil. *Propliopithecus* might well be near the ancestry of *Proconsul* or of the African species of *Sivapithecus*, both of which occur in the Kenya Miocene at a date perhaps 10 to 15 million years later than the deposition of the Egyptian Quatrani formation. Some scanty evidence suggests that certain species of the *Proconsul-Sivapithecus-Dryopithecus* complex may never have exhibited much premolar heteromorphy and therefore may relate to this early form which, like man, does not show differentiated premolars.

F. Fayum Primate Frontal

Simons (1959) described a small primate frontal bone from the Egyptian Oligocene (Fig. 15). This remains the only known cranial portion of an Oligocene primate. The specimen shows that by this stage in their derivation Anthropoidea had evolved their characteristic and exclusive feature of postorbital closure. An endocranial cast of the

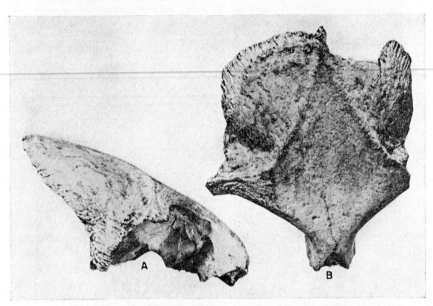

Fig. 15. A primate frontal bone from the Egyptian early Oligocene, Fayum Province. (A) Lateral view. (B) Dorsal view. (From Simons, 1959.) Magnification: 2.33.

region of the olfactory bulbs also indicates that these structures were considerably smaller, relative to the frontal region of the brain case, than in any known Eocene primate, so that reduction of the olfactory sense must by this time have progressed considerably. It is clear from the narrowness of the interorbital septum, anterior rotation of the orbits, restricted sutural contact for the posterior margins of the nasals, and similar features, that the species of higher primate represented by this skull fragment was larger brained and of much shorter face than any previously existing primates are known to have been. In this sense it is nicely transitional between Paleocene-Eocene and Miocene-Recent primates, as a good connecting link should be. Presumably the forward rotation of the orbits and foreshortened face correlate with increasing use of the hands in feeding and defense. The size of this frontal suggests an animal about as large as the Eastern gray squirrel or, among living primates, the lion marmoset, *Leontocebus*. Simons (1959) discussed the probabilities as to which, if any, of the known Fayum primates this skull fragment might belong, and pointed out that the mandibles of *Parapithecus* and *Apidium* are small enough to go with a frontal of this size. Nevertheless, in recent papers by Hürzeler (1958) and Kälin (1961), the primate status of both *Apidium* and *Parapithecus* has been questioned to varying degrees. While not agreeing with these authors that these forms are much in doubt as primates, the writer would now prefer to suggest that the frontal bone (which because of the presence of postorbital closure should be placed among the higher primates) may belong with the newly recovered species *Oligopithecus savagei* (Simons, 1962b), which is of the right size and is an undoubted member of the Anthropoidea. Moreover, both specimens appear to have come from about the same horizon, the upper 40 feet of the fossil wood zone, Fluviomarine or Quatrani formation (see Beadnell, 1905). Of course, the frontal fragment may belong with a species otherwise unknown.

G. OLIGOPITHECUS

Oligopithecus savagei (Simons, 1962b) (Fig. 16) in over-all dental and mandibular morphology is, among its Fayum contemporaries, more like *Propliopithecus* than like *Apidium* or *Parapithecus*. However, it differs from all the other three in possessing an anteroposteriorly elongate P_3. This P_3, on the other hand, is not three-rooted as is this tooth in the

FIG. 16. *Oligopithecus savagei*. From the Egyptian early Oligocene, Fayum Province. (From Simons, 1962b.) Magnification: 4.0.

unnamed Fayum jaw discussed above (Section IV,D), which in any event is a much larger form—in comparable measurements over twice as large as *Oligopithecus*.

Of considerable interest is the noticeable resemblance of the lower P_4-M_1 of *Oligopithecus* to those of *Amphipithecus* (Fig. 17) described by Colbert in 1938 from the late Eocene Pondaung formation of Burma. The similarity between these two forms tends to strengthen the supposition that *Amphipithecus mogaungensis* does represent the earliest known member of the Anthropoidea, and therefore to the extent that the Pondaung formation has been correctly assessed as being of late Eocene age, shows that Catarrhini had differentiated in the late Eocene in

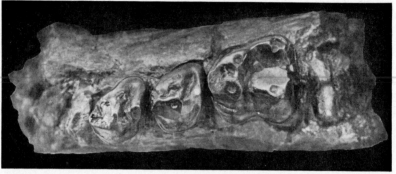

FIG. 17. *Amphipithecus mogaungensis* from the late Eocene of Burma. (Courtesy American Museum of Natural History.) Magnification: 4.0.

southeast Asia at a time somewhat earlier than that of the deposition of the fluviomarine beds in Egypt. In first molar morphology both *Amphipithecus* and *Oligopithecus* are rather more reminiscent of such ancient cebids as *Homunculus* and *Cebupithecia* from the South American Miocene than other non-Oligocene primates. This latter similarity, however, is much more likely to be due to the retention of a rather generalized first molar pattern in all these forms than to a close connection between earliest Old World Anthropoidea and Ceboidea. Nevertheless, the apparent presence in *Amphipithecus* of three premolars has led some students to conclude that this Burmese primate is a platyrrhine, which is nonsense zoogeographically. The forerunners of Old World Anthropoidea must certainly have at one time possessed three premolars, and before that four. Provisionally, the similarity between P_4 and M_1 in *Oligopithecus* and *Amphipithecus* strengthens acceptance of primate status for the latter which has been questioned as a primate by Hürzeler (1958, p. 32) and by others. Evidently, the Old World Anthropoidea passed through a stage where three premolars were retained above and below, during the late Eocene, for the loss of P_1 and P_2 has been accomplished in such early Oligocene forms as *Oligopithecus savagei* and *Propliopithecus haeckli*. Moreover, *Oligopithecus* even shows some differentiation of the P_3, away from the primitive pattern which more likely developed after the loss of P_1 and P_2. This could indicate that the date of reduction of the dentition in the lineage of *Oligopithecus* fell well back in the Eocene.

H. CONCLUSIONS

Taken together, the primates of the African Oligocene represent a rather curious assemblage. No species of definite prosimian grade are known, and those, such as *Parapithecus fraasi*, which have been suspected of prosimian ties by some authors, are quite unlike any prosimians of the European Eocene and do show ties with Hominoidea. This may well be the result of the continent of Africa having been separated from Europe for a considerable period of time, and remaining so until slightly before the deposition of the Fayum fluviomarine beds. By then the presence of carnivore and anthracothere genera (or perhaps even species) synonymous with forms occurring in Europe, demonstrates that a land connection had been established between these two continents. Traces of higher primates, "*Kansupithecus*" and *Amphipithecus*, contemporary with, or earlier, than these Egyptian forms in Asia, renders the area of initial differentiation of the Old World higher primates somewhat in doubt. Perhaps neither "*Kansupithecus*" nor *Amphipithecus* are primates, but such an eventuality seems quite unlikely. There is always the possibility, however, that one or both of them occurred somewhat later in time than preliminary faunal correlations suggest. In the latter case, it would be slightly more probable that Anthropoidea originally differentiated in Africa from prosimian stocks which may have reached that continent as far back as the Paleocene; and that the Asian occurrences represent the result of sporadic migrations from Africa through the area of the Indian subcontinent. This would also explain why there are no really clear-cut similarities between Fayum primates and those of the late Eocene of Europe.

V. MIOCENE PRIMATES

A. PROBLEMS OF TAXONOMIC AND GEOGRAPHIC DISTRIBUTION

In spite of extensive new additions to knowledge of the fossil record of Old World higher primates of the Miocene epoch and later, an up-to-date assessment of the significance of materials now known is not available in English. General awareness of the full import of known Miocene Anthropoidea has also been hampered by a lack of attention of the zoogeography of these early species, and their associated faunas. As a consequence of this inattention, up-to-date knowledge of geographic range of given forms has never been fully applied to the reinterpretation of the present taxonomic arrangement of Old World fossil Anthropoidea.

Previous workers can hardly be criticized for this situation. The system of present hominoid taxonomy grew up largely before even partial information as to distribution and range was available for the primates concerned. Because of present day disjunct or relict distribution of most of the Old World higher primate genera, with the notable exception of *Macaca* and *Homo*, a conservative, and to some extent justifiable, practice of regarding closely similar forms occurring in different continents, such as *Epipliopithecus* and *Limnopithecus*, as generally distinct, has been followed by most authors. This practice has tended to obscure what was happening in higher primate phylogeny throughout a widespread area of tropical and subtropical environments in Eurasia and Africa during Miocene-Recent times. Such splitting at the generic level has also helped to conceal the manner in which new and more complete knowledge of fossil cercopithecoids and hominoids in specific geographic regions and at given times can be fitted together with evidence from other regions to best tell the story of the rise of the higher primates and man in the Old World. There has been a tendency to separate these primates generically if from different continents. Recently a second and better practice has been developing. This is to assign two forms to the same genus, if they are nearly indistinguishable morphologically, even if from widely separated areas. Clearly, this type of procedure falls more nearly in line with the practice of taxonomists of other groups of fossil Mammalia than does the earlier alternative.

Perhaps the conclusions as to relationship among Miocene-Pleistocene primates given below cannot be stated with an ideal degree of finality; they are, however, drawn from direct comparisons of most of the relevant materials over a period of years. The absence of a background, founded on direct observation of relevant materials is all too frequent in the analysis of fossil relatives of man, and generally has resulted in authors quoting earlier authors or in citing "a majority of opinions." Such historical methods may have sufficed for Livy or Tacitus, but they can hardly be classified as scientific. What appears to be needed in such cases is fresh analysis of the fossil realities, not recitation of outdated and sometimes emotional views concerning them.

During the Miocene epoch the expansion of Anthropoidea to nearly their present limits of distribution seems to have been accomplished.[4] Several ceboid species of essentially modern type have been recovered from South American Miocene deposits. These fossil materials are of species belonging to the genera *Homunculus, Dolichocebus,* and *Cebupithecia.* Stirton and Savage (1951) have provided the latest study of these forms including an excellent description of skull and postcranial remains of one of them, *Cebupithecia sarmientoi.* Crania of *Dolichocebus* and *Homunculus* have also been described (Kraglievich, 1951) but in order to better understand their phyletic relationship these specimens will require further analysis. Published figures of the two latter forms suggest that although the characteristic bun-shaped skull of ceboids was already present in Miocene time, the frontal expansion of the brain was not as great as in modern ceboids with comparable skull size.

In Eurasia hominoids have been recovered from rocks of Miocene age distributed from Spain, through France, the Rhine valley, and Austria eastward to the Siwalik beds of India and perhaps in China. On the other hand, the great rarity of fossil evidence of cercopithecoid monkeys during the epoch is puzzling. Apart from one or two teeth resembling the Pliocene genus *Mesopithecus* from the Kenya Miocene deposits, no cercopithecoid remains have yet been described from rocks of this period. Since climates and ecologies in the Miocene were satisfactory for the existence of hominoids in northern areas, such as Germany and Czechoslovakia, and in view of the fact that living cercopithecoids tolerate climatic extremes as great as or even greater than Pongidae, for example, the Japanese monkey and the Himalayan langurs can tolerate, the rarity or absence of this group in Europe and particularly in the East African and Eurasian Miocene localities deserves consideration. Perhaps the solution to the puzzle is that although they are morphologically "primitive" the basic radiation of cercopithecoids was comparatively recent and largely post-Miocene in occurrence.

B. PLIOPITHECUS

Species presently assigned to *Pliopithecus* have been recovered in a series of localities in Europe, ranging from early to late Miocene. The possible occurrence of this genus in the European Pliocene, as well, has been reported in the literature. On the basis of evidence now available it seems unlikely that members of one subgenus of this genus, *Epiplio-*

---

[4] Since species of most Miocene primate genera occur in more than one Old World continent, the following discussion will not be broken down as to continent.

pithecus (Fig. 18) proposed by Zapfe and Hürzeler (1957), can be maintained as generically distinct from *Limnopithecus*, from the Miocene of Kenya. Publications dealing with *Limnopithecus* appearing subsequent to Hopwood's original description of this form (1933) do not sufficiently analyze whether it is separable, on the generic level, from its European ally. However, as is (or should be) required practice when proposing a new genus, Hopwood did consider this possibility. After discussing a few slight and variable characters of the metaconid and lingual cingulum seen in *Limnopithecus* but not in *Pliopithecus*, Hopwood (1933, pp. 440-441) remarks:

> "Other reasons for keeping the three fossil genera [*Pliopithecus, Prohylobates, Limnopithecus*] apart are the various ages of the deposits in which they are found and their widely separated localities. Apart from convenience, neither reason is particularly sound, but when dealing with species founded on such fragmentary remains as those of *Prohylobates tandyi* and *Limnopithecus legetet* there is much to be said in its favor."

Hopwood thus exemplifies the attitude questioned here, that forms in widely separated areas are to be distinguished generically even if morphological differences for doing so are not provided by the materials concerned. On the other hand, the two points made by Hopwood might well apply to discriminations on the species level, it being most unlikely that a single species of arboreal primate would range so far in area or persist so long in time. Moreover, recent potassium-argon age determinations indicate that the east African fauna from the vicinity of Rusinga Island, Kenya (which includes *Limnopithecus*), is essentially contemporary with those Czechoslovakian deposits which have yielded *Epipliopithecus*. Simple comparison of variability in living pongid species groups assigned to single genera, such as the members of *Hylobates*, *Pongo*, and *Pan* readily demonstrates the lack of need for generic separation among those early gibbons. One can, at least try to keep the proposal of new genera in harmony with previous usage in the taxon concerned. Pending better knowledge of total anatomy *Epipliopithecus*, *Prohylobates*, and *Limnopithecus* should be considered subgenera of *Pliopithecus*, as was initially suggested for the first of these taxa (Zapfe and Hürzeler, 1957). It would seem to me more logical to suppose that fragmentary materials, if not easily distinguishable, should be grouped together taxonomically. The reverse of this is to suppose that, were the forms concerned better known, they would turn out to be different. In this, the taxonomist of fossils tries to get ahead of his time, by predicting, without evidence in support of the assumption, that additional material will prove a sheer hypothesis: that distinctions of generic value do exist. In paleontological studies it is better to work with the material at hand and leave to the future the opportunity to improve accuracy of judgment.

It is of considerable interest that the skeletal material of *Pliopithecus*

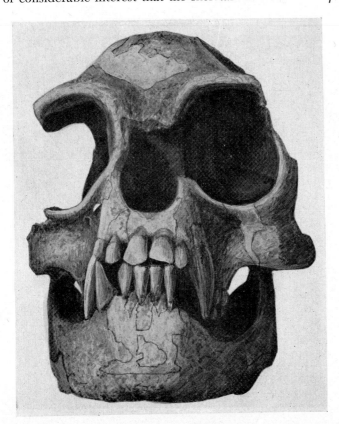

FIG. 18. *Pliopithecus* (*Epipliopithecus*) *vindobonensis*. A nearly complete gibbon-like skull from the Miocene of Europe. Collected near Neudorf an der March, Czechoslovakia. (From Zapfe, 1958.) Magnification: 1.0.

now available shows that although definably hylobatine dentally, the forelimb elongation so characteristic of modern gibbons is barely noticeable in this Miocene form (Simons, 1960b).

C. PROCONSUL

In addition to *Limnopithecus*, Hopwood (1933) described a second genus of fossil pongid, *Proconsul*, from the region of Rusinga Island, Lake

Victoria, Kenya. Another genus from these same sediments then proposed by him (*Xenopithecus*) later proved to be a synonym of *Proconsul*. During the early thirties, collections made by Leakey and MacInnes also in the region of Rusinga Island added greatly to the number and variety of known primate species from the East African Miocene. These materials insofar as they pertain to the Pongidae were reported in a

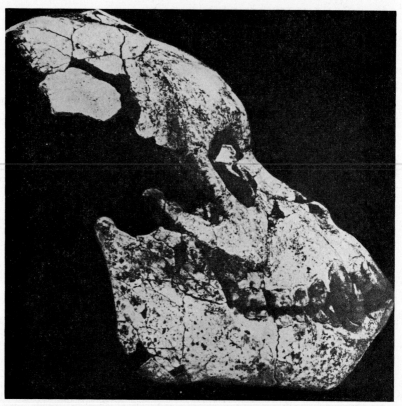

Fig. 19a. Lateral view of 1948 skull of *Proconsul africanus* found in Miocene deposits, Rusinga Island, Lake Victoria, Kenya. (From Clark and Leakey, 1951.) Magnification: 0.9.

monograph by Clark and Leakey (1951). The discovery by Mrs. Leakey in 1948 of a nearly entire skull of *Proconsul africanus* (Figs. 19 and 20), together with a certain number of limb bones and an entire hand of a different individual belonging to this species, make *Proconsul* perhaps the best known Miocene primate. To date, three species of *Proconsul* have been described. Judging from the size of comparable parts, these range from about the body bulk of a large gibbon or siamang (*P.*

africanus) to that of a small gorilla (*P. major*). These extensive materials of *Proconsul* have over the years stimulated considerable discussion of the possible affinities of the genus within the Hominoidea. Because of both geographic location and morphology, it seemed appropriate to

FIG. 19b.   Facial view of 1948 skull of *Proconsul africanus*, from Miocene beds, Rusinga Island, Kenya. (From Clark and Leakey, 1951, slightly retouched.) Magnification: 1.0.

Hopwood, and other early discussants of the form, to suppose that *Proconsul* might well relate to the ancestry of chimpanzee and gorilla. Prognathism, large canines, and the lack of crossing specializations in the molar teeth of *Proconsul* all combine to suggest this possible relation to the modern African apes. On the other hand, Clark and Leakey (1951) stressed the generalized nature of *Proconsul*, which in many ways had hardly progressed beyond a monkey-like grade of organization. Some of these primitive "nonape-like" features include: external nares narrowing ventrally, orientation of orbital cavities, slight postorbital construction of the skull, absence of eyebrow ridges, slender cheek bones, narrow mandibular symphysis, and lack of the simian shelf. Most of these differences from modern pongids are such as to admit of the possibility that *Proconsul*, or a form of primate very much like it, was ancestral to Hominidae. Certainly in the dentition there is little to exclude at least the smaller species of *Proconsul* from hominid ancestry. Although the canines are enlarged and there is some premolar heteromorphy the incisors are rather hominid-like, and molar construction is primitive

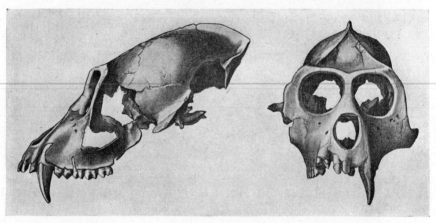

Fig. 20.   Facial and lateral aspects of the skull of *Libypithecus markgrafi*, from Pliocene deposits in the Wadi Natrum, Egypt. From Stromer, 1913. Magnification: approximately 0.5.

enough to serve as the foundation for that of almost any of later occurring hominids. However, the tendency to regard *Proconsul* as being close to the human ancestry may in large part be due to the simple fact that we know much more about this primate than we do about its contemporaries among the Miocene Hominoidea in Africa and elsewhere.

Napier and Davis' recent (1959) study of the forelimb and shoulder anatomy of *Proconsul* has demonstrated that the species *P. africanus* was probably semiarboreal, and a partial brachiator, but that it possessed few or no "highly developed" commitments to brachiation.

D. DRYOPITHECUS

The dryopithecines or "oak-apes" make their first appearance in a far-flung series of Eurasian deposits of Miocene age, but they do not provide much information useful in reconstructing primate history, for their cranial and limb remains are practically unknown. There are no skull fragments of this or related genera and limb remains such as those of "*Paidopithex*" consisting of a single femur from late Miocene deposits at Eppelsheim, Germany, are of uncertain placement within the group. In fact, the latter has been suggested by Hürzeler (1958) as possibly belonging to *Oreopithecus*. One other possible dryopithecine find includes limb bones; this find is "*Austriacopithecus*," which has recently been restudied by Thenius (1954) and by Zapfe (1961). It is equally uncertain as to which, if any, of the known dryopithecines this material belongs, but Thenius favors the idea that these forelimb bones indicate a pongid which lacked brachiating specializations.

Confusion reigns in the dental analyses and taxonomic assessment of dryopithecines. It is clear that the group has been excessively split taxonomically, but, because known dentitions of the subfamily are widely scattered in museums and collections throughout the world, no one to date has been able to present a sensible analysis of the group. At best this would be difficult because of the incompleteness of specimens. For instance, none of the types of European and Indian dryopithecine species appear to include upper and lower dentitions in association.

The classic concept of *Dryopithecus* is founded on European species of which the earliest described is *D. fontani* from the Miocene of Saint Gaudens, proposed by Lartet in 1856. This specimen and several other European discoveries since that date show that *Dryopithecus* was a medium sided hominoid about as big as the chimpanzee, and that like the living pongids it had large canines, and heteromorphic premolars, but in general possessed smaller and narrower incisors than do the living forms. Gregory's early demonstration of the common possession of the five cusped *Dryopithecus* pattern in the lower molars of members of this general group, and in primitive man, brought to attention the view that the ultimate origins of the Hominidae may trace back to the "oak apes." Gregory (1922) in summarizing the dental evidence for such a relationship remarked, that ". . . man is a late Tertiary offshoot of the *Dryopithecus-Sivapithecus* group, or at least of apes that closely resembled those genera in the construction of jaw and dentition." Recent restudy of *Ramapithecus* (Simons, 1961d) emphasizing the hominid features of this mid-Pliocene primate from the Siwalik beds of India, when considered together with conclusions drawn from Leakey's new discovery of a similar primate type *Kenyapithecus* (from Africa) appear to strengthen Gregory's perceptive hypothesis. Both *Ramapithecus* and *Kenyapithecus* show strong resemblances to *Dryopithecus* and *Sivapi-*

thecus as well as to Hominidae. Considered as a whole, *Dryopithecus* and its allies form a highly variable complex from which the species of *Proconsul* do not differ greatly. For instance it is difficult to understand why the latter two genera have been placed in different subfamilies, when the evidence even for their generic separation could be disputed. In addition to the French mandibles, all assignable to *D. fontani*, a few other species referable to this genus have been recovered elsewhere in Europe. One of these, *D. darwini*, was described by Abel from a single lower molar from Miocene deposits in the Vienna basin. It appears to be more like *Sivapithecus* than are most of the European dryopithecines. Another species, *D. rhenanus*, is known from a number of isolated teeth from localities in southern Germany. Whether the genus *Dryopithecus*, in the strict sense, occurred outside Europe is not definitely known. A quite large lower molar from the Siwaliks, described originally as *Dryopithecus giganteus* by Pilgrim, was removed to a new genus *Indopithecus* by von Koenigswald in 1949. Recently, Woo (1958) figured and discussed materials from Keiyuan, Yunnan, China, which he assigned to a new species *Dryopithecus keiyuanensis*. This material seems definitely to establish a considerable eastward range for species of this genus if the Chinese material is correctly placed taxonomically. Fourtau (1920) described another species *D. mogharensis*, from lower Miocene beds in the Wadi Moghara, Egypt. Recent examination of casts of this specimen (the original cannot now be located) indicates continued doubt as to the specimen's actually belonging to *Dryopithecus*.

Of considerable interest in interpreting the origins of Hominidae, is the genus *Sivapithecus*, which as it is now understood, has been reported as occurring in Miocene deposits of Africa, Europe, and Asia.

Villalta and Crusafont (1944) have described a species perhaps belonging to this genus from the Miocene of Spain[5] and its presence also in the Miocene beds of Kenya (*Sivapithecus africanus*) has been reported by Clark and Leakey (1951). The great majority of remains of this primate are, however, from the Siwalik beds of India, from which deposits Gregory *et al.* (1938) distinguished two species *S. indicus* and *S. sivalensis*. From this genus they also distinguished two other genera and species (originally described by Lewis on the basis of material in the Yale collections) *Bramapithecus* and *Sugrivapithecus*, both of which, like *Sivapithecus*, range in age from late Miocene to early Pliocene. In view of the considerable uncertainty as to the interrelationships of the species of all of these dryopithecine genera and of other

---

[5] Recently reassigned to *Dryopithecus*.

hominoid genera of Miocene-Pliocene age it seems more useful to tabulate places and times of occurrence for them, and to refrain here from more elaborate attempts to analyze them taxonomically (Table I). Hopefully, new finds and further comparative study will help clarify our knowledge of the dryopithecines, some particular species of which in all probability gave rise to the Hominidae.

E. KENYAPITHECUS

In the spring of 1962 Dr. Lewis Leakey announced the discovery of a mammalian fauna near Fort Ternan, Kenya, of latest Miocene or early Pliocene aspect and indicated that it contained a new variety of higher primate. Falling as it does between the age of the extensive Olduvai fauna of Tanganyika and the Miocene deposits of the Rusinga Island area, Kenya, Mammalia from this new site are of intense interest in determining ancestor-descendant relationships between the two faunas. Regardless of whether the Ft. Ternan fauna should prove to be Pliocene or late Miocene in age, this intermediate fauna remains equally important. Nevertheless, potassium-argon age determinations for this site indicate a date of about 14 million years B.P., which is rather earlier than other dates reported up to now for the early Pliocene. Leakey (1962) published a description of this new species which he has called *Kenyapithecus wickeri*. The type material consists of opposite maxillae with teeth, an upper canine which fits the canine alveolus of the left maxilla, and an isolated lower molar. Dr. Leakey's careful analysis of this specimen shows that in known parts, it possesses many features which are similar to the hominids. These include a comparatively small upper canine, a low-crowned fourth upper premolar, as in *Ramapithecus* (Fig. 25) from the Siwaliks, with a placement and condition of the anterior wear facet which would suggest anteroposterior crowding of the dentition in connection with facial foreshortening as in *Ramapithecus*. Moreover, the deep canine fossa and placement of the anterior root of the zygoma are similar to the condition of these structures in hominids. During a recent visit of Dr. Leakey's to the paleontological laboratories at Yale it was possible to compare directly the types of *Ramapithecus brevirostris* and *Kenyapithecus wickeri* and their close similarity in comparable structures is striking. Although it is probably not advisable at present to assert that these two genera are indistinguishable it seems clear that again the main justification for their generic separation is the presumed difference in age and the wide geographic separation. As knowledge of Cenozoic faunas the world over has grown throughout the last few decades it has become increasingly apparent that many genera of Mammalia had wider geographic distribution and persisted longer than could possibly have been conjectured from the first sporadic finds of extinct faunas in the 19th century. As a consequence of this it has become more obvious to the modern school of paleontologists that generic separations which are founded mainly on temporal or areal separation are usually not advisable, as has been discussed in Section V above. Such practice tends to obscure real similarities between fossil faunas of different areas and thereby decreases the accuracy of faunal correlation. In this specific case there is practically no morphological basis, either in the structure of the teeth or in the conformation of the maxillae, the only comparable parts known in these two primates, upon which a generic separation could be founded. In fact, specific distinction could even be questioned. In any event, these two finds indicate that populations of *Kenyapithecus-Ramapithecus* type must have been distributed widely throughout the Old World tropics in Mio-Pliocene times. This distribution does not suggest that the emergence of man necessarily took place in Africa, although it is clearly there that our best evidence of his emergence has been found to date. Briefly, these two specimens show features foreshadowing Hominidae, through their common possession of relatively small canines, hominid-like morphology in the fourth upper premolar, presence of canine fossae (resembling those of hominids), and with a man-like placement of the anterior base of the zygomatic arch.

To the extent that it can be accepted that these two species *K. wickeri* and *R. brevirostris* do represent members of populations transitional between early Miocene dryopithecine and the Pleistocene Hominidae then the line of derivation seems to point back to *Sivapithecus africanus* which would definitely put the species of *Proconsul* off the main line of hominid derivation. However that may be, it is obvious that continuation of Dr. Leakey's valuable field researches in East Africa is one of the surest methods of helping to clarify this phase of the history of human origins.

VI. Pliocene Primates

A. Geographic Distribution

Discussion of the nature and distribution of members of this order in Pliocene times is simplified by the fact that almost nothing has been found out about the Central and South American Ceboidea of this epoch. Knowledge of prosimians during the period concerned is almost equally poor, being limited to a single described species of undoubted Pliocene age with supposed lorisid affinities, *Indraloris lulli*, from the Siwalik Hills of India. A few other lorisiformes from the late Miocene or just possibly early Pliocene of East Africa are currently under study, but have not been definitively described.

Knowledge of the Old World monkeys essentially begins in this epoch. Although of a primitive grade morphologically, cercopithecoids appear late in the fossil record and known remains of undoubted assignment to this group reveal little as to their derivation. One of the best preserved Pliocene skulls belonging to this superfamily is that of *Libypithecus* from middle or late Pliocene beds in the Wadi Natrun, Egypt. The type and only skull of this primate, with its strong sagittal crest and forward jutting rostrum, has suggested to most students affinities with the baboons and, to a lesser extent, with macaques. An endocranial cast from this skull, studied by Edinger (1938) shows considerable detail, but is apparently not more primitive in structure than are those of living cercopithecoids. By far the most complete knowledge of a Pliocene monkey is provided by the extensive remains of *Mesopithecus pentelici* from Pontian deposits in Europe and the Near East. Originally discovered at the locality of Pikermi near Athens this primate has now been reported from sites in Macedonia, Rumania, Czechoslovakia, Hungary, southern Russia, and Iran, in addition to the Miocene fragments from Kenya, mentioned in Section V, which have provisionally been referred to this genus. Most studies of *Mesopithecus* have stressed its similarities with colobines such as *Presbytis* but, as Patterson (1954, p. 200) has pointed out *Mesopithecus* appears to have had an ecology different from the modern arboreal, leaf-eating colobines. He reports that this Pontian monkey is typically found in association with a steppe or open country fauna, and skulls have been recovered together in one place, neither fact suggesting the ecology of modern members of the subfamily to which it has been assigned. In addition to the presence of *Mesopithecus* in the Pliocene of Europe, is the French occurrence of a second species of extinct cercopithecid, *Dolichopithecus arvernensis*, for which excellent cranial remains are known at a slightly later horizon. This species has also been proposed as a possible colobine —a colobine which, however, possesses an elongate rostrum as in *Papio* and, unlike colobines, short macaque-like limbs. In the latest Pliocene lignites of Tuscany, Italy, and in the Montpellier sands of southern France fragmentary primate remains assignable to the living *Presbytis* (= *Semnopithecus*) occur.

From Pliocene deposits in the Siwalik Hills of India, species of cercopithecids which may belong to the extant genera *Pygathryx, Papio,*

Cercopithecus, and *Macaca* have been described but the zone of occurrence of some of these species is not known with certainty (Pilgrim, 1915), and some may be of Pleistocene age. Other occurrences of cercopithecines in the Pliocene include those of *Macaca* in Holland and in the Arno valley of Italy. During the Pleistocene, distribution of

TABLE I

RELATIVE AGE AND GEOGRAPHIC DISTRIBUTION OF LATER TERTIARY HOMINOID PRIMATES[a]

Provincial age	Europe	Africa	Asia
Pliocene: Astian and Plaisantian	—	—	*Ankarapithecus*
Pliocene: Pontian	*Rhenopithecus* *Paidopithex* *Dryopithecus* ?*Pliopithecus* *Oreopithecus*	—	?*Hylopithecus* *Sugrivapithecus* *Sivapithecus* *Bramapithecus* *Ramapithecus* *Udabnopithecus* *Indopithecus*
Miocene: Sarmatian	*Dryopithecus* *Pliopithecus*	*Kenyapithecus*	*Sugrivapithecus* *Sivapithecus* ?*Dryopithecus* *Bramapithecus*
Miocene: Vindobonian	?*Sivapithecus* *Dryopithecus* *Austriacopithecus* *Pliopithecus-* [*Epipliopithecus*]	*Sivapithecus* *Proconsul* *Pliopithecus-* [*Limnopithecus*]	—
Miocene: Burdigalian	—	?*Dryopithecus* *Prohylobates*	"*Kansupithecus*"

[a] Modified after Thenius (1958).

species of this genus became very broad indeed and they range in the north from western Europe to China.

Table I indicates the distribution of most proposed genera of hominoid primates of the Pliocene age. Knowledge of these higher primates is limited to finds from scattered European localities and from the Siwalik deposits. Outside these areas a Pontian dryopithecine *Udabnopithecus* (which is based on quite a fragmentary material) has been recovered from deposits in Georgia, U.S.S.R. For Asia Minor, Ozansoy (1957) has recently described a new dryopithecine derivative, *Ankarapithecus meteai* from Pliocene deposits in Turkey. If truly a member of the dryopithecinae, the species is chiefly remarkable for its late occurrence and large size.

B. OREOPITHECUS

Since its original description in 1872 by Gervais, *Oreopithecus bambolii*, from Pontian lignites of Montebambolii, a province of Grosetto in Tuscany, Italy, has been a difficult primate to classify. During the decades following this discovery, several more or less incomplete studies (on both the original specimens and on relatively poorly made casts) were published. From these papers three main theories as to its taxonomic position emerged. Most of the early students placed *Oreopithecus* among the cercopithecoids, basing their conclusions on a superficial similarity between its molars and those of the baboons and macaques. In a brief note Forsyth Major (1872), observing the bicuspid anterior premolar, suggested that the teeth of *Oreopithecus* showed analogies with the human dentition. This seed of an idea has more recently been developed by Hürzeler (1949, 1954, 1958). The majority of early students, most of whom had not actually seen original specimens, placed the animal as intermediate between the cercopithecoids and the hominoids. This view is supported by Gregory (1922, 1951).

Since the late 1940's Johannes Hürzeler at Basel has performed the valuable service of bringing together the scattered materials of this primate and providing new dental analyses of its relationships to other members of the order. His studies showed conclusively that *Oreopithecus* possessed greater affinity to hominoids than to cercopithecoids. In 1958 his collecting activities in Tuscany produced a nearly complete skeleton of this animal (Fig. 21). Since this discovery a number of studies of the osteology of *Oreopithecus* have been initiated and one preliminary analysis published by Schultz (1960). Among these recent studies on the 1958 skeleton a few primitive characters are evident such as the presence of a mid-sagittal keel on the lumbar vertebral centra and on the lower molars a large talonid; both traits typify cercopithecoids but are rarely, if ever, to be seen in hominoids. Of course, these may be explained as primitive holdovers outweighed, to a large extent, by such hominoid traits as: well developed clavicle, wide pelvis with man-like anterior inferior iliac spine, some indications of a brachiating adaptation (if curved phalanges and longer arms than legs can be considered as

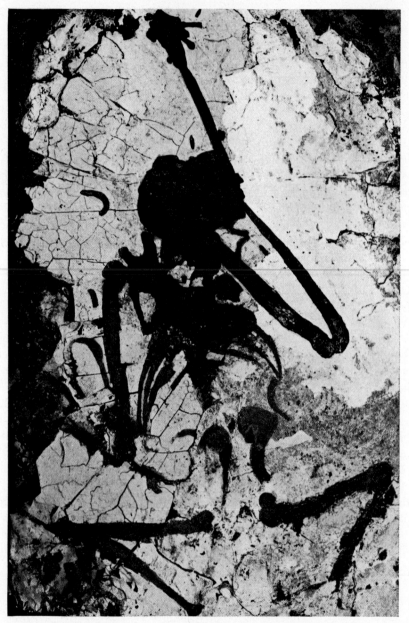

FIG. 21. The 1958 skeleton of *Oreopithecus bambolii* discovered in the earliest Pliocene Grosseto lignites of Tuscany, Italy. (Courtesy Basle Natural History Museum.) Magnification: 1/6.

such), steep symphysis, the presence of a hypoconulid on the molars, and the lack of a precanine diastama. The absence of the internal groove or channel running across cingulum up to the apex of the root of the canine, which typically is present in cercopithecoids and pongids, is a resemblance between hominids and *Oreopithecus.*

In his 1958 report, Hürzeler defends assignment of *Oreopithecus* to the Hominidae; his justifications for this consist primarily of demonstrating that the tooth length proportions are hominid in character. This similarity he believes to be further reinforced by the manner of incisor attrition, together with the steep symphysis of the chin with more vertically emplaced incisors as in hominids. Yet, the latter two features are also found in *Gigantopithecus,* which most students do not accept as a hominid.

Clearly *Oreopithecus* must now be regarded as a hominoid and such characters as the large M_3 talonid and the mid-sagittal keel on the centra of the lumbar vertebrae assumed to indicate primitive characters retained in this lineage. But their function nonetheless should not be ignored, particularly that of the latter. This keel is associated with the anterior longitudinal ligament to which are attached the crura of the diaphragm. These crura are functional in breathing and are developed to a greater degree, with respect to their attachment to the longitudinal ligament, in quadrupedal than in bipedal animals. The presence of a keel would indicate greater attachment surface along these lines and the possibility that *Oreopithecus* was well adapted for quadrupedal locomotion should not be overlooked.

This is of particular interest when studying the significance of the femuro-humeral and intermembral indices derived from the 1958 skeleton, together with postcranial materials recovered earlier. In comparing these indices, it would appear that adaptations for brachiation in *Oreopithecus* are of an intermediate nature, resembling more closely those of the chimpanzee and gorilla than of such highly arboreal modern forms as gibbon and orangutan. These indices and other evidence tend to place *Oreopithecus* neither on the hominid line, nor on the pongid, but seem instead to indicate an independently derived taxon. Butler and Mills (1959) study of the dentition of *Oreopithecus* suggest that "In its upper molar pattern . . . therefore *Oreopithecus* appears to retain primitive features that are not known in any of the Pongidae, and at the same time it resembles what are presumably the most primitive members of the family rather than the later forms. This suggests that it is a survivor, specialized in its own way, from a prepongid stock."

Simons (1960a) has discussed resemblances between *Apidium* and

Oreopithecus. To the extent that these are valid they indicate that both belong to a lineage of long standing independent derivation which split off from the lines of other Hominoidea in the late Eocene. However, before such a derivation can be proven much more fossil material will have to be recovered in the Egyptian Oligocene and in later deposits.

C. Ramapithecus

The type maxilla of *Ramapithecus brevirostris* was collected in 1932 by the Yale North India Paleontological Expedition directed by G. E. Lewis. This specimen was recovered from the Nagri zone, Hari Tal-yangar area, Simla Hills, which is now generally correlated with the early Pliocene Pontian stage of Europe. Depending on its exact position in the section it could have been almost as old as *Kenyapithecus* from Ft. Ternan, East Africa. If the two were approximately contemporary this fact would also go far in accounting for their resemblances, although, of course, mammal genera have considerable time duration and these two forms certainly need not be from the same time plane.

The type maxilla of this species preserves the last two upper premolars and the first two molars of the right side, as well as the incisor and canine alveoli, so that it is possible to determine something of the emplacement, size, and morphology of all of the upper teeth save the last molars. Other features such as an arched palate, slight canine fossa, approximated nasal aperture and anterior tooth row (Fig. 22) can be determined from examination of the maxilla itself.

Lewis (1934) clearly pointed out the many hominid features to be seen in this specimen, but after his description *R. brevirostris* was often discussed as having little or no significant resemblance to Pleistocene hominids. Two factors helped to create the lag in recognition of the connecting position it occupies. The first of these is that Hrdlička (1935) insisted, quite erroneously, that none of its features of resemblance to hominids were significant (Simons, 1961d). However, he did state in this paper that *R. brevirostris* was more like modern man than *Australopithecus africanus* but concluded that both of these primates were pongids. For those who disregarded Hrdlicka's objections there was still the problem of the mandible assigned by Gregory *et al.* (1938, p. 21) to *Ramapithecus* cf. *brevirostris*. This specimen, however, is from the earlier Chinji zone and from a different area than the maxilla of *R. brevirostris*. These authors (1938, p. 21) noted that the specimen shows premolar heteromorphy and remarked that this feature is one which is "characteristic of pongids but which is not known in undoubted Hominidae." The questionably referred mandible is of the proper size to occlude with the type maxilla, but it is quite possible that it does not belong to the genus *Ramapithecus*. At least it does not seem necessary to me to assign this mandible showing nonhominid premolar heteromorphy to this genus, a conclusion with which Lewis is now in agreement (personal communication). The position of upper P₃ and of the

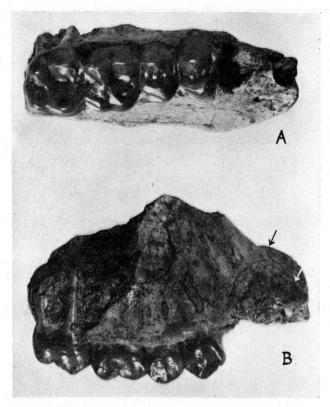

Fig. 22.   *Ramapithecus brevirostris*, occlusal views (A) and lateral view (B) of right maxilla. (From Simons, 1961d.) Magnification: 1.7.

canine alveoli rather suggest that *R. brevirostris* would not have shown such distinct lower premolar heteromorphy.

With the above possible objections clarified it is now easier to concentrate on the significance of the sole maxilla as an evidence of human phylogeny. One common view about the type of *R. brevirostris* is that since it represents only a fragment of the whole animal its taxonomic assessment could go far wrong. This is always possible. Although what we are dealing with here is a small portion of an animal it is a part in which pongids and hominids differ in several respects. In these points of difference (listed by Lewis, 1934) *Ramapithecus*, like *Kenyapithecus* resembles hominids. As the writer remarked previously (Simons, 1961d, p. 5):

> "It seems illogical to choose the alternative of regarding this form as belonging to an otherwise unknown group of apes, parallelistic toward hominids but not closely related to them, when it occurs in the proper time and place to represent a forerunner of Pleistocene Hominidae."

REFERENCES

ABEL, O. (1931). "Die Stellung des Menschen in Rahmen der Wirbeltiere," Jena, 398 pp.

BEADNELL, H. J. L. (1905). The topology and geology of the Fayum Province of Egypt. *Publ. Surv. Dept., Ministry of Public Works, Egypt* pp. 1-101.

BOHLIN, B. (1946). The fossil mammals from the Tertiary of Tabun-buluk. *Rept. Sino-Swedish Exped. N.W. Prov. China* 6, No. 4, 1-259.

BOHLIN, B. (1951). Some mammalian remains from Shih-ehr-ma-ch'eng, Hu-hui-p'u area, western Kansu. *Rept. Sino-Swedish Exped. N.W. Prov. China* No. 35, 1-47.

BUTLER, P. M., AND MILLS, J. R. E. (1959). A contribution to the odontology of *Oreopithecus. Bull. Brit. Museum Geol.* 4, 1-26.

CHOW, M. (1961). A new tarsioid primate from the Lushi Eocene, Honan. *Vert. Palas.* 5, 1-5.

CLARK, W. E. LEGROS (1934). On the skull structure of *Pronycticebus gaudryi. Proc. Zool. Soc. London* pp. 19-27.

CLARK, W. E. LEGROS (1960). "The Antecedents of Man," 374 pp. Chicago, Illinois, Quadrangle Books.

CLARK, W. E. LEGROS, AND LEAKEY, L. S. B. (1951). The Miocene Hominoidea of East Africa. *In* "Fossil Mammals of Africa," No. 1, pp. 1-117. London, Brit. Mus. Nat. Hist.

CLARK, W. E. LEGROS, AND THOMAS, D. P. (1952). The Miocene lemuroids of East Africa. *In* "Fossil Mammals of Africa," No. 5, pp. 1-20. London, Brit. Mus. Nat. Hist.

COLBERT, E. H. (1938). Fossil mammals from Burma in the American Museum of Natural History. *Bull. Am. Museum Nat. Hist.* 74, 225-436.

EDINGER, T. (1938). Mitteilungen über Wirbeltierreste aus dem Mittelpliocäen des Natrontales (Ägypten). *Son. Abd. Zent. Min. Geol.* No. 4, 122-128.

FOURTAU, R. (1920). Contribution à l'étude des vertèbres Miocènes de l'Egypte. *Surv. Dept. Ministry of Finance Egypt* 11, 1-121.

GAZIN, C. L. (1958). A review of the middle and upper Eocene Primates of North America. *Smith. Misc. Coll.* 126, 1-112.

GERVAIS, P. (1872). Coup d'oeil sur les Mammifères fossiles de l'Italie, suivie de la description d'une espèce nouvelle de singe provenant des lignites du Monte Bamboli. *J. Zool.* 1, 211-233.

GRANDIDIER, G. (1904). Un noveau lémurien fossile de France, le *Pronycticebus gaudryi. Bull. muséum natl. hist. nat.* (*Paris*) 10, 9-13.

GREGORY, W. K. (1916). Studies on the evolution of Primates. *Bull. Am. Museum Nat. Hist.* 35, 239-355.

GREGORY, W. K. (1920). On the structure and relations of *Notharctus*, an American Eocene primate. *Am. Museum Nat. Hist. Mem.* 3, 49-243.

GREGORY, W. K. (1922). "The Origin and Evolution of the Human Dentition," 548 pp. Baltimore, Maryland, Williams & Wilkins.

GREGORY, W. K. (1951). "Evolution Emerging," Vol. 1, pp. 1-704. New York, Macmillan.

GREGORY, W. K., HELLMAN, M., AND LEWIS, C. E. (1938). Fossil anthropoids of the Yale-Cambridge Expedition of 1935. *Carnegie Inst. Wash. Publ.* No. 495, 1-27.

HILL, W. C. O. (1953). "Primates: Comparative Anatomy and Taxonomy," Vol. I: Strepsirhini, 798 pp. New York, Wiley (Interscience).

HILL, W. C. O. (1955). "Primates: Comparative Anatomy and Taxonomy," Vol. II: Haplorhini; Tarsioidea, 347 pp. New York, Wiley (Interscience).

HOPWOOD, A. T. (1933). Miocene Primates from Kenya. *J. Linnean Soc. Zool.* 38, 437-464.

HRDLIČKA, A. (1935). The Yale fossils of anthropoid apes. *Am. J. Sci.* 29, 34-40.

HÜRZELER, J. (1947). *Alsaticopithecus leemanni* nov. gen., nov. sp., ein neuer Primate aus dem unteren Lutetien von Buchsweiler im Unterelsass. *Ber deut. Schweiz. Pal. Ges.* 40, 343-356.

HÜRZELER, J. (1948). Zur Stammesgeschichte der Necrolemuriden. *Schweiz. Paläont. Abh.* 66, 1-46.

HÜRZELER, J. (1949). Neubeschreibung von *Oreopithecus bambolii* Gervais. *Schweiz. Paläont. Abh.* 66, 1-20.

HÜRZELER, J. (1954.) Zur systematischen Stellung von *Oreopithecus*. *Verhandl. naturforsch. Ges. Basel* 65, 88-95.

HÜRZELER, J. (1958). *Oreopithecus bambolii* Gervais. *Verhandl. naturforsch. Ges. Basel* 69, 1-48.

HUXLEY, T. H. (1876). "Man's Place in Nature." New York, Appelton.

JONES, F. WOOD (1929). Some landmarks in the phylogeny of Primates. *Human Biol.* 1, 214-228.

KÄLIN, J. (1961). Sur les primates de l'Oligocène inférieur d'Egypte. *Ann. Pal.* 74, 1-48.

KRAGLIEVICH, J. L. (1951). Contribuciones del conocimiento de los Primates fossiles de la Patagonia. *Com. Inst. Nac. Invest. Cie. Nat.* 2, 55-82.

LARTET, E. (1856). Note sur un grand Singe fossile qui se rattache au groupe des Singes supérieurs. *Compt. rend. acad. sci.* 43, 219-222.

LEAKEY, L. S. B. (1962). A new lower Pliocene fossil primate from Kenya. *Ann. and Mag. Nat. Hist.* 4, 689-696.

LEWIS, G. E. (1934). Preliminary notice of new man-like apes from India. *Am. J. Sci.* 27, 161-179.

MCKENNA, M. C. (1960). Fossil mammals from the early Wasatchian Four Mile fauna, Eocene of northwest Colorado. *Bull. Dept. Geol. Univ. Calif.* 37, 1-130.

MAJOR, C. E. FORSYTH (1872). La Faune des Vertébrés de Monte Bamboli. *Atti. soc. ital. sci. nat. e museo civico storia nat. Milano* 15, 290-303.

NAPIER, J. R., AND DAVIS, P. R. (1959). The fore-limb skeleton and associated remains of *Proconsul africanus*. In "Fossil Mammals of Africa," No. 16. Brit. Museum Nat. Hist., London.

OSBORN, H. F. (1908). New fossil mammals from the Fayum Oligocene, Egypt. *Bull. Am. Museum Nat. Hist.* **24**, 265-272.

OZANSOY, F. (1957). Faunes de mammifères de Tertiaire de Turquie et leurs revisions stratigraphiques. *Bull. Min. Res. Exptl. Inst. Turkey* No. **49**, 29-48.

PATTERSON, B. (1954). The geologic history of non-hominoid Primates in the Old World. *Human Biol.* **26**, 191-209.

PILGRIM, G. E. (1915). New Siwalik Primates and their bearing on the question of the evolution of man and the Anthropoidea. *Rec. Geol. Surv. India* **45**, 1-74.

RUSSELL, D. E. (1959). Le crâne de *Plesiadapis*; note préliminaire. *Bull. soc. géol. France* **7**, 312-314.

SABAN, R. (1958). Insectivora. In "Traité de Paléontologie" (J. Piveteau, ed.), Vol. 6, pp. 822-902. Paris, Masson.

SABAN, R. (1961). Carpolestidae. In "Traité de Paléontologie" (J. Piveteau, ed.), Vol. 6, pp. 638-640. Paris, Masson.

SCHLOSSER, M. (1910). Über einige fossile Säugetiere aus dem Oligocäen von Ägypten. *Zool. Anz.* **35**, 500-508.

SCHLOSSER, M. (1911). Beiträge zur Kenntnis der oligocäenen Landsäugetiere aus dem Fayum, Ägypten. *Brit. Pal. Geol. Öst.-Ung.* **24**, 51-167.

SCHULTZ, A. H. (1960). Einige Beobachtungen und Masse am Skelett von *Oreopithecus*. *Z. Morphol. Anthropol.* **50**, 136-149.

SIMONS, E. L. (1959). An anthropoid frontal bone from the Fayum Oligocene of Egypt: the oldest skull fragment of a higher primate. *Am. Museum Novitates* No. **1976**, 1-16.

SIMONS, E. L. (1960a). *Apidium* and *Oreopithecus*. *Nature* **186**, 824-826.

SIMONS, E. L. (1960b). New fossil Primates: A review of the past decade. *Am. Sci.* **48**, 179-192.

SIMONS, E. L. (1961a). Notes on Eocene Tarsioids and a revision of some Necrolemurinae. *Bull. Brit. Museum Nat. Hist. Geol.* **5**, 45-69.

SIMONS, E. L. (1961b). An anthropoid mandible from the Oligocene Fayum beds of Egypt. *Am. Museum Nat. Hist. Novitates* No. **2051**, 1-5.

SIMONS, E. L. (1961c). The dentition of *Ourayia*:—Its bearing on relationships of omomyid prosimians. *Postilla, Yale Peabody Museum* No. **54**, 1-20.

SIMONS, E. L. (1961d). The phyletic position of *Ramapithecus*. *Postilla, Yale Peabody Museum* No. **57**, 1-9.

SIMONS, E. L. (1962a). A New Eocene primate *Cantius*, and a revision of early Cenozoic lemuroids of Europe. *Bull. Brit. Museum Nat. Hist. Geol.* **7**, 1-36.

SIMONS, E. L. (1962b). Two new primate species from the African Oligocene. *Postilla, Yale Peabody Museum* No. **64**, 1-12.

SIMONS, E. L. (1962c). Fossil evidence relating to the early evolution of primate behavior. In "Relatives of Man: Modern Studies of the the Relation of the Evolution of Nonhuman Primates to Human Evolution" (J. Buettner-Janusch, ed.), *Ann. N.Y. Acad. Sci.* **102**, 282-293.

SIMONS, E. L., AND RUSSELL, D. E. (1960). The cranial anatomy of *Necrolemur*. *Breviora, Museum Com. Zool., Harvard* No. **127**, 1-14.

SIMPSON, G. G. (1933). The "plagiaulacoid" type of mammalian dentition. *J. Mam.* **14**, 97-105.

SIMPSON, G. G. (1935). The first mammals. *Quart. Rev. Biol.* **10**, 154-180.

SIMPSON, G. G. (1937). The Fort Union of the Crazy Mountain field, Montana, and its mammalian fauna. *U.S. Natl. Museum, Bull.* No. **169**, 1-287.

SIMPSON, G. G. (1940). Studies on the earliest Primates. *Am. Museum Nat. Hist. Bull.* **77**, 185-212.

SIMPSON, G. G. (1945). The principles of classification and a classification of mammals. *Bull. Am. Museum Nat. Hist.* **85**, 1-350.

SIMPSON, G. G. (1955). The Phenacolemuridae, new family of early Primates. *Bull. Am. Museum Nat. Hist.* **105**, 412-442.

SIMPSON, G. G. (1962). Primate taxonomy and recent studies of nonhuman Primates. *In* "Relatives of Man: Modern Studies of the Relation of the Evolution of Nonhuman Primates to Human Evolution" (J. Buettner-Janusch, ed.), *Ann. N.Y. Acad. Sci.* **102**, 282-293.

STEHLIN, H. G. (1916). Die Säugetiere des schweizerischen Eocäens. Kritischer Katalog der Materialen. Teil VII, Hälfte II. *Mem. Soc. Pal. Suisse.* **41**, 1299-1552.

STIRTON, R. A., AND SAVAGE, D. E. (1951). A new monkey from the La Venta late Miocene of Colombia. *Minis. Min. Pe. Serv. Geol. Nac.* **7**, 347-356.

STROMER, E. (1913). Mitteilungen über die Wirbeltierreste aus dem Mittelpliozän des Natrontales (Ägypten). *Z. deut. geol. Ges.* **65**, 350-361.

THENIUS, E. (1954). Die Bedeutung von *Austriacopithecus* Ehrenberg für die Stammesgeschichte der Hominoidea. *Anz. Öster. Akad. Wiss.* **13**, 191-196.

THENIUS, E. (1958). Tertiärstratigraphie und tertiäre Hominoidenfunde. *Anthropol. Anz. Stuttgart* **22**, 66-77.

VILLALTA, J., AND CRUSAFONT, M. (1944). Dos nuevos anthropomorphos del Mioceno, español y su situación dentro de la moderna sistemática de los símidos. *Notas y comun. inst. geol. y minerno España* **13**, 91-139.

WOO, J. K. (1958). New materials of *Dryopithecus* from Keiyuan, Yunnan. *Vert. Palas.* **2**, 38-42.

WOO, J. K., AND CHOW, M. (1957). New material of the earliest primate known in China. *Vert. Palas.* **1**, 267-272.

WOOD, A. E. (1962). The early Tertiary rodents of the family Paramyidae. *Trans. Am. Phil. Soc.* **52**, 1-261.

WORTMANN, J. L. (1903). Studies of Eocene Mammalia in the Marsh Collection, Peabody Museum. Part II, Primates. *Am. J. Sci.* **16**, 345-368.

ZAPFE, H. (1958). Primatenfunde im Jungtertiär des Wiener Beckens und anderer Fundorte in Österreich. *Veröff. Naturhist. Mus. Wien.* [N.F.] **1**, 1-5.

ZAPFE, H. (1961). Ein Primatenfund aus den Miozänen Molasse von Oberösterreich. *Z. Morphol. Anthropol.* **51**, 247-267.

ZAPFE, H., AND HÜRZELER, J. (1957). Die Fauna der miozänen Spaltenfüllung von Neudorf an der March (CSR), Primates. *Sitzber. Akad. Wiss. Wien Math.-naturw. Kl.* **65**, 113-123.

Chapter 3

The Primate Nervous System: Functional and Structural Aspects in Phylogeny

CHARLES R. NOBACK[1] AND NORMAN MOSKOWITZ[2]

Department of Anatomy, Columbia University, New York, New York

I. INTRODUCTION

The primates are visually oriented mammals with multipurpose fore-limbs. These extremities were emancipated from their role as weight

[1] Supported by National Institute for Neurological Diseases and Blindness, United States Public Health Service Grant Nos. B-1417 and B-3473.

[2] Supported by United States Public Health Service Grant No. 2B-5242-C. *Present address:* Department of Anatomy, Jefferson Medical College, Philadelphia, Pennsylvania.

131

supporters in stance and locomotion in the preprimates to become, in the primates, major informers in the sensory sphere, and manipulators and graspers useful in climbing, exploring, and handling. The visual sense is the paramount modality that primates utilize in assessing their external environment. This presentation illustrates several phylogenetic aspects of the primate nervous system that are associated with the fore-limb and the visual system. The principles outlined have a broader application.

Although the literature on the primate brain is large, comprehensive analyses of even portions of the nervous system in a representative series of primates are limited. Functional and structural analyses of the brain of man and of the macaques dominate the literature. The surface to-pography of the cerebrum has been reviewed and illustrated by Con-nolly (1950). The visual system is the one functional unit that has been analyzed in a relatively comprehensive fashion (Walls, 1942; Clark, 1942; Polyak, 1957). Over-all reviews of the primate brain may be found in the works of Tilney (1928), Riley (1928), and Kappers et al. (1936). More information and data are needed to complete our understanding of the morphology and physiology of the nervous system of this order of mammals.

The problem of evaluating the phylogenetic implications of neural structures in both morphological and physiological terms is compounded by several factors: (1) The functional significance of many structures cannot be stated in finite terms. For example, structures such as the basal ganglia are integrated with other structures (cerebral cortex and thalamus) into complex feedback systems whose precise function in motion are as yet unknown. (2) Some structures include complexes of several functional entities. The anatomically discrete dorsal columns consist of fibers that carry, among others, the impulses of such modali-ties as touch (from skin) and position sense (from deep structures). (3) Skilled judgment must be utilized in evaluating a character such as size. Is absolute size more informative than relative size or vice versa? In more concrete terms the increased size of the dorsal columns is, in part, correlated with the prehensile tail in the spider monkey, with in-creased body size in the gorilla and with highly sensitive finger tips in man. (4) Another factor is that parallel evolution has apparently oc-curred in the primates. *Cebus* and *Macaca* have cerebral topographies that are difficult to distinguish. The interpretation explaining this simi-larity is that although the New World monkeys and the Old World monkeys evolved independently, each group elaborated cerebral con-volutions along similar lines.

The nervous system, the brain in particular, is likely to yield more information to explain the success of primate evolution than other organ systems. In essence the phylogeny of the nervous system is based on the modification and elaboration of pre-existing structures and functional systems. All brains of primates seem to be models of each other. In fact, no new structure *per se* is found in man's brain that is not found in the brain of the other primates. The increase in the size of the brain, absolute and relative, is characteristic of primate evolution and the conclusions drawn from weight and volumetric studies of the gross structures of the brain have been fairly well exploited (Count, 1947; Dart, 1956; and others). Because these parameters are actually the composite of several elements, the inferences drawn from such data must be stated in general terms. For example the fact that the cerebral cortex increases in size and weight in the primates tells us nothing about the fundamental processes of how the cortex functions. By volume 30% of the cortex consists of the neurons and their processes and 70% of glial cells and blood vessels; the glial cells outnumber the neurons from 5 to 10 times.

II. The Nervous System and the Forelimbs

The forelimbs of the primates display degrees of dexterity that range from relatively more generalized stereotyped movements to fine dexterous movements. For example, in man the swinging of the upper extremities during locomotion is an expression of a stereotype movement while the fingering of a violinist is a complex of fine movements that are emancipated, so to say, from the confines of the stereotype movements. Some anatomical and physiological mechanisms in the nervous system of primates that relate to forelimb movements will be outlined in this discussion. These include: (1) the integration of "sensory" or afferent input from the periphery into some of the basic reflexes of the spinal cord; (2) some neural structures associated with the role of the limb as a major sensory organ; (3) the concept of the lemniscal system and the reticular system; (4) some higher integrative systems of the brain and their functional significance; and (5) the cerebral cortex.

A. The Integration of "Sensory" (Afferent) Input from the Forelimb into the Basic Reflexes of the Spinal Cord (Fig. 1)

Forelimb dexterity is dependent upon the interaction of a number of complex circuits in the nervous system. In this section attention is directed primarily to additional information on the classic spinal reflex pathways, especially to the role of efferent neurons that innervate peripheral sensory endings (Ruch and Fulton, 1960). This interaction between the central nervous system and the periphery is a constant reminder of the integrative role of the nervous system in afferent input and efferent output.

Two of the basic reflex patterns concerned with the forelimb move-

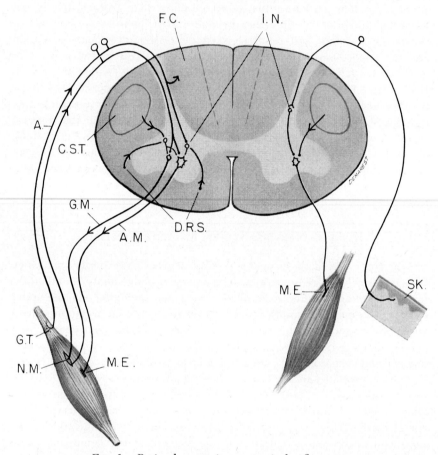

FIG. 1.   Basic elements in some spinal reflex arcs.

The stretch reflex arc (left side of figure) includes the neuromuscular spindle receptor, the afferent (sensory) neuron, the alpha (lower) motor neuron, and the voluntary muscle. The stretch reflex may be influenced by the arc of the Golgi tendon ending, afferent neuron, internuncial cell, alpha motor neuron, and voluntary muscle. The gamma motor neurons innervate the intrinsic muscles of the neuro-muscular spindles. The gamma loop arc includes the small gamma motor cells, the muscle fibers of the neuromuscular spindle, the afferent neuron, the alpha motor neuron, and the voluntary muscles. The reticulospinal tracts and the corticospinal tracts are among the pathways from the brain that synapse (mainly through inter-nuncial neurons) with the alpha motor neurons and the gamma motor neurons.

The flexor reflexor reflex arc (right side of figure) includes the afferent neuron

ments are the extensor (stretch) reflex and the flexor (withdrawal) reflex. The extensor reflex is fundamentally concerned with muscular activity that is essential for the maintenance of posture—the antigravity action of holding the body off the ground. Antigravity action is expressed in a four-limbed animal such as a lemur by the extension of the forelimbs and hind limbs (standing on all fours) and in man by the extension of the hind limbs (stance) and flexion of the forelimbs. The flexor reflex is a primitive protective reflex that is primarily the reaction of the limb in withdrawing from noxious or potentially injurious stimuli. These two reflexes are integrated into limb activities.

Movements are largely dependent upon information received from the periphery. Two significant sources of proprioceptive input are the neuromuscular spindles and the Golgi tendon endings. These sensory endings are integrated into an exquisite feedback system. (In a feedback system, impulses initiating a given action are partially returned to the original source.) The neuromuscular spindles, elongated receptors within the muscle mass, are oriented parallel to the long axis of the muscle fibers. The Golgi tendon endings are located in tendons. The neuromuscular spindles send impulses to the spinal cord, particularly when they are stretched and so provide a continuous measure of muscle tension. The more the muscle is stretched, the greater is the rate of spindle firing with the result that more impulses are transmitted to the spinal cord by nerve fibers that synapse directly with the large motor nerve cells (alpha cells). These motor neurons, in turn, transmit impulses to the voluntary muscles that now contract. As the muscle contracts the neuromuscular spindles are passively shortened and the rate of firing by the spindles is reduced. To sustain this muscular contraction, the central nervous system acts to increase the firing rate of the spindles. The motor pathways of the central nervous system—activated volitionally for example—stimulate small motor neurons (gamma efferent cells) that innervate miniature muscle cells (intrafusal muscle fibers) within the neuromuscular spindles (Fig. 1). These

---

from the skin, an internuncial neuron in the spinal cord, the alpha motor neuron, and the motor ending in the voluntary muscle.

Most axons of the corticospinal tract synapse on internuncial neurons that, in turn, synapse with the alpha motor neurons. Some axons of the corticospinal tract in apes and man synapse directly with the alpha motor neurons.

A.	Afferent neuron	G.T.	Golgi tendon ending
A.M.	Alpha motor neuron	I.N.	Internuncial neuron
C.S.T.	Corticospinal tract	M.E.	Motor ending in
D.R.S.	Reticulospinal tracts		voluntary muscle
F.C.	Fasciculus cuneatus	N.M.	Neuromuscular spindle
G.M.	Gamma motor neuron	SK.	Skin

gamma efferent fibers stimulate the intrafusal muscle cells to contract and in turn stretch the sensory portion of the spindle with the result that each spindle now transmits more pulses to the motor cells in the spinal cord (the reflex arc is the gamma loop). In turn, muscular contraction is maintained or even increased. Another factor is integrated into the system just noted. When a muscle contracts, tension develops in the tendons. When the tendon stretch reaches a critical point the Golgi tendon endings commence firing (these tendon endings have a high threshold as compared to the spindle endings), and transmit impulses via peripheral nerves that synapse with neurons of the spinal cord that, in turn, synapse with the large alpha motor cells. The stimuli from the tendon endings tend to inhibit the motor cells from firing.

The flexor reflex is mediated by a reflex arc that has its beginning in receptors in the skin for touch, pain, and other sensations. The stimuli from these endings are conducted to the spinal cord neurons that are integrated into the central nervous system mechanisms that finally interact with the alpha motor fibers and gamma motor fibers. (Although the flexor reflex is a protective reflex, the sensation of pain is not necessary for its proper functioning. Pain is actually an auxiliary phenomenon.) The interplay of the excitatory stimulation and the inhibitory stimulation from the periphery and from the central nervous system on the alpha and gamma motor cells determines the extent and degree of muscular contraction. It is within the central nervous system that the phenomena are operative for the integration of flexor activity and extensor activity.

The dexterity of movement is also related to two quantitative factors: (1) the number of afferent endings and (2) the number of motor units (a motor unit includes one alpha motor neuron and the muscle cells it innervates). On the afferent side, for example, the greater the delicacy with which a muscle can be controlled, the greater is the relative number of neuromuscular spindles in the muscle. On the efferent side, more motor units are associated with the muscles that manipulate the fingers than with those that move the shoulder girdle. In the muscles associated with fine movements each nerve innervates only a few muscle cells; these muscles have relatively many motor units. Although these principles are well established, they have not been documented in a large series of primates.

B. Some Neural Structures Associated with the Role of the Forelimb as a Major Sensory Organ (Figs. 2 and 3)

The forelimb is a major sensory organ of primates. The neural structures associated with the transmission and processing of information for the perception of two-point discrimination, size, shape, weight, and position-sense will be outlined. The systems associated with pain and temperature modalities will be omitted.

The major pathway by which these modalities of the forelimb are conveyed to and through the brain consists of the peripheral nerves, the dorsal column of the spinal cord (*fasciculus cuneatus*), the *nucleus cuneatus* of the lower medulla oblongata, the medial lemniscus of the brain stem, the ventral posterior nucleus of the thalamus, the thalamo-cortical pathways, and the postcentral gyrus and other areas of the cerebral cortex (Fig. 2). This pathway, essentially absent in the non-mammalian vertebrates, is especially prominent in the higher primates including man and is a measure of the importance of these modalities in the primates.

Several portions of this system are measurable. The cross-sectional areas of the dorsal columns and the medial lemniscus (rough indicators of the number of nerve fibers present) and the surface area of the postcentral gyrus of the cerebrum have been determined. These param-eters are significantly greater in the higher than they are in the lower primates and in the larger than in the smaller primates (Tilney, 1928; Kappers *et al.*, 1937; Noback, 1959a). For example, the percentage ratio of the area of the dorsal columns to the area of the total white matter in the cervical spinal cord in cross-section is about 19% in the small monkey *Oedipomidas oedipus* and 26% in the larger *Cebus fatuellus* (Kappers *et al.*, 1936). The enlarged cross-sectional area of the dorsal columns of the spider monkeys (Atelinae) is in a large measure asso-ciated with the role of the tail as a sensory organ in these forms. More comprehensive quantitative analyses of the structures associated with this proprioceptive system in the primates should be made to estab-lish detailed deductions.

The ascending reticular system is another pathway by which in-formation from the limb may be conveyed to the brain. This pathway passes through the gray matter of the spinal cord, the spinoreticular tracts, the reticular formation of the brain stem, the reticular nuclei of the thalamus (Section II, E, 2) and terminates in a widespread area of the cerebral cortex. (Various aspects of this system will be discussed in the following sections.) This system consists of anatomically diffuse tracts. For example, the spinoreticular tracts ascend in the ventral and lateral portions of the spinal cord and terminate largely in the reticular formation of the medulla and also in the pons and the mid-brain (Mehler *et al.*, 1960; Nauta and Kuypers, 1958). In the reticular formation of the brain stem (medulla, pons, and midbrain) this is an

organized yet diffuse anatomical organization where complex interactions of neural impulses occur.

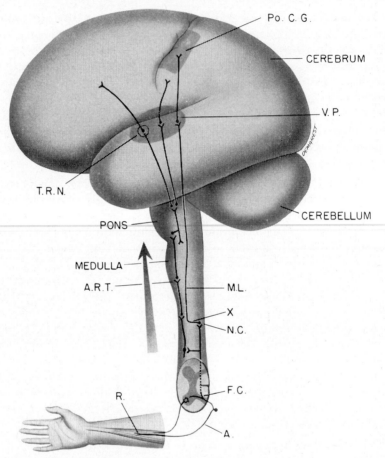

Po. C. G.

CEREBRUM

V. P.

T.R.N.

CEREBELLUM

PONS

MEDULLA

A.R.T.

M.L.

X

N.C.

R.

F.C.

A.

FIG. 2.   The ascending pathways. The ascending (afferent or sensory) pathways
include the lemniscal system and the reticular system. Both systems are prominent
in primates.

The lemniscal system consists of phylogenetically new, relatively direct pathways.
One such pathway includes the tracts and nuclei subserving the general somatic
sensations of touch and proprioception. The afferent neurons of the forelimb enter
the spinal cord through the dorsal roots, ascend in the *fasciculus cuneatus* (of the
dorsal columns), and terminate by synapsing in the *nucleus cuneatus* (lower medulla). The neurons of the *nucleus cuneatus* have axons that cross over to the
opposite side, ascend in the medial lemniscus, and terminate by synapsing in
the ventral posterior nucleus of the thalamus. The neurons of this thalamic nucleus
project to the portion of the postcentral gyrus associated with the forelimb.

The reticular system consists of the phylogenetically old, relatively indirect

C. The Concept of the Lemniscal System and the Reticular System
(Figs. 2 and 3)

The ascending pathways, just noted, are examples of two fundamental systems. The relatively direct pathway conveying the modalities associated with two-point discrimination, position sense, vibratory sense, and others belongs to the lemniscal system. The indirect pathways belong to the reticular system. This fundamental classification has a phylogenetic significance and a conceptual value. The differences outlined below should not be interpreted too rigidly.

The reticular system is the phylogenetically old integrator of the nervous system (Herrick, 1956). The lemniscal system is the phylogenetically new analyzer of the nervous system. A lemniscus is generally defined as an ascending tract with its origin (nucleus) in the spinal cord or lower brain stem and its terminus in the brain stem or thalamus and as a transmitter of sensory modalities (Herrick and Bishop, 1958). Both systems are located throughout the neuraxis (spinal cord, brain stem, diencephalon, and cerebrum). The reticular system is present in all living vertebrates while the lemniscal system is prominent in mammals and especially in the higher mammals including primates.

The reticular system may be characterized as the multineuronal, multisynaptic, diffuse, nonspecific, integrative system. The lemniscal systems may be characterized as the oligoneuronal, oligosynaptic, compactly organized specific, analytical system.

The multineuronal, multisynaptic, and diffuse features imply that the reticular system consists of relatively many nerve cells, numerous synaptic contacts, diffusely organized tracts and nuclei, all interposed between the site of the initial stimulus in the periphery (forelimb) and the terminus in the higher centers of the brain. Although the neuroanatomical organization appears as a reticular network microscopically, the reticular system is composed of well organized patterns (Scheibel and Scheibel, 1958). The oligoneuronal, oligosynaptic, and compactly

---

pathways associated with the state of alertness. These pathways include the reticular tracts and nuclei of the brain stem and thalamus that project to wide areas of the cortex. Note that sequences of many neurons form these ascending pathways. The internuncial neurons of the spinal cord are omitted in the figure.

A.	Afferent neuron	R.	Receptor
A.R.T.	Ascending reticular tracts and nuclei in brain stem	T.R.N.	Thalamic reticular nuclei
		V.P.	Ventral posterior nucleus of thalamus
F.C.	*Fasciculus cuneatus*		
M.L.	Medial lemniscus	X	Crossing-over of medial lemniscus
N.C.	*Nucleus cuneatus*		
Po.C.G.	Postcentral gyrus		

organized features imply that the lemniscal system consists of relatively few (but absolutely many) neurons and synapses, and compactly organized tracts and nuclei, all interposed between the site of initial stimulus and the terminus in the higher centers of the brain. In a sense, the lemniscal tracts are the long express highways.

Functionally the reticular system is nonspecific and integrative while the lemniscal system is specific and analytical (Herrick, 1948, 1956). The nonspecific nature of the reticular system is related to the concept that this system receives input from many sources and integrates this information and absorbs this input. Thus its identification with a specific sense is lost but the neural effect of its stimulus is utilized. In the reticular system the modalities lose their identity as a specific sense and exert their role anonymously in the general expression of arousal and wakefulness (Magoun, 1958). The lemniscal system is specific and analytical in that the ascending pathways conduct impulses associated with specific modalities such as temperature, touch, two-point discrimination, and others. This system separates or analyzes the environment and distinguishes the stimuli.

Both the reticular system and the lemniscal system are further elaborated during phylogeny. For example, the *nucleus centrum medianum* (Section II, E, 2) of the thalamus is small in small lemurs, fair sized in large lemurs and the monkeys, and large in the apes and man (Clark, 1932a; Walker, 1938). Recent investigations have demonstrated that this nucleus belongs to the thalamic reticular system (Jasper, 1958). The nuclear complexes of the thalamic lemniscal system are larger and more elaborate anatomically in the higher than in the lower primates. These include the lateral geniculate body of the visual system and the ventral posterior nucleus of the general somatic sensory system.

At the cerebral cortical level these two systems illustrate progressive elaboration during phylogeny and differences in their projections from the thalamus to the cortex. The fibers of the thalamic reticular system project to wide areas of the neocortex. This widespread distribution parallels the tremendous expansions of the cerebral cortex during primate phylogeny. In contrast the lemniscal systems (vision, audition, and general senses) project to rather well defined cortical regions (Section II, F).

D. Motor Systems and Their Relations to the Reticular System and the Lemniscal System

The concept of the reticular system and the lemniscal system can be extended to the motor systems of the nervous system. The pyramidal tract (corticospinal tract), the motor system that projects from the cerebral cortex directly to the spinal cord, may be considered to be the lemniscal aspect of the motor systems. The so-called "extrapyramidal" system may be considered to be the reticular aspect of the motor systems. This is the motor system that includes the complex pathways associated with such structures as the cerebral cortex, the basal ganglia of the cerebrum, the subthalamus of the diencephalon, and the reticular formation of the brain stem. The pathways of this system finally project from the lower brain stem to the spinal cord as the reticulospinal tracts. The general characteristics of the reticular system and the lemniscal system noted above for the ascending system also apply to these descending systems. The extrapyramidal system is the motor system of the nonmammalian vertebrates. It is phylogenetically old. The pyramidal motor system (exclusive to mammals) and the extrapyramidal motor system are the motor system of the primates. The pyramidal system is phylogenetically new.

1. *The Pyramidal System* (Figs. 3 and 6)

The pyramidal tract originates from wide areas (more extensive than the classic precentral gyrus) of the cerebral cortex, passes through the internal capsule of the cerebrum and the pyramids of the medulla, and terminates in the gray matter of the spinal cord. The cross-sectional area of the pyramidal tract (Fig. 6) is greater in the primates than in other mammals. According to Lassek (1954) the pyramids contain about 554,000 fibers in the macaque, about 505,000 fibers in the spider monkey, about 807,000 fibers in the chimpanzee and about 1,200,000 fibers in man. The pyramidal tract comprises about 20% of the cross-sectional area of the white matter of the spinal cord in the monkey and 30% in man. The cerebral peduncles of the midbrain (these include the corticopontile tracts and the pyramidal tract; Section II, E, 1) comprise about 11% of the cross-sectional area of the midbrain in the apes and 20% in man (Kappers *et al.*, 1936).

A significant phylogenetic feature is the manner in which this tract system terminates in the spinal cord. In nonprimate mammals, *i.e.*, the cat, fibers of the pyramidal tract project exclusively to the internuncial cells, which in turn, synapse with the alpha motor cells of the spinal cord. The pyramidal fibers of the primates project primarily to the internuncial neurons, but in apes and man some synapse directly on the alpha motor cells. The direct projections of the pyramidal tract to the alpha motor cells become "increasingly prominent throughout the primate series" (Kuypers, 1960; Verhaart, 1962). The implication is that the cerebral cortex can exert a direct effect on the alpha motor cells in higher primates and only indirectly via the internuncial cells in the nonprimate mammals. This may be considered as one morphological expression for directing fine dexterous movements of the hand.

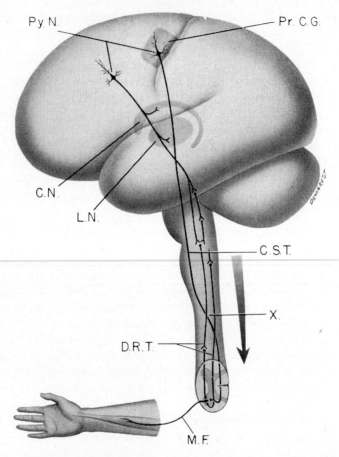

Fig. 3. The descending pathways. The corticospinal tract (pyramidal tract) may be classified as the descending pathway of the lemniscal system and the extra-pyramidal system as the descending pathways of the reticular system. The cortico-spinal tract extends from the cerebral cortex, decussates in the lower medulla, and terminates (mainly through internuncial neurons omitted in the figure) in the alpha motor cells and gamma motor cells of the spinal cord. The extrapyramidal system extends from the cerebral cortex through a complex sequence of relay nuclei in subcortical structures and projects via reticulospinal tracts to internuncial neurons and the motor neurons of the spinal cord.

C.N.	Caudate nucleus	M.F.	Alpha and gamma motor fibers
C.S.T.	Corticospinal tract	Pr.C.G.	Precentral gyrus
D.R.T.	Reticulospinal tracts (descending or motor)	Py.N.	Pyramidal neuron
		X.	Decussation of corticospinal tract
L.N.	Lenticular nucleus		

2. *Extrapyramidal System* (Figs. 3 and 4)

Only two facets of the extremely complex extrapyramidal system will be discussed. The first to be considered consists of some volumetric data on the basal ganglia in a series of primates and the second is the role of the reticulospinal tracts in forelimb movements.

The basal ganglia are large subcortical structures of the extrapyramidal system located in the cerebrum. The precise functional role of these ganglia in the motor mechanism is still controversial. Apparently the

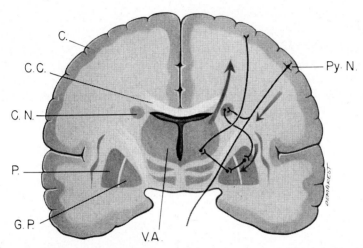

FIG. 4. A circuit of the extrapyramidal motor system. This circuit includes pathways from the cerebral cortex to the neostriatum, to the *globus pallidus*, to the ventral anterior nucleus of the thalamus, and back to the cerebral cortex. The neostriatum consists of the caudate nucleus and the putamen. The *globus pallidus* and the putamen form the lenticular nucleus (see Fig. 3).

C.	Cerebral cortex	P.	Putamen
C.C.	*Corpus callosum*	Py.N.	Pyramidal neuron (motor cell)
C.N.	Caudate nucleus	V.A.	Ventral anterior
G.P.	*Globus pallidus*		thalamic nucleus

basal ganglia are integrated into a complex feedback system (Fig. 4): the circuit from the cerebral cortex to the basal ganglia to the ventral anterior nucleus of the thalamus and back to the cortex (Mettler, 1957). The basal ganglia include the *globus pallidus,* caudate nucleus, putamen. The *globus pallidus* is phylogenetically older (paleostriatum) than the putamen and caudate nucleus (neostriatum). The volume of these three nuclei was calculated in a series of primates including *Galago demidovii, Perodicticus potto, Macaca mulatta, Cercocebus torquatus atys, Cebus fatuellus, Ateles ater, Pan satyrus,* and *Homo sapiens* (Harman and Carpenter, 1950). In this series of primates, the ratio of the volume of the *globus pallidus* to the combined volumes of the putamen and the caudate nucleus is constant. The relative size of the caudate nucleus to the putamen changes. The relatively large caudate nucleus of the prosimians decreases in relative size while the putamen correspondingly increases as the primate scale "ascends." These structures are absolutely larger in the higher than in the lower primates. The *globus pallidus* of the primates illustrates the point that a phylogenetically older structure need not regress but may progressively enlarge during phylogeny.

The reticulospinal tracts are significant links of the extrapyramidal system for the transmission of impulses to the spinal cord. These tracts originate in the reticular formation of the pons and the medulla and terminate on internuncial cells in the gray matter of the spinal cord. These in turn exert their influences on the alpha motor cells and gamma motor cells of the basic spinal reflex arcs noted above. In essence these tracts may either excite or inhibit the activity of these motor cells and the basic spinal reflexes.

3. General Significance of the Reticular System and the Lemniscal Systems

The reticular system may be considered as the primordial network (neuropile) of the nervous system. "The neuropile is the mother tissue from which have been derived both the specialized centers and tracts which execute the refined movements of the local reflexes and the more general web which binds these local activities together and integrates their behavior" (Herrick, 1931).

The stereotype movements are an expression of the reticular system while the fine analytical movements are an expression of the lemniscal systems (Herrick, 1956). The sensitivity of the hand in the higher primates is reflected in the prominence of the ascending lemniscal systems.

The principle that the finer specific movements are individuated, from the generalized total patterns, applies to ontogeny (Coghill, 1929) as well as phylogeny (Herrick, 1956). These phylogenetic and ontogenetic expressions that the total patterns preceded the partial patterns is a fundamental for the analysis of behavior. In this respect the simple spinal reflex (local reflex) is an abstraction for it is an integral part of the total pattern.

E. Some Higher Integrative Systems of the Brain and Their Functional Significance

In the course of evolution, the "higher centers" of the brain have developed and assumed a modulating role over the "lower centers" in the brain stem and spinal cord. This process of encephalization and corticalization is well expressed in the higher primates and man. These "higher centers" are in a sense successive brains that may excite and inhibit the activity of the lower centers. In fact, the inhibitory activity of the nervous system may be more significant than excitatory activity in acquiring manual skills. For example, in the dexterous movements of writing, the prevention of accessory movements is imperative. Skill, in this sense, may be a measure of inhibition. An associated principle is known as the release phenomenon (Section II, E, 1). For example, ablation of the cerebellum in primates may be followed by an excess of movement (intention tremor) rather than a poverty of movement. The cerebellum normally modulates and regulates certain phases of motor activity and when its influence is drastically reduced, the rest of the nervous system is released from this regulation.

Two aspects of these higher integrative mechanisms that are prominent in the primates will be outlined. These include: (1) interrelations between the cerebral cortex and the cerebellar cortex and (2) interrelations between the cerebral cortex and the thalamus.

1. *Interrelations between the Cerebral Cortex and the Cerebellar Cortex* (Figs. 5 and 6)

In the primates, the pathways that integrate the cerebral cortex with the cerebellar cortex are prominent and become larger and more important in the higher primates including man. The main neural structures of the feedback system performing this integration include in order: the cerebral cortex; the corticopontine tracts; the pontine nuclei of the pons; the pontocerebellar tracts that pass through the middle cerebellar peduncle (*brachium pontis*) to the cerebellar cortex of the opposite side; the fibers from the cerebellar cortex to the lateral or dentate nucleus of the cerebellum; the dentatorubrothalamic tract that passes from the dentate nucleus through the superior cerebellar peduncle (*brachium conjunctivum*), has synaptic connections in the nucleus ruber of the midbrain and continues with the addition of some rubrothalamic fibers to the ventral lateral nucleus of the thalamus; and finally the thalamocortical pathway that projects to the motor areas of the cerebral cortex. This is the skeleton of a complex feedback system (Fig. 5). In each nucleus the cells act as "funnels" and filters where processing of the impulses takes place. Each of the above-mentioned structures becomes larger in the higher primates.

This system may operate in this general way. In the execution of a volitional movement, information is transmitted from the cerebrum to the cerebellum and returned to the cerebral cortex and utilized in the

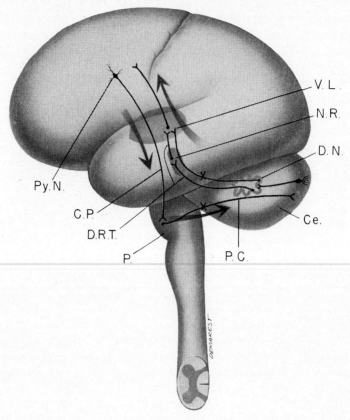

Fɪɢ. 5. Diagram illustrating the interrelationship between the cerebrum and the cerebellum.

This diagram illustrates a series of structures, integrated in a feedback circuit, that functions in the synergic movements. These structures, all well developed in primates, include the cerebral cortex, corticopontine tracts (from wide areas of the cortex), pontine nuclei, the pontocerebellar tracts (crossed tract terminating in the cerebellar cortex), cerebellar cortex, corticodentate fibers to the dentate nucleus, dentato-rubrothalamic tract (dentate nucleus of cerebellum, *nucleus ruber* of midbrain, and ventral lateral thalamic nucleus), and the tract from the thalamus to the cerebral cortex.

Ce.	Cerebellar cortex	P.C.	Pontocerebellar tract
C.P.	Corticopontine tracts	Py.N.	Pyramidal neuron in
D.N.	Dentate nucleus		cerebral cortex
D.R.T.	Dentato-rubrothalamic tract	V.L.	Ventral lateral nucleus
N.R.	*Nucleus ruber*		of thalamus
P.	Pontine nuclei	X.	Decussation

coordination of movement. The role of the cerebellum is that of a regulator acting as a servomechanism. The cerebellum does not play a role in sensory perception nor in the general pattern of action of the muscle groups. It regulates the strength and timing of the contractions of the individual muscles involved in the movement. This role in muscular coordination is known as synergy, the regulation and the gradation of contraction of the various muscles for smooth voluntary movement. When the cerebellum is damaged, synergy may be impaired. The release phenomenon is expressed by an asynchronous tremor during the execution of the movement.

The exclusively mammalian corticopontocerebellar parts of this feedback system evolved in concert during phylogeny. In the lower primates the *nucleus pontis* and the middle cerebellar peduncle are smaller than in the higher primates. The examination of Riley's (1928) figures shows this vividly (Fig. 6).

The lateral expansion of the cerebellum (neocerebellum) is associated with the increasing size of the corticopontocerebellar system (Dow, 1942). The expansion of these neocerebellar lateral hemispheres is pronounced in the primate series so that these structures reach their greatest absolute size and complexity in the higher apes and man. In general, the neocerebellum appears to be associated with the coordination of the finer movements in the extremities—especially the fingers. The cerebellum is relatively simple in the prosimians (Wood Jones, 1929; Clark, 1934). In the larger monkeys it reaches considerable size and becomes intricately fissured.

In the primates and other mammals there is an essential relationship between the cerebellar weight and the amount of muscle mass (Torgersen, 1954). If muscular coordination is equal, the larger the mammal's muscle mass the larger the cerebellum. As such the absolute cerebellar weight has a less complicated meaning than does cerebellar weight relative to total brain weight. The agility of the small primates is expressed in their relatively large cerebella. The greater relative weight of the cerebellum of a prosimian as compared to a monkey is, in part, associated with the larger cerebrum (greater degree of encephalization) in the latter (Putnam, 1928; Torgersen, 1954). The relatively greater weight of the cerebellum in relation to brain weight in an anthropoid ape as compared to that of man is again related, in part, to man's larger brain (Torgersen, 1954). The morphological distinction between the neocerebellum and the rest of the cerebellum is not sufficiently definable to make meaningful analyses of the "functional subdivisions" of the cerebellum on the basis of weight.

The dentate nucleus (lateral nucleus) of the cerebellum is small

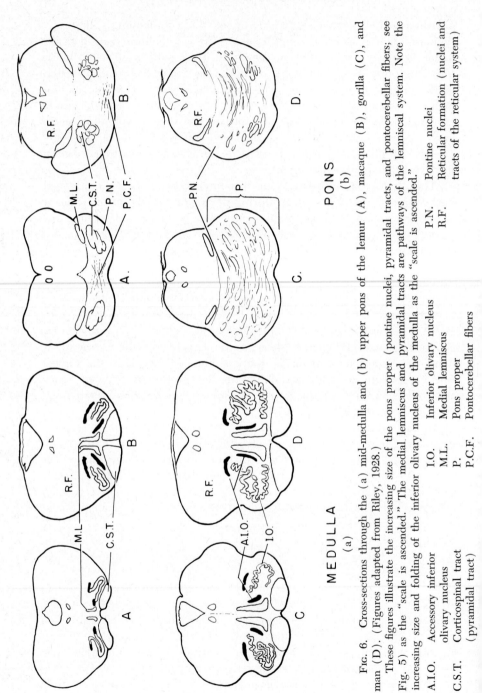

FIG. 6. Cross-sections through the (a) mid-medulla and (b) upper pons of the lemur (A), macaque (B), gorilla (C), and man (D). (Figures adapted from Riley, 1928.)

These figures illustrate the increasing size of the pons proper (pontine nuclei, pyramidal tracts, and pontocerebellar fibers; see Fig. 5) as the "scale is ascended." The medial lemniscus and pyramidal tracts are pathways of the lemniscal system. Note the increasing size and folding of the inferior olivary nucleus of the medulla as the "scale is ascended."

A.I.O.   Accessory inferior olivary nucleus
         olivary nucleus
C.S.T. Corticospinal tract (pyramidal tract)
I.O.   Inferior olivary nucleus
M.L.   Medial lemniscus
P.   Pons proper
P.C.F. Pontocerebellar fibers
P.N.   Pontine nuclei
R.F.   Reticular formation (nuclei and tracts of the reticular system)

in the prosimians (even smaller than the other cerebellar nuclei), definitely large in the monkeys, and extremely large in the apes and man (Jansen, 1954). This increase in size of the dentate nucleus is accompanied by only a slight increase in size of the *nucleus fastigius* (medial nucleus) of the cerebellum. The *nucleus fastigius* is associated with the vestibular system. This comparison reflects the increasing importance of the neocerebellar system as contrasted with the conservative vestibular system in the higher primates.

The *nucleus ruber* is divided into two parts: a large-cell (magnocellular) portion and a small-cell (parvocellular) portion. The magnocellular portion gives rise to the rubrospinal tract that projects to the spinal cord while the parvocellular portion projects cephalically to the ventral lateral nucleus of the thalamus. The magnocellular nucleus contains more neurons in the lower than in the higher primates. This is reflected in the reduction of the rubrospinal tract to a minor tract in the higher primates. In contrast the parvocellular portion of the *nucleus ruber* is large in the monkeys and assumes such large proportions in the apes and man. In summary, the cephalic projection of the *nucleus ruber* to the thalamus becomes more significant as the scale is "ascended" whereas the caudal projection to the spinal cord is reduced to only a minor tract.

The ventral lateral nucleus, the thalamic component of this system, is larger in the apes and man than in the monkeys and lower primates (Walker, 1938; Heiner, 1960).

The main (neo) inferior olivary nucleus of the medulla is a structure that is small in the lower primates, large in the monkeys, and extremely large and convoluted in the apes and man (Fig. 6). The small accessory (paleo) inferior olivary nuclei, in contrast, are small in all the primates, including man. All these nuclei, with unknown functional significance, receive their input from the reticular formation and project to wide areas of the neocerebellum. They may be considered as adjunct structures to the corticocerebellar systems. The tremendous size of the main olivary nucleus in the apes and man is indicative of some significant but unknown role of this nucleus and its tracts.

Both the neocerebellar cortex and the neocortex of the cerebrum have dramatically enlarged during the course of primate evolution. Whether the expansion of these two structures was exactly parallel during phylogeny or whether one structure emerged relatively later than the other is not established. In fact, only the paleontological record can solve this problem. The relatively late emergence of the neocerebellum is suggested by Harman (1957). The evidence is based on ontogeny of the human brain. Volumetric studies by Dunn (1921) and

Grenell and Scammon (1943) and relative growth analysis by Noback and Moss (1956) indicate that the cerebellum commences its relative growth expansion later in fetal life than the cerebral hemisphere does. If this ontogenetic observation is indicative of a phylogenetic process then the cerebellar expansion is a relatively late phenomenon. This may imply that cerebellar growth may be a truly significant feature of future human evolution (Harman, 1957).

Fissuration is usually associated with the cerebral cortex and the cerebellar cortex. However, the principle of fissuration also applies to the folding of the dentate nucleus of the cerebellum and the main inferior olivary nucleus of the medulla. Fissuration is briefly discussed in the section on cerebral cortex (Section II, F).

2. Interrelations between Cerebral Cortex and Thalamus (Fig. 7)

The thalamus (Fig. 7) of the diencephalon is subdivided into a number of nuclei. Among those nuclei prominent in the primates are the ventral posterior nucleus (general senses), medial geniculate body (audition), lateral geniculate body (vision), *nucleus centrum medianum* (reticular system), ventral lateral nucleus, lateral nuclear group, pulvinar and medial (dorsomedial) nucleus (Clark, 1931, 1932a; Walker, 1938; Toncray and Krieg, 1946; Sheps, 1945; Krieg, 1948; Heiner, 1960).

These nuclear groups are integrated into several fundamental activities of the cerebrum: (1) The thalamus is intercalated between the ascending afferent influences from the organism (internal and external environments) and the cerebral cortex. (2) The thalamic nuclei are not merely relay stations but are actually nodal points in the pathways where significant neural processing occurs. (3) Some of these nuclear complexes, especially those associated with "higher functions" have reciprocal connections with certain areas of the cerebral cortex. In fact areas of the cerebral cortex and certain thalamic nuclei (lateral nuclear groups, pulvinar and medial nucleus, for example) are so interconnected that each nucleus and a specific cortical area may be considered as a "functional unit." (4) Some nuclei are integrated into complex feedback systems with the cerebral cortex and subcerebral structures. An example is the ventral lateral nucleus which is intercalated in the circuits of the cerebral cortex and the cerebellar cortex discussed above. (5) The dynamic role of the thalamus is affected by the evolutionary process of corticalization (Section II, F, 3); some functions attributed to the thalamus in monkeys, for example, are apparently "transferred" to the cerebral cortex of apes and man. A monkey with an ablated visual cortex can perceive light and dark but has no object vision, while a chimpanzee (or a man) with a similar ablation cannot even perceive light. This implies that some visual stimuli reach the conscious level in subcortical structures (thalamus and midbrain tectum) of the monkey but not in the chimpanzee and man. In the latter two organisms, any conscious recognition of optic input requires cortical activity.

Knowledge of the detailed functional significance of the thalamus is in a state of flux. Hence the discussion will be restricted to only a few points.

The ventral posterior nucleus, the medial geniculate body (audition), and the lateral geniculate body are integrated into circuits that belong to the lemniscal systems. The ventral posterior nucleus is the nucleus of termination of the medial lemniscus (touch and proprioception) and the lateral spinothalamic tract (pain and temperature). In turn, this

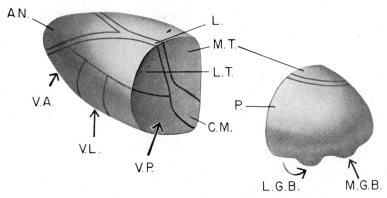

Fig. 7.   Diagram of the thalamus from a left posterolateral view.

Prominent thalamic nuclei in the primates are noted. The lateral geniculate body (vision), the medial geniculate body (audition), and the ventral posterior thalamic nucleus (general senses) are integrated into the ascending afferent pathways. The ventral lateral thalamic nucleus is integrated in the cerebellar-cerebral pathway (Fig. 5). The ventral anterior thalamic nucleus is a link in an extrapyramidal circuit (Fig. 4). The *nucleus centrum medianum* and other laminar nuclei are integrated in the ascending reticular system (Fig. 2). The lateral thalamic nuclei and the pulvinar are reciprocally connected with the association areas of the occipital, temporal, and parietal lobes. These lobes are associated with the cortical integration aspects of vision, audition, and the general senses (Fig. 8). The medial (dorsomedial) thalamic nucleus has reciprocal connections with the prefrontal lobe associated with certain aspects of behavior and personality (Fig. 8).

A.N.	Anterior nucleus	M.G.B.	Medial geniculate body
C.M.	*Nucleus centrum medianum*	M.T.	Medial thalamic nucleus
L.	Laminar nuclei (thalamic reticular nuclei)	P.	Pulvinar
		V.A.	Ventral anterior nucleus
L.G.B.	Lateral geniculate body	V.L.	Ventral lateral nucleus
L.T.	Lateral thalamic nuclei	V.P.	Ventral posterior nucleus

nucleus projects to the postcentral gyrus of the cerebral cortex (general sensory cortex) and other cortical areas (Figs. 2 and 8). The general senses of the forelimb project to the specific portion of this nucleus. The fact that this nucleus is well developed in primates and especially in the higher primates is directly correlated with the refinement of these senses in these forms. It is likely that pain and some of the crude general senses have not yet been corticalized but are brought to consciousness in the thalamus, although not necessarily in this specific nucleus (Mehler *et al.*, 1960). The lateral geniculate body increases in size and complexity as the primate scale is "ascended." The phylogenetic aspects of the lateral geniculate body in the primates are outlined under the discussion of the visual system (Section III, E).

The *nucleus centrum medianum* is a thalamic nucleus that is one of a number in the thalamus that belongs to the reticular system. This nucleus is the largest and most delineated of all the thalamic reticular nuclei in higher primates. The exact role of this nucleus in the states of sleep, awareness, and consciousness is slowly being established (Jasper, 1958).

The ventral lateral nucleus is integrated into the cerebral cortex-cerebellar cortex interrelations (Section II, E, 1).

The lateral nuclear groups and the pulvinar are nuclear masses that reach tremendous proportions in the higher primates and man. Their large size is correlated with the expansion of the association areas of the cerebral cortex in the apes and man (Fig. 8). Rich reciprocal connections exist between these nuclei and the cerebral cortex. The probable role of these structures is in some way associated with the elaboration of the higher integrative aspects of vision, audition, and the general senses.

The medial (dorsomedial) thalamic nucleus has abundant reciprocal connections with the prefrontal lobes of the cerebral cortex known as the prefrontal cortex. This portion of the cortex is large in the apes and is greatly expanded in man. The experimental evidence indicates that this complex of the medial nucleus and the prefrontal lobes is concerned with certain phases of personality and behavior. Without this portion of the brain monkeys, apes, and man perform tasks essentially as before ablation but anxiety, frustration, and other emotional expressions are of less concern to the affected individual (Ruch and Fulton, 1960).

F. THE CEREBRAL CORTEX (Fig. 8)

The increase in the size and weight of the brain, the expansion of the volume of the cerebral cortex, and the fissuration of the surface of the cerebral cortex are dramatic features of primate evolution. In this presentation, attention is directed primarily to some general structural and functional facets of the primate cerebral cortex. Because many aspects of the size and weight of the primate brain are discussed by Count (1947) and Dart (1956) and others, and the descriptions of the external

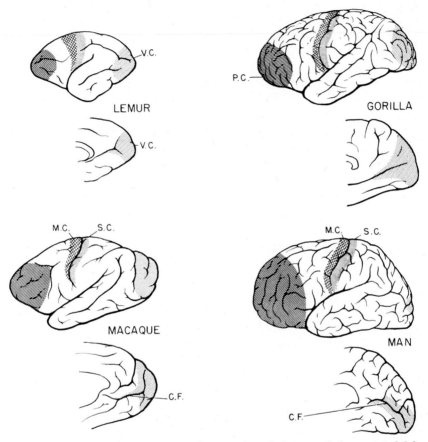

FIG. 8.   Lateral views of the cerebrum and medial view of the occipital lobe of representative primates.

Note that the primary visual cortex shifts from the lateral surface to the medial aspect of the cortex and occupies relatively less of the total cortical surface area as the "scale is ascended." The visual cortex is actually larger in the ascending scale. The association areas of the parietal, occipital, and temporal lobes and the prefrontal lobe are both absolutely and relatively largest in apes and man.

Figures are drawn to the following scales: lemur (1×); macaque (½×); gorilla (⅓×) and man (¼×).

C.F.	Calcarine fissure	S.C.	Primary sensory cortex
M.C.	Primary motor cortex	V.C.	Primary visual cortex
P.C.	Prefrontal lobe		

morphology, particularly cerebral topography, are reviewed by Connolly (1950), these topics will be largely omitted.

Mammals with small brains have smooth cortices (lissencephalic brains) and mammals with large brains have cortices convoluted with gyri and sulci (gyrencephalic brains). This correlation between size of brain and surface cortical contours is present in many orders of mammals: Perissodactyla, Artiodactyla, Proboscidea, Carnivora, Cetacea, and Primates. No completely gyrencephalic order of mammals exists, for all orders arose from small brained lissencephalic ancestors (Edinger, 1948). Within an order, the fissural patterns of the cortical surface are similar. For example, the basic primate convolutional pattern is present in lower primates. The addition of sulci and gyri to the basic patterns can be seen in the progressively more convoluted brains of monkeys, apes, and man (Fig. 8). The basic fissural patterns differ in the various orders. In fact, there is probably little point in attempting to homologize the fissures, sulci, and gyri of the different orders. On the other hand the comparison of the functional areas (sensory areas and motor areas) of the cortices of species of different orders has validity.

There is no difficulty in reconstructing a transition from the generalized insectivore to the generalized primate (Clark, 1931). In such lower primates as *Microcebus* the neocortex has only one sulcus—the calcarine sulcus in the occipital lobe. The small brains of lemurs have a series of longitudinally oriented sulci and gyri. The medium sized brains of the monkeys have transverse and arcuate shaped sulci. Apes and man have additional secondary sulci that make for a more complex fissural pattern (Clark, 1960). In a sense the lower forms foreshadow the patterns in the higher forms. Throughout this expansion of the cerebral cortex there is an increase in the absolute size of the so-called primary sensory and primary motor projection areas. A proportionately large increase in the size of the neocortex as the scale is "ascended" is attributed to the association cortex.

Fissuration is geometrically explained by Baillarger's Law of Folding Compensation. Sulci and gyri are the expression of the great increase in cortical surface area. In the trend toward larger brains, the relative increase in volume of the cerebral cortex is greater than the increase in the volume of the entire brain. The cerebral cortex increases in volume by enlarging in two dimensions, surface expansion, without any significant increase in the third dimension, cortical depth. The thickness of the cortex in small-brained mammals is only slightly less than in large-brained mammals. In summary, fissuration of the cerebral cortex is a phenomenon that reflects the increase in cortical volume without any significant increase in cortical thickness (Clark, 1945). In the evolution of the primates from lemurs, the corticalization has been achieved by the increase in the number of cortical units (see Section II, F, 2 on the phylogeny of finer structure of the cerebral cortex) rather than by any drastic shift in the nature of the cortex itself. In addition cortical evolution is closely associated with the evolution of the subcortical structures (see for example the thalamo-cortical interrelations, in Section II, E, 2).

Of significance in fissuration is the fact that no disproportionate increase in cortical volume occurs in any species. The volume of the neocortex tends to remain as a constant percentage of the total brain volume in the primates (Harman, 1947) whose neocortex ranges from 46% to 58% of the total brain volume. Thus the cortical volume is relatively high in all primates, in the lissencephalic lower primates as well as in the gyrencephalic apes and man. In comparison the neocortex of rodents is roughly 30% and of carnivores 40 to 46% of the total brain volume (Harman, 1947). Apparently, each order of mammals has evolved from its Paleocene ancestors with its own ratio of neocortical volume to total brain volume that is maintained, in general, during its phylogeny.

Fissuration and folding is a phenomenon that is characteristic of several neural structures during phylogeny. In addition to the cerebral cortex, these are the cerebellar cortex, dentate nucleus of the cerebellum, inferior olivary nucleus of the medulla, and the lateral geniculate body of the thalamus. All these structures are organized gray masses of cell bodies of nerve cells and all increase in size in the monkeys, apes, and man. Not all nuclei that expand in primate evolution are folded or convoluted. The *nucleus gracilis, nucleus cuneatus,* the parvocellular portion of the *nucleus ruber,* the thalamic nuclei, and the nuclei of the basal ganglia increase in size in three dimensions. The basis for these different expressions of increased size is not fully known. The fissuration of the cerebellar cortex into narrow folia is characteristically different from the wide gyri of the cerebrum.

1. Parcellation of the Cerebral Cortex

The expansion of the cerebral cortex is associated with two factors: (1) The increase in the number of the ascending (sensory or afferent) projection fibers and the descending (motor or efferent) projection fibers that pass to and from subcortical centers. (2) The elaboration of the intrinsic association and commissural fiber systems that integrate one area of the cortex with other cortical areas of the same side and opposite side.

During primate evolution the neocortex expanded rapidly (von Bonin, 1945, 1947, 1951; Peden and von Bonin, 1947; Bailey *et al.,* 1950). Apparently much of this expansion has occurred in the primary projection areas in the lower primates and in the association areas in apes and man (Fig. 8). The primary sensory areas include the visual area in the occipital lobe, the auditory area of the temporal lobe, and the general sensory area in the parietal lobe. The classic motor areas include the primary motor cortex of the precentral gyrus and the premotor cortex of the cortical area just rostral to the primary motor area. The rest of the cortex is known as the "association cortex" and is presumably concerned with the integrative activities of the cerebral cortex. In a general way the expansion of the temporal lobes is associated with the higher functional activity associated with the auditory system, the storage of certain visual and auditory memories, and other complex learning mechanisms. The large cortical area common to occipital lobe, parietal lobe, and posterior temporal lobe is probably the great integrative region for all the sensory systems—vision, audition, and general senses. The rostral cortex of the frontal lobes (prefrontal cortex, Fig. 8) and the rostral cortex of the temporal lobe (these two areas are interconnected) are associated with such higher integrative expressions as drive, initiative, urge to pursue objectives, and other attention-directed activities.

The great commissure of the cerebral cortex, the corpus callosum (found only in eutherian mammals) increases in size parallel to the cerebral cortex. Functionally this structure transfers information from one hemisphere to the other (Sperry, 1961).

Neurophysiological studies of the cerebral cortex of several primates including man have broadened the perspective on the functional parcellation of the cerebral cortex (Woolsey, 1958; Penfield and Jasper, 1954). The cortices of *Macaca mulatta, Saimiri sciurea* (catarrhine squirrel monkey), and *Hapale jacchus* (marmoset) were examined by Woolsey (1954), Benjamin and Welker (1957), Welker *et al.* (1957), and Woolsey (1958), and that of man by Penfield and Rasmussen (1950).

Four areas of the cortex, when appropriately stimulated electrically, yield motor responses (Fig. 9). These same areas are also the receptive areas of the general senses. The regions are the precentral gyrus, the postcentral gyrus, the supplementary on the medial aspect of the frontal lobe, and the "second" area at the base of the precentral gyrus adjacent to the Sylvian fissure. The precentral gyrus and the supplementary area are primarily motor areas because motor responses are relatively easily evoked. The postcentral gyrus and the second area are primarily general sensory areas because peripheral stimulation produces activity in these areas. Stimulation of the general sensory endings may also evoke some activity in the motor areas, and motor responses may be obtained by stimulating the sensory areas. These observations emphasize the fact that no sharp differences exist between motor areas and sensory areas. Somatotopic organization of these areas has been described. The homunculi and simunculi are roughly in proportion to the degree of motor dexterity or sensory acuity for the body region represented. For example, the thumb and fingers have a large representation because of their function as excellent sensory receptors and manipulators. The primates with prehensile tails have a large area represented for this organ. The topographic pattern of the postcentral gyrus is a mirror image of that of the precentral gyrus (Fig. 9). All areas with the partial exception of

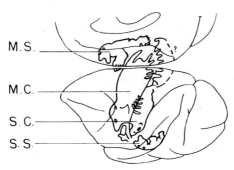

FIG. 9. Diagram of motor and general sensory cortical areas in the monkey. (After Woolsey, 1958.)

Four cortical areas are associated with both motor activity and reception of general senses. Somatotopic organization is characteristic in each area. The primary motor area and the supplementary motor area are chiefly associated with motor responses and secondarily with reception of stimuli of the general senses. The primary sensory area and the second area are chiefly receptive areas of general senses and secondarily associated with motor responses.

| M.C. | Primary motor area | S.C. | Primary sensory area |
| M.S. | Supplementary motor area | S.S. | Second area |

the supplemental areas have mosaic representation for the entire body. In man, Penfield and Jasper (1954) have described a general sensory area on the medial aspect of the parietal lobe. Other areas that evoke motor responses have been reported by Crosby (1956).

The greater sensitivity and finer dexterity of the hand as the scale is "ascended" from marmoset, squirrel monkey, macaque monkey, and man are reflected in the greater area of the cortical surface alloted to the hand in these four cortical areas. In the macaque and man the cortical area in the precentral gyrus representing the hand has expanded in such a way that it separates the enlarged facial region (near the Sylvian fissure) from the occipital region of the head (located near the cortical representation of the neck and trunk region). This intercalation of the hand between these two head areas (facial and occipital re-

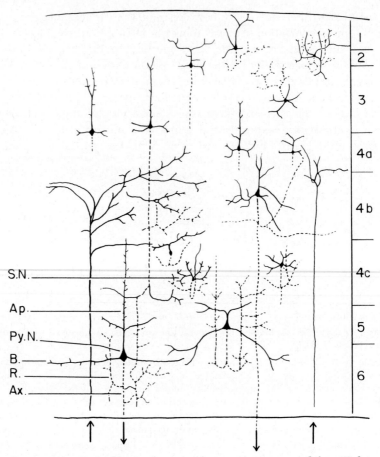

Fɪɢ. 10.   Neurons in the visual cortex of man as reconstructed from Golgi preparations.   (After Polyak, 1957.)

The two basic cell types of the cerebral cortex are the pyramidal neuron and the stellate neuron. Each pyramidal neuron is oriented with its apical dendrite toward the cortical surface, with its axon projecting to the subcortical white matter, and its relatively short basilar dendrites extending horizontally. An axon has at least one collateral branch that feeds back to the immediate cortex. The stellate cells are small cells with axons that arborize in the immediate cortex. Fibers projecting cells into the cortex enter in a plane parallel to the apical dendrite and axon of a pyramidal neuron. In effect the basic structural units of the cerebral cortex are vertical columns. The relative and absolute increase in the number of stellate cells in the higher primates is a significant index of the delicacy of function of the human cerebral cortex. The numbers (1–6) represent the layers of the visual cortex.

Ap.	Apical dendrite	R.	Recurrent collateral
Ax.	Axon		branch of axon
B.	Basilar dendrite	S.N.	Stellate neuron
Py.N.	Pyramidal neuron		

gions) occurs in the postcentral gyrus of man (Fig. 9; Benjamin and Welker, 1957; Woolsey, 1958). During phylogeny the sulci deepen and incorporate more cortical area than the gyri do. In the monkey more of the motor area is present on the gyral cortex than in the sulcal cortex while in man most of the motor area is in the sulcal cortex.

2. Phylogenetic Aspects of the Neurons of the Neocortex (Fig. 10)

The neocortex is organized with two cell types: pyramidal cells and stellate cells (Fig. 10). The pyramidal cells are vertically (perpendicular to cortical surface) oriented cells with a branched apical dendrite extending toward the cortical surface, basilar dendrites extending horizontally for short distances, and a long axon projecting into the subjacent white matter. The axons project to subcortical cerebral levels, brain stem, and spinal levels, or to other areas of the cortex of the same and opposite cerebral hemisphere. Each stellate neuron has many dendrites and a relatively short axon that remains within the cortex. Many variations of these cell types exist. Of importance is the fact that the pyramidal cells have axons that project to the subjacent white matter and that the stellate cells have short axons that do not leave the cortex.

The elementary pattern of organization in the mammalian cerebral cortex is a vertically oriented column of pyramidal cells and stellate cells. Because of the orientation of the cortical neurons, the horizontal spread of intracortical activity among the vertical columns is limited. The complex interactions of input-output functions of the vertical columns is via the pyramidal cell axons. Input to each column is from the axons of subcortical structures such as the thalamus and from axons of pyramidal cells of other vertical cortical columns of the nearby or distant cortex. In turn, each cortical column projects via pyramidal axons to other cortical columns or to subcortical structures via the subjacent white matter. An increase in the amount of cortex and fibers in the white matter occurs as the primate scale is "ascended."

The significant phylogenetic change in the morphological complexity of the neocortex is expressed in the vertical columns of neurons. Although the details of this change have not been documented in the primate cortex, the collateral evidence is sound. The neocortex of the mouse, rat, and rabbit is composed of pyramidal cells and stellate cells with relatively long axons. Stellate cells with short axons are scarce. The assumption is made that the neocortex of the lower primates is similarly organized with the probability that: (1) the dendrites are more branched, (2) stellate cells with long axons are more numerous, and (3) stellate cells with short axons are present. The neurons of the human cortex have been examined in detail (Ramón y Cajal, 1911; Lorente de Nó, 1949; Conel, 1959). The changes in the morphology of the human cortex from that in nonprimates are fundamentally modifications of the basic cell types and not additional new cell types. The pyramidal cells of man have, in general, more elaborate dendritic arborization patterns than described for any other form. The relative increase in the number of stellate cells proportional to pyramidal cells is most significant. Many stellate cells have relatively long axons that remain within their respective vertical columns. The most dramatic increase is in the number of stellate cells with short axons in all cortical areas (Ramón y Cajal, 1911). These cells increase the degree of interaction between the cells of each vertical unit. "Cajal assumed that the large number of stellate cells with short axons was the anatomical expression of the delicacy of function of the human brain." This assumption is almost a statement of fact, for no evidence exists to refute it (Lorente de Nó, 1949).

3. *Functional Expression of Cortex (Encephalization and Corticalization)*

Encephalization is the concept whereby the forebrain, through evolution, assumes a dominant role over the lower centers. The domination is greater in the higher primates and man. In turn, the functional dependence of the lower centers on the higher levels is greater in the higher forms (Noback and Moscowitz, 1962). The increase in the dominance of the cerebral cortex, corticalization for example, is reflected in its complex elaboration. A functional expression of this dominance is the release phenomenon (Section II, E) that follows the ablation of certain cortical areas.

Cerebral functions increase as the scale is "ascended" (Terzuolo and Adey, 1960). In the higher primates, the stimulation of the motor cortex elicits more intricate motor patterns, the release phenomena following cortical ablation of motor areas are more severe and persistent, and the relative and absolute increase in size of responsive cortical areas is greater. Ablation of the precentral motor cortex results in less severe deficits in lemurs and New World monkeys than in such Old World monkeys as the mangabeys and macaques; greater deficits are exhibited in the chimpanzee (Walker and Fulton, 1938; Ruch and Fulton, 1960). Lesions in this gyrus interfere especially with skilled motor acts in the macaque (Pribram *et al.*, 1955). Experimental section of the pyramids in the medulla (presumably the corticospinal tracts are interrupted) results in more severe impairment in the chimpanzee than in the monkey (Tower, 1944). The permanent motor deficits in the chimpanzee includes poverty of movement in the limbs with the loss of fine movements such as apposition of the thumb with the index finger in grooming and in manipulation of fine objects (Tower, 1944). On the sensory side, ablation of the postcentral gyrus reduces the ability to discriminate weight less in the monkey than in the chimpanzee, and most in man (Ruch et al., 1938).

The general somatic sense of crude touch and pain are probably "thalamic" senses in all primates (Mehler, 1957). The appreciation of discriminative general senses such as weight, form, size, and texture requires cortical activity.

III. The Primate Visual System

Of the senses available to man in the assessment of his environment, probably none is so useful as the visual sense. In recognition of its importance we have an everyday vocabulary that expresses meaning beyond visual sensations, such as *insight, foresight, hindsight,* and *visionary* (Clark, 1943). All these imply a mental process that may be regarded as intellectual. Anatomically the importance of sight in man is indicated by the estimate of Bruesch and Arey (1942) that more than one-third of all the nerve fibers entering or leaving the central nervous system are those of the optic nerves. The elaboration of the visual system in primates is associated with their development of the arboreal habit requiring the recognition and assessment of spatial relations of distant objects, conditions under which smell, the chief special sense of the lower mammals, functions less effectively (Clark, 1942; Polyak, 1957). In perfecting this sense, anatomical changes occur. The orbits shift medially, eyes are directed frontally, the snout is reduced, binocular vision appears as may color vision, and new nervous pathways arise to conduct light impulses from the eye to the brain.

Reduced to basic anatomical and physiological elements, the visual system consists of a light-refracting and light-absorbing organ, the eye; a nervous pathway leading to analytical and integrating mechanisms, namely the subcortical and cortical centers of the brain. Among inframammals the optic pathway includes retinas, optic nerves, optic chiasma, optic tracts, and optic lobes. In these forms the optic lobes, part of the midbrain, appear to perform two functions in processing visual stimuli by: (1) coordinating sensory stimuli and (2) coordinating motor responses. In mammals the optic pathways extend to the cerebral cortex and include retinas, optic nerves, optic chiasma, optic tracts, lateral geniculate bodies, optic radiations (geniculo-calcarine tracts), and visual cortex (area 17, striate cortex, Fig. 11). The last structure lies in the region of the calcarine sulcus of the occipital lobes where optic impulses are relayed to other cortical areas. This development in evolution, the transfer and elaboration of activity from a subcortical center to the cerebral cortex, is referred to as encephalization or corticalization (Section II, F, 3). Thus the optic lobes of the midbrain function in both sensory and motor activity in the inframammal but their homologues,

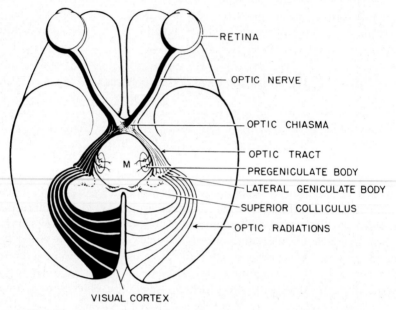

FIG. 11.   Diagram of human visual system. (After Polyak, 1957.)

Fibers from the lateral (outer half) of each retina do not cross over in the optic chiasma. Those originating from the medial (inner) half of each retina cross over in the optic chiasma. Because the lens inverts the field of vision, the image projected to the lateral half of the retina comes from the field in front of the eye. The image projected to the medial half of the retina comes from a more lateral field. Thus in the optic chiasma impulses from homonymous (similar) fields are segregated for transmission over the optic tracts chiefly to the lateral geniculate body (some fibers pass to the pregeniculate and superior colliculus) where the axons from the neurons of the retina synapse. The neurons of the lateral geniculate body form a lemniscal pathway—the geniculo-calcarine tract (optic radiations) to the visual cortex where the stimuli are integrated as vision. M., Midbrain.

the superior colliculi are only associated with some motor reflex pathways related to optic stimuli in higher primates. Conscious activity in response to visual stimulation in these primates is integrated in the cerebral cortex, rather than in the midbrain.

This discussion is limited to some elements that appear to be significant in the evolution of the visual system.

A. The Retina

The light-sensitive tissue of the eye, the retina, is composed of: (1) photoreceptors, the rods and cones and (2) neurons, the bipolar and ganglion cells, that analyze and relay visual impulses via the optic pathway to the brain. Functional and anatomical differentiation of the retina exists, particularly in primates with well developed vision. However, there is no evolutionary sequence in the organization of the nervous elements of the retina from lower to higher anthropoids (Clark, 1960). The organization is related to the photic habits of the species. In the region of the visual axis, the central area, locus of keenest vision is defined by the pattern of detouring blood vessels and optic nerve fibers, allowing for more effective transmission of light by reducing mechanical interference. In addition this area is marked by an increase in number, fineness, and concentration of neurons optimally functional in bright light. The peripheral or extra-areal region of the retina characteristically contains coarser neurons that are associated with perception in dim light in diurnal animals.

The photoreceptors, components of the bacillary layer of the retina, are of two kinds—cones and rods. Cones function in light of high intensity and are associated with visual acuity and color vision, while rods are activated in low intensities of light. Associated with the light receptors are photolabile pigments, rhodopsin or visual purple contained in the rods, and chlorolabe and erythrolabe (Rushton, 1958) in the cones of the human retina. The latter two pigments are distinguished from each other by the difference in maximal absorption spectra. Erythrolabe is somewhat more responsive to red light. The photosensitivity of the receptor pigments varies but little in different animal species (Crescitelli, 1958).

The differences in distribution and kinds of photoreceptors in the central area of the retina are an adaptation to maximal function under different photic intensities. In diurnal primates the greatest concentration of cones appears in central fovea along with the greatest refinement of the photoreceptor. In man the cones of the central fovea are twice the length of those more peripherally situated (Polyak, 1957). This is consistent with the functional role of cones in visual acuity.

The most delicate rods of diurnal primates adapted for vision in dim light are found in the perifoveal area; their size increases in the periphery of the retina. In man the maximal number of rods is located outside the central area, but is reached in the periphery of the central area of the rhesus monkey (Polyak, 1957). The rods of the nocturnal tarsier however, reach their greatest attenuation in the central fovea, although their concentration remains relatively uniform throughout the retina.

In this animal endowed with a typically differentiated retina of primates, the photoreceptors consist only of rods similar to those of the retinas of the cat and the nocturnal lemurs *Galago* and *Nycticebus* (Polyak, 1957). The presence of a fovea in the tarsier (Polyak, 1957) has led to speculation upon its existence in a nocturnal animal. Since the fovea is regarded as the region of greatest visual discrimination in higher primates, the finding of a similar structure in the rod retina of the nocturnal New World monkey *Aotes* has led to the conclusion that in these forms it is a vestigial structure, first appearing among the tarsioids in primate evolution (Polyak, 1957; Clark, 1960). All lemurs differ from monkeys in the absence of a true fovea (Clark, 1960). The structure is also absent in the tree shrew, *Tupaia*, but in both lemurs and *Tupaia* there is a refinement of the vascular elements in this region suggesting perhaps an incipient central area (Clark, 1960). However, Polyak (1957) reported that the cones of *Tupaia* are relatively uniform in size and distribution with a constant ratio of numbers of rods and cones throughout, indicating a lack of differentiation.

B. The Optic Nerve

The optic nerve fibers are the axons of the ganglion cells of the retina. In lower mammals these axons pass directly from the retina to the optic lobes of the midbrain while collateral branches pass to the lateral geniculate body, a derivative of the thalamus. In mammals with highly evolved visual systems, the number of optic fibers reaching the lateral geniculate body increases (up to 70–80% according to Bernheimer, 1899, quoted by Brindley, 1960). The increase in absolute number of optic nerve fibers terminating in the lateral geniculate body is correlated with the further differentiation of this body and the precise terminalization of the optic nerve fibers in the lateral geniculate body (Chacko, 1948). This is an expression of encephalization.

Thick optic fibers arise from the cells of the peripheral retina, medium size fibers from the outer central area, and fine fibers from the fovea (Polyak, 1941). Fine fibers arise from monosynaptic ganglion cells receiving impulses from the cones, while thick fibers are axons of multisynaptic ganglion cells carrying converging impulses from rods and cones. Stated another way (Chacko, 1954a) fiber size is related to the amount and degree of summation (multisynapsis), an indication of the degree of sensitivity under low intensities of illumination. In nocturnal animals the fineness of the rods and of the fibers does not permit an extensive amount of summation and therefore provides for increased visual acuity. In summary, the foveal area is associated with the greatest degree of visual acuity and the peripheral area with form recognition.

The proportion of fine optic fibers, related to visual acuity, and coarse optic fibers, related to image perception, is a clue to the keenness of vision of the animal but it is not necessarily an indication of the quality of performance of the visual system as a whole. Chacko (1954a) states that human optic nerve fibers range from less than 2µ to 10µ in diameter; the maximum diameter for those of the chimpanzee is 6.5µ, 11µ for the spider monkey, 4.5µ for the tarsier, 7µ for *Lemur fulvus*, 9µ for *Loris gracilis*, 6µ for the baboon, and for comparison 15µ for the cat. The percentage of fine fibers, those less than 2µ is as follows: 95% in the tarsier, 85% in the chimpanzee, and 75% in man. The percentage of coarse fibers is greater in *Loris gracilis*,[3] *Lemur fulvus*, and the baboon than in man.

C. THE OPTIC CHIASMA

In all nonmammalian vertebrates and in many mammals including the primitive primate *Tupaia*, all the fibers of the optic nerve of one side cross over to the opposite side in the optic chiasma. The percentage of uncrossed fibers varies from none in *Tupaia*, 25–35% in tarsier (Polyak, 1957), to 40% in monkey (Clark, 1942), and 40% in man (Polyak, 1957). The uncrossed components, found only in mammals, are the axons of ganglion cells of the temporal (lateral) part of the retina. Since the lens inverts the fields of vision, the temporal part of the retina receives photic stimuli from the visual field frontal to the animal. Mammals with the most laterally directed eyes have two common features: (1) the eyes view different fields or only a small portion of the frontal visual field is common to both eyes and (2) the optic fibers are mostly crossed; the few uncrossed fibers from the temporal aspect of the retina receive photic impulses from the visual fields shared by both eyes.

Mammals with frontally placed eyes share these features: (1) the eyes view a large portion of the visual field in common and the overlapping field is projected through the lens to the lateral parts of the retina and (2) the optic fibers from the temporal parts of the retina are uncrossed while the remainder are crossed.

In summary, the uncrossed optic fibers are the axons of ganglionic retinal cells that receive photic stimuli from the portion of the visual fields viewed by both eyes. The more frontally directed eyes possess a greater common visual field and a greater number of uncrossed fibers. Thus in primates the number of uncrossed fibers in

---

[3] *Loris gracilis* is superseded by the name *Loris tardigradus* by the rule of priority.

the optic chiasma increases with the degree of frontality of the eyes (Walls, 1942; Polyak, 1957).

D. The Superior Colliculus (Fig. 11)

In the lowest vertebrates the optic lobes are an important center for conscious recognition of visual stimuli and for linking motor activities with visual stimulation. In primates an equivalent functional center is found in the occipital cortex. The superior colliculus which is the homologue of the optic lobe in more evolved animals, is regarded as a reflex center for certain eye (Crosby and Henderson, 1948) and head and neck movements. In the sequence of evolution culminating in corticalization, fewer fibers reach this structure and the superior colliculi become minimal in primates.

E. The Lateral Geniculate Body (Fig. 12)

Phylogenetically the lateral geniculate body (Fig. 12) consists of two parts, an old *pars ventralis* and a relatively newer *pars dorsalis* or lateral geniculate body proper. In infraprimates the *pars ventralis* is the larger of the two nuclei, and fibers from the optic tract can be traced to it in their passage to the superior colliculus. Its homologue, the pregeniculate nucleus of the primates, receives finely myelinated fibers directly from the optic tract and the lateral geniculate body. These fibers originate chiefly from the foveal region of the retina (Polyak, 1957). Fine fibers from the pregeniculate body pass to the central gray substance of the superior colliculus and are believed to function in pupillary reflex (Polyak, 1957).

The lateral geniculate body, nucleus of termination of most of the optic tract fibers in primates, is the most elaborate of the subcortical visual centers as attested by its size and complexity of organization. However, within this order the anatomical organization of the lateral geniculate body ranges from a relatively simple structure in the tree shrew, *Tupaia*, to an elaborate one in man (Fig. 12).

Ontogenetically the lateral geniculate body is derived from the thalamus (Clark, 1932b; Gilbert, 1935; Cooper, 1945). Its spatial relationship with the thalamus varies in different species. It lies lateral to the thalamus in insectivores (Chacko, 1955), dorsal and lateral in *Tupaia minor* (Clark, 1929), ventral and lateral in tarsier, and shows varying degrees of lateral and ventral displacement in the lemuroids. In the higher primates, man for example, the lateral geniculate body shifts ventrally and also rotates approximately 90°; thus the fibers from the upper retinal quadrants terminate medially in the lateral geniculate body and those from the lower retinal quadrants terminate laterally. In the lower mammals the projections of upper retinal quadrants are found in the lower part of the geniculate body and those from the lower retinal quadrants lie in the upper part of the geniculate body.

The segregation of neurons of the lateral geniculate body into layers or laminae is characteristic. In primates the basic plan of stratification is that of two magnocellular layers and a variable number of parvo-

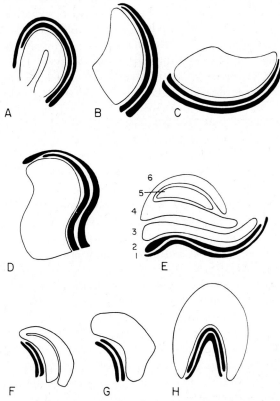

FIG. 12. Representative lateral geniculate body in primates. (After Chacko, 1955.)

A	Tarsius	D	Lemur
B	Microcebus	E	Man
C	Perodictus	F,G,H	Monkey

The inversion pattern (A,B,C) marked by the convex curvature of the two magnocellular layers (solid black) of the lateral geniculate body. The eversion (F,G,H) pattern is marked by the concave curvature of the two magnocellular layers. D and E show an intermediate pattern, with the layers being chiefly everted. The clear areas represent the parvocellular layers. The laminae are diagrammed in E. The laminae of lateral geniculate body of man (E) are numbered by the conventional method. Upper surfaces of figures are dorsal.

cellular layers to a maximum of 6 (Fig. 12E). Typically a total of 6 laminae numbered from ventral to dorsal is present in higher primates, except the gibbon which has 4. The magnocellular layers are always peripheral or ventral. However, greater variation appears among the lower primates. The Philippine tree shrew presents a rather simple lateral geniculate body consisting of two ventral magnocellular layers and a single parvocellular one (Chacko, 1955). The lemuroids, *Loris gracilis, Microcebus murinus, Lemur fulvus,* and *Perodicticus potto* have a 6-layered lateral geniculate body, but it is unlike that of higher primates in that the fibers of the ipsilateral retina terminate in layers, 2, 3, and 4 and those of the contralateral retina in layers 1, 5, and 6. The usual condition in higher primates is that uncrossed fibers terminate in layers 2, 3, and 5, crossed in layers 1, 4, and 6 (Fig. 12). In *Tarsius spectrum* Chacko (1954c) described 3 layers in the geniculate body. The peripheral large cells are organized into two layers that surround the parvocellular mass. Correlated to the predominantly small retinal neurons of this species are the small cells of the lateral geniculate body that are comparatively minute relative to those of other forms. In New World monkeys the two peripheral cell layers are well defined, while the parvocellular masses show variable differentiation. In the central vision segment of the lateral geniculate bodies, the parvocellular areas consist of 6 laminae in *Cebus fatuellus* and *Ateles geoffroyi,* 4 laminae in *Nyctipithecus*[4] and *Hapale brasiliensis,* and only 2 layers in *Saimiri sciurea* (Chacko, 1954b).

Another expression of the evolution of the primate lateral geniculate body is the density of the cells in this structure. The density is greatest in lemurs, less in monkeys, and least in man where the concentration of cells is greater in the crossed layers than in the uncrossed. A reduced density in the higher forms is related to profuse branching of cell processes indicative of greater neural activity and interaction.

The shape and folding of the lateral geniculate bodies are influenced by the increase in number of small neurons particularly in the central portions of the geniculate body that represent the central area of the retina. The increased density of small neurons in the lateral geniculate is correlated with the total increase in the neurons of the central area of the retina. The neurons of the peripheral retinal areas project to more than one-half of the total volume of the lateral geniculate body in man and chimpanzee and to less than one-half the total volume in capuchin, macaque, and spider monkeys. This suggests that peripheral vision may be relatively more significant in apes and man than in monkeys.

---

[4] *Nyctipithecus* is an outmoded form for *Aotes.*

The increased number of cells in the laminae of the lateral geniculate body is accommodated by the buckling or arching of the laminae that results in two fundamental arrangements of the layers. The primitive pattern called inversion by Clark (1932b) is marked by a convexity of the ventral laminae consisting of large cells in contrast to eversion patterns characterized by an infolding or concave arrangement of the ventral magnocellular laminae (Fig. 12). Inversion patterns are found in the Philippine tree shrew (Clark, 1932b) and *Tarsius spectrum* (Chacko, 1954c); an inversion pattern typical of man but not of monkeys is found in the lemuroids, *Loris gracilis, Microcebus murinus, Perodicticus potto,* and *Lemur fulvus.* Strongly everted laminae have been described from the New World monkeys, *Cebus fatuellus, Ateles geoffroyi, Saimiri sciurea, Nyctipithecus,* and *Hapale brasiliensis* (Chacko, 1954b). The major part of the nucleus in man conforms to the eversion pattern except for the lateral portion that is best described as showing a minor inversion (Chacko, 1948). In human development an early inversion pattern is followed by the eversion pattern (Moskowitz and Noback, 1962).

F. THE OPTIC RADIATIONS

The optic radiations are fibers that originate in the nerve cells of the lateral geniculate body and project to the visual cortex of the occipital lobes of the same side. Their appearance parallels the corticalization of the visual system. Optic radiations are found only in mammals although lateral geniculate bodies have been reported for all classes of vertebrates (Elliot Smith, 1928). Retinal representation, unlike that in the optic tract, is maintained within the optic radiations and visual cortex, the precision of which is indicated by localized degeneration following specific lesions (Clark, 1942; Polyak, 1957). The central area fibers are represented in the intermediate bundle of the visual radiations, the peripheral fibers of the upper retinal quadrant in the dorsal bundles, and the lower retinal quadrant in the ventral bundles. These terminate in the striate area of the occipital pole, the upper lip, and lower lip of the calcarine fissure respectively (Fig. 8).

G. THE STRIATE AREA (Fig. 10)

The cerebral cortex has an arrangement of cells giving a laminated appearance in cross-section, and according to Brodmann's scheme 6 distinct layers are recognized. In the visual cortex the internal layer or layer IV is especially well developed and characteristic in this region. The plexus of nerve fibers in this layer forms a white band readily seen in fresh tissue that is known as the stria of Gennari. The striate area is the cortical center of vision and strictly limited to the occipital cortex in which the optic radiations terminate.

The boundaries of the striate area vary among different species of primates. In the tree shrew the striate area is difficult to identify (Polyak, 1957), however, it has been described as lying in the posterior extremity of the occipital lobe on both lateral and medial surfaces (Clark, 1931). In the tarsier, as compared with other primates, the striate area occupies relatively the largest area. It is calculated to consist of about one-third of the entire cerebral cortex, extending from midway between front and occipital poles posteriorly to the occipital pole. The mouse lemur, *Microcebus murinus*, possesses a larger striate area than the tree shrew, *Tupaia minor*. The visual cortex of the lemur (Fig. 8) partially lines part of the calcarine fissure that phylogenetically first appears in the tree shrews. In the Old World monkeys most of the occipital lobe is covered by the striate cortex, while in the New World monkeys and anthropoid apes (Fig. 8) the exposed portion of the striate cortex of the posterolateral surface is reduced in comparison; much of it being concealed in the calcarine fissure. In man the area is confined chiefly to the medial surface of the hemisphere in the region of the calcarine fissure (Fig. 8). Thus, in summary, the striate area of lower primates is distributed over the lateral surface of the occipital lobe, in more primitive primates almost all of the cortex of the occipital operculum is the striate area. In man it is confined to the medial surface of the occipital lobe along the calcarine fissure. The apparent reduction of the striate area in the higher forms is related to the corticalization of the extrastriate areas with the shift of emphasis from perception to visual association areas of the parietotemporo-occipital region. The posterior displacement of the visual area is related to the inrolling of the occipital cortex in phylogeny and results in the formation of the lateral or posterior sulcus of the hominid or hominoid brain (Polyak, 1957). The degree of fusion of the lateral and medial calcarine fissures is variable in the human brain.

The localization of corresponding areas of the retina in the striate cortex is as precise as that in the lateral geniculate body but is more extensive in area. In man the macula is represented in the posterior part of the striate area; the extra-macular portions are more anterior to the calcarine fissure (Spalding, 1952; Crosby, 1960). In the monkey the foveal area of the retina lies on the lateral face of the occipital lobe close to the simian sulcus and the extra-areal cortex is represented on the medial surface in the anterior part of the calcarine fissure (Polyak, 1957).

The visual cortex is thick where the fovea are represented and thin where monocular vision is projected. In reflection of these general changes in thickness between the representation of central and peripheral vision, major histological changes are recognized by an increase of cell elements and the division of the strata into sublayers. The ratio of the thickness of the central cortex to that of the peripheral sector is relatively constant among the primates, ranging from 1.25 to 1.51. The thickest central cortex among the forms examined by Solnitsky and Harman (1946) is found in man, the thinnest in *Lemur mongoz;* the thickest peripheral sector occurs in man and the thinnest in *L. mongoz* and *Galago demidovii.* From their study, Solnitsky and Harman (1946) indicate that the peripheral sectors of the visual area show greater differentiation than the central sector in nocturnal forms, that the complexity of the central sector is greatest in the diurnal forms, and that the distinction between the two sectors is least in crepuscular primates.

Among primates the greatest expression of differentiation of the lamina is found in layer IV, particularly layer IVb. In *Perodicticus potto* there is little differentiation of the cell layers in any of the visual cortex. Layer IV of the peripheral sector of *Galago demidovii* shows somewhat more intrinsic complexity than the central sector. A similar condition is said to be found in *Microcebus murinus* (Clark, 1931).

Layer IV is unique in the crepuscular lemur, *L. mongoz* in that layer IVb of the central sector is twice the thickness of the peripheral region. Distinction between peripheral and central sectors is not usually a feature of the visual cortex of crepuscular forms. In the Old World monkeys *Macaca mulatta,* and *Cercopithecus aethiops sabaea* and in the New World monkeys, *Cebus fatuellus, Ateles ater,* and *Cercocebus torquatus,* layer IVb of the central sector is further divided into five sublayers that are most distinct in *C. torquatus.* Elaboration of IVb in the above forms is greater in the central than the peripheral sectors.

The striate area of *Pan satyrus* is marked by an increase in the number and diversity of cells composing the cortex. The central sector of the visual cortex of man is the most complicated of the primates. This conclusion is based on the shapes and sizes of the cells and number of distinct subdivisions of the laminae.

Functionally layer IVb is concerned with the reception of impulses from homonymous retinal fields, and that IIIb represents the layer of fusion of these impulses. Layer IVa is regarded as a locus of passage; the origin of intrastriate fibers and cortical projection systems is located here (Solnitsky and Harman, 1946).

H. THE CORTICAL VISUAL PATHWAYS

The cortical visual pathways are little understood, but the often cited work of von Bonin *et al.* (1942) indicates some of the cortical relationships in monkeys and chimpanzee, and presumably can be extended to other species of primates. With the application of strychnine to the cortex, electrical impulses can be detected. Recordings of such impulses indicate that there are intrastriate connections in area 17, interconnections between area 17 and parastriate area 18, intrastriate connections in area 18 and interconnections of area 18 with areas 17 and 19. No propagation of impulses was recorded from area 19. These findings are a physiological indication of the association fibers that may exist in the striate, parastriate, and peristriate areas.

On the basis of clinical and experimental data, functionally the striate area may be regarded as showing some degree of encephalization. The destruction of area 17 in man leads to complete blindness (Marquis, 1934; Ruch and Fulton, 1960). The ablation of the same area in the monkey results in visual losses related to cone-vision involving the ability to distinguish different intensities of light, colors, and patterns. However the function of rod-vision, discrimination between light and dark, is unimpaired.

Preoccipital ablation involving parastriate and peristriate cortical areas but not the striate area, does not affect the ability of monkeys to distinguish brightness, color, or pattern, or recognize objects (Chow and Hutt, 1953). On these data is based the conclusion that the visual association areas do not prossess a unique integrating function. It is emphasized, however, that the performance of an animal after ablation of a cortical area is not a measure of the activity of the part removed, but of the remaining parts (Chow and Hutt, 1953).

The significance of the structural and functional changes, those of the forelimbs and eyes in primate evolution and in man particularly, are aptly expressed by Henry J. Watt (1925).

"Of the conditions that enrich the sensory basis of the human mind and so provide the greater wealth of material by which it attains levels beyond those of the animal mind, probably the most important are the functions of the fovea, of accommodation and of static stereoscopy and the development of a delicate skin and prehensile hands. All these make in some way for a differentiation that is the first form of abstraction. The fovea refines and distinguishes positions and forms, while accommodation sharpens the object of attention and dissipates the rest; stereoscopy adds a new character to a group of forms that may persist for indefinite periods of observations; delicate skin gives greater sensitivity to variations of pressure, and the prehensile hand implies a very great refinement in the positions and forms in the derived articular sense. In the hand this becomes a fine mobile tridimensional sense that, like the stereoscopic eye, thus almost can go round and through things, isolating them from their surroundings. At the same time the articular sense is the conscious correlate of action and of the individual's share in his experience. It represents the self at its lowliest stage perhaps; and as we have seen it makes possible the integrations of percept and probably of concept that are the beginnings of intellect—so private and inward a power that it has often been held to come towards sense from another region altogether."

REFERENCES

BAILEY, P., VON BONIN, G., AND McCULLOCH, W. S. (1950). "The Isocortex of the Chimpanzee." Urbana, Illinois, Univ. of Illinois Press.

BENJAMIN, R., AND WELKER, W. (1957). Some receiving areas of cerebral cortex of squirrel monkey (*Saimiri sciureus*). *J. Neurophysiol.* **20**, 286-299.

BRINDLEY, G. S. (1960). "Physiology of the Retina and the Visual Pathway." London, Edward Arnold.

BRUESCH, S. R., AND AREY, L. B. (1942). The number of myelinated and unmyelinated fibers in the optic nerve of vertebrates. *J. Comp. Neurol.* **77**, 631-665.

CHACKO, L. W. (1948). Laminar pattern of the lateral geniculate body in primates. *J. Neurol., Neurosurg. Psychiat.* **11**, 211-224.

CHACKO, L. W. (1953). The volume ratio of the central vision segment to the peripheral vision segment in the lateral geniculate body in higher primates. *J. Anat. Soc. India* **2**, 21-24.

CHACKO, L. W. (1954a). A comparative study of the distribution of the fiber size in the optic nerve of mammals. *J. Anat. Soc. India* **3**, 11-23.

CHACKO, L. W. (1954b). The lateral geniculate body in the New World Monkeys. *J. Anat. Soc. India* **3**, 62-74.

CHACKO, L. W. (1954c). The lateral geniculate body of *Tarsius spectrum*. *J. Anat. Soc. India* **3**, 75-77.

CHACKO, L. W. (1955). The lateral geniculate body in gibbon (*Hylobates hoolock*). *J. Anat. Soc. India* **4**, 69-81.

CHOW, K. L., AND HUTT, P. J. (1953). The "Association Cortex" of *Macaca mulatta*. A review of recent contributions to its anatomy and functions. *Brain* **76**, 625-677.

CLARK, W. E. LeGROS (1929). The thalamus of *Tupaia minor*. *J. Anat.* **63**, 117-206.

CLARK, W. E. LeGROS (1931). The brain of *Microcebus*. *Proc. Zool. Soc. London* **1**, 463-486.

CLARK, W. E. LeGROS (1932a). The structure and connections of the thalamus. *Brain* **55**, 406-470.

CLARK, W. E. LeGROS (1932b). A morphological study of the lateral geniculate body. *Brit. J. Ophthalmol.* **16**, 264-284.

CLARK, W. E. LeGROS (1934). "Early Forerunners of Man: A Morphological Study of the Evolutionary Origin of the Primates." London, Ballière.

CLARK, W. E. LeGROS (1942). The visual centres of the brain and their connexions. *Physiol. Revs.* **22**, 205-232.

CLARK, W. E. LeGROS (1943). The anatomy of cortical vision. *Trans. Ophthalmol. Soc. United Kingdom* **62**, 229-245.

CLARK, W. E. LeGROS (1945). Deforming patterns in the cerebral cortex. *In* "Essays on Growth and Form" (W. E. LeGros Clark and P. B. Medawar, eds.) London and New York, Oxford Univ. Press (Clarendon).

CLARK, W. E. LeGROS (1960). "The Antecedents of Man." Chicago, Quadrangle Books.

COGHILL, G. E. (1929). "Anatomy and the Problem of Behavior." London and New York, Cambridge Univ. Press.

CONEL, J. L. (1959). "The Postnatal Development of the Human Cerebral Cortex. The Cortex of the Twenty-four Month Infant." Cambridge, Massachusetts, Harvard Univ. Press.

CONNOLLY, C. J. (1950). "External Morphology of the Primate Brain." Springfield, Illinois, Charles C Thomas.

COOPER, E. R. A. (1945). The development of the human lateral geniculate body. *Brain* **68**, 222-239.

COUNT, E. W. (1947). Brain and body weight in man: Their antecedents in growth and evolution. *Ann. N.Y. Acad. Sci.* **46**, 993-1122.

CRESCITELLI, F. (1958). The natural history of visual pigments. *Ann. N.Y. Acad. Sci.* **74**, 230-255.

CROSBY, E. C. (1956). The role of the midbrain as a part of the discharge paths from higher centers. *In* "Progress in Neurobiology" (J. Ariens Kappen, ed.), pp. 217-231. Amsterdam, Elsevier.

CROSBY, E. C. (1960). Anatomie du lobe occipital et anatomie comparé des voies visuelles. *In* "Les grandes activités du lobe occipital" (P. Alajouanine, ed.), pp. 1-32. Paris, Masson.

CROSBY, E. C., AND HENDERSON, J. W. (1948). The mammalian midbrain: isthmus regions. II. Fiber connection of superior colliculus. B. Pathways concerned with autonomic eye movement. *J. Comp. Neurol.* **38**, 53-92.

DART, R. (1956). The relationships of brain size and brain pattern to human status. *S. African J. Med. Sci.* **21**, 23-45.

DOW, R. S. (1942). The evolution and anatomy of the cerebellum. *Biol. Revs. Biol. Proc. Cambridge Phil. Soc.* **17**, 179-220.

DUNN, H. L. (1921). The growth of the central nervous system in the human fetus as expressed by graphic analysis and empirical formulae. *J. Comp. Neurol.* **33**, 405-491.

EDINGER, T. (1948). Evolution of the horse brain. *Mem. Geol. Soc. America* **25**, 1-777.

ELLIOT SMITH, G. (1928). The Bowman Lecture, 1928. The new vision. *Trans. Ophthalmol. Soc. United Kingdom* **48**, 64-85.

GILBERT, M. S. (1935). The early development of the human diencephalon. *J. Comp. Neurol.* **62**, 81-115.

GRENELL, R., AND SCAMMON, R. (1943). An iconometrographic representation of the growth of the central nervous system in man. *J. Comp. Neurol.* **79**, 329-354.

HARMAN, P. J. (1947). On the significance of fissuration of the isocortex. *J. Comp. Neurol.* **87**, 161-168.

HARMAN, P. J. (1957). Paleoneurologic, neoneurologic and ontogenetic aspects of brain phylogeny. James Arthur lecture on the evolution of the human brain. New York, American Museum of Natural History.

HARMAN, P. J., AND CARPENTER, M. B. (1950). Volumetric comparisons of the basal ganglia of various primates including man. *J. Comp. Neurol.* **93**, 125-138.

HEINER, J. R. (1960). A reconstruction of the diencephalic nuclei of the chimpanzee. *J. Comp. Neurol.* **114**, 217-238.

HERRICK, C. J. (1931). "An Introduction to Neurology." Philadelphia, Pennsylvania, Saunders.

HERRICK, C. J. (1948). "The Brain of the Tiger Salamander." Chicago, Univ. of Chicago Press.

HERRICK, C. J. (1956). "The Evolution of Human Nature." Austin, Texas, Univ. of Texas Press.

HERRICK, C. J., AND BISHOP, G. (1958). A comparative survey of the spinal lemniscus system. In "Reticular Formation of the Brain" (H. Jasper, L. Proctor, R. Knighton, W. Noshay, and R. Costello, eds.), pp. 353-360. Boston, Little, Brown.

HOOKER, D. (1952). "The Prenatal Origin of Behavior." Lawrence, Kansas, Univ. of Kansas Press.

JANSEN, J. (1954). On the morphogenesis and morphology of the mammalian cerebellum. In "Aspects of Cerebellar Anatomy" (J. Jansen and A. Brodal, eds.), pp. 13-81. Oslo, Johan Grundt Tanum Forlag.

JASPER, H. (1958). Reticulo-cortical systems and theories of the integrative actions of the brain. In "Biological and Biochemical Bases of Behavior (H. Harlow and C. Woolsey, eds.) Madison, Wisconsin, Univ. of Wisconsin Press.

KAPPERS, A., HUBER, C., AND CROSBY, E. (1936). "Comparative Anatomy of the Nervous System of Vertebrates." New York, Macmillan.

KLÜVER, H. (1941). Visual functions after removal of the occipital lobes. J. Psychol. u. Neurol. 11, 23-45.

KRIEG, W. (1948). A reconstruction of the diencephalic nuclei of Macacus rhesus. J. Comp. Neurol. 88, 1-51.

KUYPERS, H. G. (1958). Some projections from the peri-central cortex to the pons and lower brain stem in monkey and chimpanzee. J. Comp. Neurol. 110, 221-256.

KUYPERS, H. G. (1960). Central cortical projections to motor, somatosensory and reticular cell groups. In "Structure and Function of the Cerebral Cortex" (D. E. Tower and J. P. Shadé, eds.), pp. 138-143. Amsterdam, Elsevier.

LASSEK, A. M. (1954). "The Pyramidal Tract." Springfield, Illinois, Charles C Thomas.

LORENTE DE NÓ, R. (1949). Cerebral cortex: architecture, intracortical connections, motor projections. In "Physiology of the Nervous System" (J. F. Fulton, ed.) London and New York, Oxford Univ. Press.

MAGOUN, H. W. (1958). "The Waking Brain." Springfield, Illinois, Charles C Thomas.

MARQUIS, D. G. (1934). Effects of removal of visual cortex in mammals, with observation on the retention of light discrimination in dogs. Research Publ. Assoc. Research Nervous Mental Disease 13, 558-592.

MARQUIS, D. G. (1935). Phylogenetic interpretation of the functions of the visual cortex. A.M.A. Arch. Neurol. Psychiat. 33, 807-815.

MEHLER, W. (1957). The mammalian pain tract in phylogeny. Anat. Record 127, 332.

MEHLER, W., FEFERMAN, M., AND NAUTA, W. (1960). Ascending axonal degeneration following anterolateral cordotomy. Brain 83, 718-750.

METTLER, F. L. (1957). Anatomy and physiology of the extrapyramidal motor passage. Premier congr. intern. sci. neurol., Première journée commune Vol. 1, pp. 11-37.

MOSKOWITZ, N., AND NOBACK, C. R. (1962). The human lateral geniculate body in normal development and congenital unilateral amophthalmia. J. Neuropathol. Exptl. Neurol. 21, 377-382.

NAUTA, W. J., AND KUYPERS, H. G. (1958). Some ascending pathways in the brain stem reticular formation. In "Reticular Formation of the Brain" (H. Jasper, L. Proctor, R. Knighton, W. Noshay, and R. Costello, eds.), pp. 3-30. Boston, Little, Brown.

NOBACK, C. (1959a). Brain of a gorilla. II. Brain stem nuclei. J. Comp. Neurol. 111, 345-386.

NOBACK, C. (1959b). The heritage of the human brain. James Arthur lecture on the evolution of the human brain. New York, American Museum of Natural History.

NOBACK, C., AND MOSS, M. (1956). Differential growth of the human brain. J. Comp. Neurol. 105, 539-551.

NOBACK, C., AND MOSKOWITZ, N. (1962). Structural and functional correlates of "encephalization" in the primate brain. In "The Relatives of Man" (J. Buettner-Janusch, ed.), Ann. N.Y. Acad. Sci. 102, 210-218.

PEDEN, J. K., AND VON BONIN, G. (1947). The neocortex of Hapale. J. Comp. Neurol. 86, 57-64.

PENFIELD, W., AND JASPER, H. (1954). "Epilepsy and the Functional Anatomy of the Brain." Boston, Little, Brown.

PENFIELD, W., AND RASMUSSEN, T. (1950). "The Cerebral Cortex of Man." New York, Macmillan.

POLYAK, S. (1941). "The Retina." Chicago, Univ. of Chicago Press.

POLYAK, S. (1957). "The Vertebrate Visual System." Chicago, Univ. of Chicago Press.

PRIBRAM, K., KRUGER, L., ROBINSON, F., AND BERMAN, A. (1955). The effects of precentral lesions in the behavior of monkeys. Yale J. Biol. and Med. 28, 428-443.

PUTNAM, I. K. (1928). The proportion of cerebellar to total brain weight in mammals. Proc. Roy. Netherlands Acad. Sci., Amsterdam 31, 155-168. Cited by Torgersen (1954).

RAMÓN Y CAJAL, S. (1911). "Histologie du système nerveus de l'homme et des vertebrés," Vol. 2. Paris, Maloine.

RILEY, H. A. (1928). The reconstruction of the gray matter in the primate brain stem. In "The Brain from Ape to Man" (F. Tilney, ed.) New York, Hoeber (Harper).

RUCH, T., AND FULTON, J. (1960). "Medical Physiology and Biophysics." Philadelphia, Pennsylvania, Saunders.

RUCH, T., FULTON, J., AND GERMAN, W. (1938). Sensory discrimination in monkey, chimpanzee and man after lesions of the parietal lobe. A.M.A. Arch. Neurol. Psychiat. 39, 919-937.

RUSHTON, W. A. H. (1958). Kinetics of cone pigments measured objectively on the living human fovea. Ann. N.Y. Acad. Sci. 74, 291-304.

SCHEIBEL, M., AND SCHEIBEL, A. (1958). Structural substrates for integrative patterns in the brain stem reticular core. In "Reticular Formation of the Brain" (H. Jasper, L. Proctor, R. Knighton, W. Noshay, and R. Costello, eds.), pp. 31-55. Boston, Little, Brown.

SHEPS, J. (1945). The nuclear configuration and cortical connections of the human thalamus. J. Comp. Neurol. 83, 1-56.

SOLNITSKY, O., AND HARMAN, P. J. (1946). A comparative study of the central and peripheral centers of the visual cortex in primates, with observations on the lateral geniculate body. J. Comp. Neurol. 85, 313-391.

SPALDING, J. M. K. (1952). Wounds of the visual pathway. Part II. The striate cortex. *J. Neurol. Neurosurg. Psychiat.* **15**, 169-183.

SPERRY, R. W. (1961). Cerebral organization and behavior. *Science* **133**, 1749-1757.

TERZUOLO, C. A., AND ADEY, A. (1960). Sensorimotor cortical activities. In "Handbook of Physiology," Section 1: "Neurophysiology" (J. Field, H. W. Magoun, and V. E. Hall, eds.), Vol. 2, pp. 797-835. Washington, D.C., American Physiological Society.

TILNEY, F. (1928). "The Brain from Ape to Man." New York, Hoeber (Harper).

TONCRAY, J., AND KRIEG, W. (1946). The nuclei of the human thalamus: a comparative approach. *J. Comp. Neurol.* **85**, 421-459.

TORGERSEN, J. (1954). The occiput, the posterior cranial fossa and the cerebellum. In "Aspects of Cerebellar Anatomy" (J. Jansen and A. Brodal, eds.), pp. 396-416. Oslo, Norway, Johan Grundt Tanum Forlag.

TOWER, S. S. (1944). The pyramidal tract. In "The Precentral Motor Cortex" (P. Bucy, ed.), pp. 149-172. Urbana, Illinois, Univ. of Illinois Press.

VERHAART, W. J. (1962). The pyramidal tract. *World Neurol.* **3**, 43-53.

von BONIN, G. (1945). "The Cortex of *Galago*." Urbana, Illinois, Univ. of Illinois Press.

von BONIN, G. (1947). The neocortex of *Hapale*. *J. Comp. Neurol.* **86**, 57-64.

von BONIN, G. (1950). "Essay on the Cerebral Cortex." Springfield, Illinois, Charles C Thomas.

von BONIN, G. (1951). The isocortex of *Tarsius*. *J. Comp. Neurol.* **95**, 387-428.

von BONIN, G. (1955). Toward an anthropology of the brain. *Ann. N.Y. Acad. Sci.* **63**, 505-509.

von BONIN, G., GAROL, H. W., AND McCULLOCH, W. S. (1942). The functional organization of the occipital lobes. In "Visual Mechanisms" (H. Klüver, ed.) *Biol. Symposia* **7**, 165-192.

WALKER, A. E. (1938). "The Primate Thalamus." Chicago, Univ. of Chicago Press.

WALKER, E., AND FULTON, J. (1938). Hemidecortication in chimpanzee, baboon, potto, cat and coati: a study in encephalization. *J. Nervous Mental Disease* **87**, 677-700.

WALLS, G. L. (1942). The vertebrate eye and its adaptive radiation. *Cranbrook Inst. Sci. Bull.* No. 19. (Bloomfield Hills, Michigan, Cranbrook Press.)

WATT, H. J. (1925). "The Sensory Basis and Structure of Knowledge." London, Methuen.

WELKER, W., BENJAMIN, R., MILES, R., AND WOOLSEY, C. (1957). Motor effects of stimulation of cerebral cortex of squirrel monkey (*Saimiri sciureus*). *J. Neurophysiol.* **20**, 347-364.

WOOD-JONES, F. (1929). "Man's Place Among the Mammals." London, Arnold.

WOOLSEY, C. N. (1954). Localization patterns in a lissencephalic primate (*Hapale jacchus*). *Am. J. Physiol.* **179**, 686.

WOOLSEY, C. N. (1958). Organization of somatic sensory and motor areas of the cerebral cortex. In "Biological and Biochemical Basis of Behavior" (H. Harbow and C. Woolsey, eds.), pp. 63-81. Madison, Wisconsin, Univ. of Wisconsin Press.

Chapter 4

New Approaches to the Study of the Skin of Primates[1]

WILLIAM MONTAGNA AND RICHARD A. ELLIS

Arnold Biological Laboratory,
Brown University, Providence, Rhode Island

I. INTRODUCTION

It is embarrassingly premature for us to write a general article about the skin of primates. Our own studies have just progressed beyond the initial stages, our knowledge is sketchy, and our opinions change daily. Five years ago, we began these studies in a burst of sophomoric enthusiasm, hoping to have it complete in a brief time. As our own methods have become more refined, our acuity sharpened, and our understanding broader, the task has become progressively difficult. At the beginning we had hoped to unravel at least some of the trends in the evolution of the skin of primates. We have now become so cautious that we can make no predictions beyond that of finding interesting results which may eventually have a bearing on the evolution of the skin of man.

The Europeans and the Japanese have made a surprisingly large number of studies on the skin of primates. They have investigated with

[1] This work was supported by grants from the United States Public Health Service, RG-2125(C11) and RG-8380(CB1).

some thoroughness the distribution of hair, sweat glands, and pigment, the details of the palmar and plantar ridges, the anatomy and distribution of sinus hair follicles, and the axillary organ. The modern student of the skin cannot overlook this literature, much of which, unfortunately, is published in journals which are difficult to obtain. As we become again aware of the skin of primates, there is a real need for a review of this literature. This article largely ignores this older literature, by design, lest it become a book in its own right. It is our purpose here to present a brief account of the work that is in progress in our laboratory and to point to the problems which are ahead of us; this is not a review of our knowledge of the skin of primates.

Avidly studied by the Germans, the comparative anatomy of the skin of primates has been mostly neglected during the last 50 years. Understandably, the earlier histological accounts leave much to be desired. Let us remember, for example, that the sweat glands, although recognized as belonging to two types more than 100 years ago, were not defined as eccrine and apocrine by Schiefferdecker until 1917. Actually, it was not until recently, when histochemical methods began to be used, that the specific attributes of the two types of sweat glands began to be understood. Even now, however, histological criteria alone are not sufficient to help separate unerringly the two types of glands.

We believe that skin, a difficult organ to understand well, should be studied by those who have made it their specialty. Those who are not thoroughly familiar with the kaleidoscopic nature of the structure and function of the skin can often overlook unsubtle and even spectacular differences that may exist between the skins of different animals. Even in the same animal great differences exist from one region of the body to another.

It is usual to assume that a study of the anatomy, physiology, and biochemistry of any organ system, regardless of species differences, should bear results which are basically similar. Thus, information obtained from the skin of the mouse, the rat, the dog, for example, has been interpreted in general terms and considered to be directly applicable to the skin of most other mammals. Yet, even excluding such aberrant forms as the aquatic ones, the skin of which has become modified along very different lines, the biologist who fails to recognize the particular differences which occur in the skin of closely related genera will never come to a full understanding of this organ. There are many and varied examples of such differences, and the three that follow are only a random sampling: (a) The sebaceous glands of the Anubis baboon (*Papio doguera*) contain great quantities of nonspecific alkaline phosphatase (Montagna and Yun, 1962b), whereas those of the genus *Cerco-*

pithecus contain none. (b) The quiescent hair follicles of all primates contain glycogen in the cells of the epithelial sac around the club hair, but those of most nonprimate mammals do not (Montagna and Ellis, 1959). (c) Cortisone, which inhibits spontaneous growth of hair in the mouse and the rat (Mohn, 1958), induces regrowth in the follicles in lesions of *alopecia areata* in the scalp of man (Rothman, 1954). To understand the significance of these and many other disparities, we must understand the various properties of the skin of the individual animals. From such studies may emerge the keys which could unveil the basic biological principles that guide the proper functioning of all skin. Thus, a knowledge of the dissimilarities will elucidate the similarities that must be present.

The biologist has rarely appreciated the inhomogeneity of skin, although the physician often has. Those who are familiar only with textbook accounts of the anatomy, physiology, and chemical composition of the skin are seldom concerned with the fact that the skin of the scalp, the face, the axilla, the abdomen, the palm, etc., of man are so different from each other that each could belong to a different animal. Even the physiological responses of the "different" skin over the body are different. Androgenic hormones, for example, which in genetically predisposed men cause baldness, at the same time enhance the growth of hair on their chest and on other body areas that express secondary sex characteristics. This indicates that the topographic idiosyncrasies of the skin in a single individual are not merely superficial and "anatomical." Another vexing fact is that in the same individual a hair follicle in one part of the body may grow uninterruptedly for years, whereas in another part of the body it may have short, intermittent cycles of growth and quiescence. What agent, or agents, control such growth?

We began our systematic comparative studies of the skin of primates in order to come to an understanding of the great differences that exist between the skin of man and that of other mammals. Among the unique particularities of the skin of man, the following are noteworthy: (a) it has a well developed, well vascularized papillary dermis; (b) the underside of its epidermis is sculptured with complex systems of ridges and grooves, which fit into the grooves and over the ridges of the papillary body; (c) it has many eccrine sweat glands over the entire body; (d) in the *cavum axillae* it has large apocrine sweat glands that secrete substances which, when degraded by the bacterial flora on the surface, become fetid. These and other peculiarities make the skin of man stand apart from that of other animals. We have wondered to what extent man shares some of the peculiarities of his skin with those of other primates.

The application of the modern methods in histology and histochemistry to the study of the skin of primates has been very fruitful. Even when we do not know the specific significance of the various histochemical properties of cutaneous structures, these are important components of the signatures of those organs. Winkelmann (1960a), for example, in a systematic study of the histochemical properties of the cutaneous nerves of vertebrates is shedding considerable light on the similarities and dissimilarities of the various sensory end organs in the same animal and in different animals. We are now exploring the physiology of sweating in primates, relating the results with information obtained from histochemistry. The initial results are so promising that this type of investigation will be pursued further. Finally, we are beginning to introduce to the study of the skin of primates a variety of new investigative approaches, including cytophysiology, electron microscopy, and pharmacology.

The skin of primates has undergone evolutionary changes as varied as those which have occurred in the size, shape, color, and behavior of the members of the order. Knowledge of the skin of one form does not allow us to predict what the skin of a closely related form may offer. For example, whereas in the skin of the Lorisidae each hair follicle has a small sebaceous gland opening into its pilary canal, in the skin of the black lemur (*Lemur macaco*) the sebaceous glands are very large, open directly onto the surface of the skin, and the hair follicles are *free* of sebaceous glands. How does one interpret such conditions? Is this a special adaptation of the true lemurs? Does this give us a clue to the evolution of these two major cutaneous appendages? Is this situation similar in all true lemurs? What advantages do these numerous and gigantic sebaceous glands give the true lemurs? What is the special function of these glands and how is their function adapted to the well-being of the lemurs? We cannot answer these and other questions before we know a great deal more about all of the various modifications that have taken place in the skin in all of the major forms of primates.

It is evident that in spite of old and new information, we are in the infancy of these studies. There is an obvious urgency in these, as in all studies of primate biology, because primates, and especially the primitive ones, are declining. In an era when biological research is mainly concerned with the nucleic acid molecule and protein synthesis, it may not be fashionable to do anatomical and descriptive investigations. Yet, without this information we will grope in ignorance, unaware of the numerous and fascinating changes that have taken place in the evolution of skin.

II. THE EPIDERMIS

The outstanding peculiarity of the epidermis of man is a complex and distinctive understructure. In histological preparations the dermoepidermal junction is scalloped by epidermal columns of different sizes, erroneously called *rete pegs* or *epidermal papillae*. These structures are in effect sections through long, branching ridges on the underside of the epidermis, the upper layer of the dermis being molded around them. Horstmann (1957), who has made painstaking studies of the dermoepidermal junction, has shown characteristic regional differences in the sculpture of the underside of the epidermis. The underside of the epidermis is more complex in regions of greater wear and tear, such as the volar surfaces of the pes and manus, the head, the genital areas, and the *rima ani*. It is more complex on the extensor and dorsal areas than on the flexor and ventral ones. On the dermoepidermal surface of the basal cells of the epidermis, cytoplasmic rootlets extend into the surface of the dermis. The ridges and the cytoplasmic extensions ensure intimate contact between the dermis and the avascular epidermis.

The epidermis of other primates shows varying degrees of understructure, but none that we have studied has systems of ridges as extensive as those in the epidermis of man. The epidermis of Lemuridae, other prosimians, and Hapalidae has no understructure of ridges and valleys except on the friction surfaces. In most anthropoid primates, except for the friction surfaces, in the face, lips, and surfaces with a sparse population of hairs, the epidermis has barely detectable ridges. The underside of the epidermis of the chimpanzee and the gorilla has grooves and ridges better developed than those in other primates but not as well formed as in man. There is an inverse relation between hair cover and the complexity of the underside of the epidermis. In man, however, even the scalp, which has the most luxurious hair cover, has an epidermis with a rich undersculpturing. Although the epidermal ridges are better developed in man, the cytoplasmic extensions at the dermoepidermal surface of the basal cells are more conspicuous in other primates. Of these two features, then, man has favored the development of the ridges, whereas the other primates have better differentiated basal cell epidermal rootlets. The presence of closely spaced hair follicles may serve the function of the ridges in anchoring the epidermis and giving it a greater intimacy with the dermis.

The epidermis of man is thicker on the extensor than on the flexor surfaces and is thickest on the friction areas. The epidermis has a continuous stratum granulosum, composed of cells that contain large, easily demonstrable keratohyalin granules, indicative of a vigorous keratinizing process. In other primates, as in man, the epidermis on the extensor and dorsal surfaces is thicker than that on the flexor and ventral regions, and it is thickest on the friction areas. The other primates, however, even the chimpanzee and the gorilla (see Straus, 1950) do not have a well developed, continuous *stratum granulosum* over the general body surface. There is, also, an apparent inverse ratio between the richness of the pelage of the animal and a well developed *stratum granulosum*. This layer is, then, best expressed in the epidermis of man whose hair cover is meager. This suggests that the process of keratinization is more rapid in the epidermis of man; this is probably a device that makes up for the inadequate protection by the scanty pelage.

The catalogue of histochemically demonstrable enzymes in the epidermis of man is comparable to that which we have found in the epidermis of other primates. There is some cytochrome oxidase, and abundant succinic dehydrogenase, monoamine oxidase, and amylophosphorylase. These enzymes are concentrated in basal layers and gradually reach extinction in the upper cells of the malpighian layer. Different esterases are variably localized in the malpighian layer or in the corneal layer. There is some aminopeptidase, particularly in the thicker epidermis, some acid phosphatase, and β-glucuronidase in the cells above those of the *stratum granulosum* (cf. Montagna, 1962). There is no nonspecific alkaline phosphatase, but some appears in sites of injury. Normal epidermis contains no glycogen, but injuries, slight or great, which in some way interfere with keratinization, and/or mitotic activity, always result in the accumulation of some glycogen in the malpighian layer, the amount depending upon the severity of the injury. The epidermis of other primates, including the Lemuridae and the Hapalidae, also contains these enzymes. We wish to call attention particularly to amylophosphorylase. Although present in the epidermis of other mammals, moderate or strong concentrations of it are a characteristic feature of the epidermis of all primates.

We have found an interesting oddity in the skin of the potto (*Perodicticus potto*), and of two bush babies (*Galago senegalensis* and *Galago crassicaudatus*). Scattered through the epidermal cells of these animals is a population of large dendritic cells which are conspicuously reactive for alkaline phosphatase (Montagna and Ellis, 1959; Yasuda *et al.*, 1961; Montagna and Yun, 1962a). We have found no way of showing these cells other than with the method for alkaline phosphatase. The cells are distributed at random everywhere in the malpighian layer and are clustered particularly around the pilary canals. Although they superficially resemble dendritic melanocytes, the cells contain no pigment, and the melanocytes proper are unreactive for alkaline phosphatase.

We know nothing more about these strange cells and their significance must, for the present, remain an enigma.

III. THE DERMIS

We can present only a few facts about the dermis, which, however fragmentary and disconnected, should point out some of the problems that exist.

The dermis in the skin of man is distinctive in having an extensive papillary body, and in being superlatively vascularized. In spite of topographic variations, the papillary body is always thick, easily recognizable, rich in cells and ground substance, and riddled by a complex vascular system that forms a so-called subpapillary plexus and the subepidermal capillary loops. The cutaneous vascular system is developed greatly in excess of the possible metabolic needs of the skin itself and constitutes one of the major mechanisms for thermoregulation and pressure regulation of the body (see Montagna and Ellis, 1961). Another peculiarity of the skin of man is that melanocytes, which are populous in the epidermis and in hair follicles, are scarce or nearly absent from the dermis.

The dermis of the prosimians, in contrast with that of man, has practically no papillary body. Even where the skin is thick, for example, as on the face, the genital region, and the friction areas, the papillary body is poorly developed. In the anthropoid primates the papillary body is thicker and attains its best development in the chimpanzee and in the gorilla, the epidermis of which has a good undersculpturing.

For the study of cutaneous blood vessels, we have used only the histochemical technique for alkaline phosphatase. In the skin of man, this method stains selectively only the endothelium of the terminal arterioles and the capillaries, which are largely distributed in the papillary body and in the areolar tissue around the cutaneous appendages. Whereas all of the primates we have studied have a variably rich vascularity in the skin of the face, the friction surfaces, and the genital areas, most of them have relatively few superficial vessels over the rest of the body surfaces. The apes, but not the gibbon, have a better blood supply to the skin, but even these do not compare with man. These sketchy observations suggest that whereas the major number of the cutaneous blood vessels of man play an important role in thermoregulation and pressure regulation, those in the skin of other primates do not.

Whereas the skin of man derives its color primarily from the epidermal pigmentary system and from the superficial capillary and venous blood, that of many primates is due to the pigmentary systems in both the epidermis and dermis. In the prosimians we have studied, epidermal melanocytes are scarce, and dermal melanocytes are usually present only in the skin of the head and that of the genital areas. The black lemur (*Lemur macaco*) has numerous dermal melanocytes in the perivascular and perineural tissue of the skin of the head, but none is found elsewhere (Montagna *et al.*, 1961). The shaved skin of the Lorisidae and Lemuridae, except for the genital and perianal areas, is relatively pigmentless. In contrast, many of the simian forms have a very dark skin. In some of these, the dermis is so laden with large and small polymorphic melanocytes that it resembles a diffuse melanoma. Yet, in spite of heavy dermal pigmentation, these animals often have a scanty population of epidermal melanocytes. Regardless of the abundance of dermal melanocytes, they are mostly found in the reticular dermis, rarely extending into the papillary body. Different animals have a different distribution of dermal melanocytes, and even in the same animal melanocytes may be abundant in some regions and nearly absent in others. Here, then, is an unexplored source of melanin-producing cells of different sizes and form, the melanogenic activity of which is unknown. Other mammals, such as the seals (Montagna and Harrison, 1957) also have a rich dermal melanocyte system, but this information may have little pertinence to the skin of man, which is our prime concern. Let us hope that melanin will be studied as vigorously in the skin of primates as it has been in the skin of fishes, amphibians, birds, and mice.

The gross organization of the dermis in different primates has received little attention. In the primitive forms, for example, the collagenic layer of the reticular body is composed of thin, horizontal layers, neatly arranged perpendicular to one another. In progressively more advanced forms, this relatively geometric arrangement is apparently lost. But, these details of the dermis need better clarification.

The cutaneous nerves of primates are now being studied mostly by Richard Winkelmann of the Mayo Clinic. Since many cutaneous nerves contain cholinesterases and some also contain nonspecific alkaline phosphatases, histochemical techniques are useful in revealing their structure and distribution. The terminal cutaneous sensory nerves contain specific and/or nonspecific cholinesterases. In nearly all prosimians, and in all of the South American primates we have sampled, these nerves mostly contain nonspecific cholinesterase. In the Old World forms the nerves contain mostly specific cholinesterase, and in man they contain only the specific enzyme. The corpuscles of Meissner and of Vater-Pacini, the mucocutaneous end organs and the hair follicle end organs of most primates contain nonspecific cholinesterases. Few of the many species differences have been closely annotated and catalogued.

The terminal cutaneous nerves and end organs of the gibbon (*Hylobates hoolock*) contain both cholinesterases and alkaline phosphatase, a situation similar to that found in bovine and ovine skin, but *apparently* aberrant in the skin of primates. This, then, is another source of relatively untapped biological material to be investigated.

IV. The Pilosebaceous Complexes

The pilosebaceous system is peculiar to the skin of mammals. The structure and the histochemical attributes of these complexes is basically similar in all mammals, but there are numerous and often striking differences between the various orders and even between families. Thus, a comparative review of the pilosebaceous systems of primates is not possible at this time, mostly because we do not have all the facts. We will point out here, however, a few of the more interesting and suggestive findings.

A. The Hair Follicles

In spite of popular belief that man is a hairless animal, he has a rich population of hairs over the entire body (see Garn, 1951); only the vermilion border of the lips, the friction areas, and a few other surfaces are truly glabrous. The major differences between man and the other primates is in the coarseness, the length, and pigmentation of the hairs, and not necessarily in the over-all number of hair follicles. Another interesting difference between man and the other mammals is that man is the only primate which has no sinus, or tactile hair follicles. In all other primates sinus hair follicles have different distribution and different structure. These are more numerous and more generally distributed in the nocturnal forms than in the diurnal ones. The lemurs have tufts of large tactile hair follicles even on the flexor surface of the forearm, just proximal to the carpus; the lorises have them all over the facial disc, including the eyelids. The structure of the sinus hair follicles is so different in the various forms studied that to begin to understand them, a thorough survey should supplement the older work of Frederic (1905, 1906), de Beaux (1917), and others. It is inaccurate to designate sinus follicles as tactile follicles, since every hair follicle is provided with greater or lesser complicated systems of sensory nerve endings. The nerve endings around ordinary follicles form the hair follicle end organ of Winkelmann (1960b). Like all other sensory end organs, these are rich in cholinesterases and can be demonstrated easily in frozen sections treated for cholinesterases. In the skin of all the primates we have studied, nearly every follicle has a cholinesterase-rich end organ, adhering to the base of its pilary canal, and not below it. Whereas in man these end organs are diffuse, in many other primates they are compact.

The hair follicles of most prosimians differ markedly from those of the simians. The follicles of prosimians are very long and slender when active, resembling those of insectivores and rodents. When quiescent, the follicles retreat up into the dermis and are reduced to less than one-quarter the length of the active phase; this too is like the follicles of insectivores and rodents. In contrast to the follicles of the simian groups, which resemble those of man in being richly vascularized, the follicles of prosimians are poorly vascularized. The active state of simian follicles is not more than twice the length of the quiescent state, a situation similar to that found in the follicles of man. It is a rule that the thinner the follicles are, the more poorly vascularized they are; the coarser follicles in the skin of simians are variably, but well, vascularized.

The follicles in the skin of man grow in groups of three. In the adult this grouping is disrupted and the follicles often seem to grow singly. In the apes and in many of the other simian primates, the grouping is relatively distinct and is generally also limited to three follicles. However, in the prosimians the grouping is indeterminate. The follicles often grow in large islands that may contain in the same animal from four to twenty or more units. The skin between these islands is glabrous. This is an apparently generalized feature of the skin of these animals. A complete phylogenetic account of the grouping of follicles may shed some light upon its significance.

Among the histochemical peculiarities of the follicles of man is the presence of amylophosphorylase and glycogen in both the outer root sheath of active follicles and in the epithelial capsule of quiescent ones. The hair follicles of all the primates we have studied, both New World and Old World forms, share these peculiarities with those of man. Since the other mammals we have investigated have neither glycogen nor amylophosphorylase in quiescent follicles, these must be considered idiosyncracies of the follicles of primates.

The active hair follicles in the skin of man typically contain melanocytes only in the upper part of the bulb; these cells elaborate melanin only during the growing phase and feed it to the differentiating cortical cells that ascend from the matrix (Fitzpatrick *et al.*, 1958). The outer root sheath is singularly free of pigment cells and pigment granules. After injury to the follicle, however, melanocytes are found in the outer root sheath (Montagna and Chase, 1956). This means that melanocytes are probably resident within the outer root sheath, but they are nonfunctional and amelanotic. Surgical dermabrasion, usually performed for cosmetic reasons, usually removes all of the epidermis and the upper part of the follicles; during the healing of the wounds, the new epidermis is regenerated from the outer root sheath of the remaining part of the follicles (Staricco, 1960). In time this epidermis is repopulated with melanocytes which must have come from the outer root sheath. It is significant that in many primates, particularly those with a heavily pigmented skin, the outer root sheath often contains numerous, active dendritic melanocytes, visible in ordinary histological preparations. This suggests that the nonmelanotic property of melanocytes in the outer root sheath in the races of man, even in the very darkly pigmented African Negroes, is a specialized feature of the human race.

One final point to be made here is the possibility of studying the phenomenon of baldness in primates. Those who have an interest in this fascinating event in man searched for years for an appropriate experimental animal. Hamilton (1959), for example, has observed the seasonal shedding of the head feathers in the male wattled starling (*Creatophora carunculata*) and has related this phenomenon with the activity of gonadal androgens. "Balding" in this case is not comparable to that which occurs in man, since the phenomenon is reversible. Pattern baldness in man progresses in a series of irreversible changes which expresses itself in a gradual diminution in the size of hair follicles until they are aborted to vellus types, having no *arrectores pilorum* muscles, and no pigment cells in their bulb. These changes are accompanied by a disproportionate enlargement of the sebaceous glands. There are, in addition to these, dramatic changes in the epidermis of the scalp and in the surrounding dermis (Ellis, 1958; Ellis and Moretti, 1959). Of the other primates which show at least a superficial mimicry of the male pattern baldness that occurs in man, none is more striking than the uakari (*Cacajao rubicundus*), whose scalp, hairy in the young, becomes *apparently* totally epilated in the adult. But, this is all we know. We have made only brief observations of the scalp of the chimpanzee, in which some of the mature males seem to show a development of baldness like that of man. Surely the evolution of these occurrences should be investigated to see whether or not they are similar to those which take place in pattern baldness in man. We have here, then, great possibilities of exploring biological situations, which will undoubtedly be exciting and fruitful, whether or not they are directly pertinent to human male pattern baldness.

This section is intended to draw attention only to some of the general problems to be studied in the hair follicles of primates. It tells nothing of the structure of the hairs, which show many species differences and which are promising objects for study (see Hill *et al.,* 1958-1959).

B. THE SEBACEOUS GLANDS

Only a few interesting oddities will be mentioned about the sebaceous glands. The general structure of the sebaceous glands of man is similar to that of other mammals. The glands are largest and most active on the face and around the genitalia, and with few exceptions, they grow together with hair follicles. This is also applicable to the sebaceous glands in other primates. The marmosets (*Hapale*) and tamarins (*Tamarinus*), however, have huge sebaceous fields in the posterior abdominal skin. The secretion of these and of the apocrine glands, with which they are admixed, gives the fur of the inguinal region of these animals a greasy, matted appearance (Wislocki, 1930). *Lemur catta* has two almond-shaped sebaceous fields, one on each shoulder at the junction of the clavicle with the scapula, which open into a central utricle, the large single orifice of which opens onto the surface of the skin. Most primates, including man, have extensive fields of sebaceous glands in the perianal skin and around the genitalia.

The sebaceous glands of the prosimians are generally very small, except on the face and around the genitalia. The glands over the body of the pottos, galagos, and lorises are small and resemble those of laboratory rodents. The glands of the head and around the genitalia of these animals, however, are large.

The sebaceous glands of the lemurs are strikingly peculiar. There are three types of them; those over the general body surface are unilobular, globose structures in some forms, deep in the dermis, with a long narrow duct that opens independently onto the surface of the skin, the hair follicles being free of glands. Numerous dendritic melanocytes are mixed with the sebaceous cells; mature sebaceous cells contain pigment as well as lipid granules. Lemurs also have large multi-acinar glands on the face and around the genitalia, which open to the surface by way of a large duct, either free of hair follicles or together with a vellus follicle. A third type of gland is associated with the sinus hair follicles. We now have investigated only the sebaceous glands of *Lemur macaco* and *Lemur catta*, which though generally similar have many differences. We know nothing of the glands in other lemurs.

The presence of melanin in the sebaceous glands of many primates is a vexing problem. Melanin is found both in the ducts and in the glands of the lemurs, the spider monkey (*Ateles geoffroyi*), the Anubis baboon (*Papio doguera*), the chimpanzee (*Pan satyrus*), and others, but nothing is known about its significance.

The peripheral, undifferentiated cells in the sebaceous glands of man contain glycogen. The sebaceous glands of the simian primates resemble those of man, but those in the skin of prosimians may contain only small traces of glycogen or none at all. In the potto, for instance, the glands in the skin of the head and of the genitalia contain glycogen whereas those elsewhere on the body do not (Montagna and Ellis, 1959). In the lemurs we have found glycogen only in the large brachial (sebaceous) glands in *Lemur catta*. These sebaceous glands also contain amylophosphorylase. The presence of these two substances is a characteristic feature of the sebaceous glands of man and of those of the simian primates.

We know a great deal of the biology of the sebaceous glands in rodents and in man (Kligman and Shelley, 1958), but we know practically nothing about the glands of primates. A study of the sebaceous glands, then, is also a promising field of study for the primatologist, the experimental biologist, and the biochemist.

V. THE SWEAT GLANDS

One of the outstanding peculiarities of man is that he sweats freely and profusely. No other known mammal sweats as much and as readily, and the sweat glands of no other known mammal respond to so many different stimuli. There is an ever increasing mass of information on the structure, physiology, pharmacology, and composition of the secretion of the sweat glands of man, but no comparable information exists on the sweat glands of other primates.

The changes that have taken place in the sweat glands of primates are even greater than those which have occurred in the structure of the epidermis, dermis, hair follicles, and sebaceous glands. Species differences are often so sharp in the structure of the sweat glands that intelligent generalizations are very difficult to make.

Eccrine and apocrine sweat glands are distinctly different in the skin of man and in the higher primates, and have many contrasting morphological, histochemical, and physiological features. However, in "lower" primates, the differences are less pronounced. A few years ago we denied the existence of intermediate types of sweat glands, but we must now admit that, at least in the Lorisidae some glands have the attributes of both types.

Since the more "primitive" primates have only "apocrine" glands over the general body surface and very poorly differentiated eccrine glands on the palms and soles, the histologist has assumed that apocrine glands are the more primitive type. Schiefferdecker (1922), who first named the two types of glands eccrine and apocrine, believed this so fervently that on this basis he constructed an arbitrary hierarchy of human races. According to him, during phylogenetic ascension the skin of mammals has gradually lost apocrine glands and replaced them at the same pace with eccrine glands. This phenomenon culminates in man, whose skin has more than three million eccrine glands widespread over the body, but only a few apocrine glands, mostly restricted to the axilla, the external auditory meatus, and around the genitalia. Ectopic glands may be found on the scalp, the face, and a few other places. This being the case, Schiefferdecker segregated the human races on the basis of the abundance of apocrine glands over their bodies. The Europeans, allegedly having the fewest apocrine glands, belong to the highest order, whereas the Negroes, with the most apocrine glands, belong to the lowest order. It is not surprising that Schiefferdecker was carried away by his enthusiasm and that he was mistaken on all counts. The number of apocrine glands in the Negro is not really different from that in Caucasians, and an assumption that modern apocrine sweat glands are not as advanced as modern eccrine glands is unwarranted.

The fact that the more primitive extant mammals possess apocrine glands does not necessarily make these glands primitive. For example, *Ornithorhynchus*, by all considered to be a primitive mammal because it lays eggs, has a very highly specialized skin, well adapted for an aquatic existence. Significantly, these animals have eccrine and apocrine sweat glands as clearly differentiated as those of allegedly more advanced orders (Montagna and Ellis, 1960). Who, then, is to say which of these two types is the more primitive? An assertion that apocrine glands are the more primitive must assume that the eccrine glands have progressively evolved whereas the apocrine glands have remained unchanged from an archetypical form. Has this really come to pass? From our studies of the sweat glands in primates, we can infer that the sweat glands of man, eccrine and apocrine, are equally highly specialized and that each may have departed as far from a common stem form, if such existed. We may similarly infer that archetypical glands probably superficially resembled the apocrine glands but that they were as different from the modern apocrine glands of man as they were from the eccrine glands. Unfortunately, talk of archetypical forms is wholly in the realm of speculation.

The sweat glands over the general body surface of the prosimians resemble apocrine glands; those on the volar surface of the pes and manus are barely distinguishable as eccrine. Neither type, however, resembles the glands of man or those of the simian primates. In the

Lorisidae, the two types of glands share many morphological, histochemical, and physiological characteristics.

In the Lorisidae, one sweat gland grows with each island of hair follicles. Since these consist of four to twenty or more follicles, the ratio of glands to hair follicles is very small. We assume, perhaps erroneously, that this is a primitive condition. As the grouping of hair follicles has become more constant, the groups have become smaller, and the ratio of the number of glands to follicles has increased appreciably. In some areas of the body of simian primates and in man, the ratio may be one to one, or there may be more glands than hair follicles.

We believe that the development of apocrine glands from hair follicles in the human embryo, and the subsequent opening of their ducts inside the pilary canal, is an occurrence of secondary importance. In the prosimians the glands always open directly onto the surface of the skin, often by a slightly coiled terminal segment, near, but seldom inside, a pilary canal. Even in the apes the glands may or may not open inside a pilary canal; only in man they nearly always do.

The eccrine sweat glands of man abound in such substances as glycogen, cytochrome oxidase, succinic dehydrogenase, monoamine oxidase, and amylophosphorylase, and the glands are surrounded by nonmyelinated nerves that are rich in specific cholinesterase activity. In contrast, the apocrine glands contain only small amounts of these substances or none at all. These, then, are distinctive features of the eccrine glands. In higher primates both types of sweat glands are essentially similar to those of man in this regard. Such distinctions, however, are relatively meaningless in the sweat glands of lower primates, in which apparently clear-cut eccrine and apocrine glands share these properties. The diameter of the duct of the eccrine glands of man usually measures one-half to one-fourth that of the secretory coil. In contrast, the diameter of the duct of apocrine glands is many times smaller than that of the secretory segment. This difference between eccrine and apocrine glands holds true for the higher primates as well as for man. In the primitive primates the ducts of the glands in the palms and soles are exceedingly narrow, whereas the secretory segment has a relatively wide diameter, grossly resembling apocrine glands; yet, these must be classified as eccrine glands. Another anatomical point of interest is that the duct of the eccrine glands of man and of the higher primates is very long and forms a good part of the glomerate segment. In contrast, the straight, narrow duct of the eccrine glands of prosimians is directly attached to the coiled secretory segment.

Eccrine sweat glands have developed wherever the skin is modified into a typical friction surface, such as that in the palms and soles. Thus, the ventral surface of the prehensile tail of some brachiating South American monkeys, such as *Ateles* and *Lagothrix*, is glabrous and mimics the palms and soles in having dermatoglyphic sculpturing. The resemblance is complete because this area is also provided with rows of eccrine sweat glands identical with those on the palms and soles in structure and in number. A similar specialization has occurred on the knuckles of the fingers of the gorilla (Ellis and Montagna, 1961). Together with these adaptations the skin has developed sensory end organs similar to those on the palms and soles.

The human anatomist has assumed that since the apocrine glands are restricted to a few loci on the body, they are vestigial organs. Yet, the axillary organ of man is lavishly developed. The gorilla, the chimpanzee, and to a lesser extent the orangutan also have an axillary organ, but this is not so extensive as that of man. The other primates have no such accumulation of eccrine and apocrine glands in the *cavum axillae*. In simian forms, however, there is a curious preferential concentration of eccrine and apocrine glands in the anterior chest, extending onto the gular region and often the flexor surface of the arms. The macaques, mangabeys, brachiating monkeys and the gibbons, and even some of the Hapalidae have rich concentrations of glands in these regions. The orangutan and the spider monkeys have, in addition, a sternal pit, which consists of an aggregate of apocrine glands that open into a central duct just anterior to the sternum (Wislocki and Schultz, 1925). Perhaps the concentration of apocrine glands on the anterior chest has some pertinence to the evolution of the axillary organ.

In summarizing, let one remember that the more primitive primates have only apocrine glands over the body surface, and they have glands on the volar surfaces of the pes and manus which resemble eccrine glands. In phylogenetically more "advanced" forms, both eccrine and apocrine glands attain the characteristic features of the glands of man. However, to state that in man the apocrine glands are vestiges of a nearly defunct organ system is erroneous. The glands on the body surface of some of the Lorisidae have the histochemical properties of the eccrine glands of man, while histologically they resemble apocrine. It seems likely that the apocrine glands of man and those of the phylogenetically more advanced primates have undergone at least as much specialization as the eccrine glands, and that they have perhaps departed even farther from an archetypical stem form, if such ever existed.

We hope that the reader will be patient with our voicing of generalizations. We will surely have to revamp our opinion on many things as we obtain new information. Perhaps we should have simply presented the data that we have and refrained from commenting. Yet, it is difficult for the biologist not to try to read functions out of design, even when he knows that he may err.

REFERENCES

DE BEAUX, O. (1917). Osservazioni e considerazioni sulle vibrisse carpali e facciali degli Arctopiteci. *Pavia Giorn. Morfol. Uomo e Primati.* 1, 1-20.

ELLIS, R. A. (1958). Ageing of the human male scalp. *In* "The Biology of Hair Growth" (W. Montagna and R. A. Ellis, eds.) New York, Academic Press.

ELLIS, R. A., AND MONTAGNA, W. (1962). The skin of primates. VI. The skin of the gorilla (*Gorilla gorilla*). *Am. J. Phys. Anthropol.* 20, 79-93.

ELLIS, R. A., AND MORETTI, G. (1959). Vascular patterns associated with catagen hair follicles in the human scalp. *Ann. N.Y. Acad. Sci.* 83, 448-457.

FITZPATRICK, T. B., BRUNET, P., AND KUKITA, A. (1958). The nature of hair pigment. *In* "The Biology of Hair Growth" (W. Montagna and R. A. Ellis, eds.) New York, Academic Press.

FREDERIC, J. (1905). Untersuchungen über die Sinneshaare der Affen, nebst Bemerkungen über die Augenbrauen und den Schnurrbart des Menschen. *Z. Morphol. Anthropol.* 8, 239-275.

FREDERIC, J. (1906). Nachtrag zu den "Untersuchungen über die Sinnesshaare der Affen." *Z. Morphol. Anthropol.* 9, 327-330.

GARN, S. M. (1951). Types and distribution of the hair in man. *Ann. N.Y. Acad. Sci.* 53, 498-507.

HAMILTON, J. B. (1959). A male pattern baldness in wattled starlings resembling the condition in man. *Ann. N.Y. Acad. Sci.* 83, 429-447.

HILL, W. C. O., APPLEYARD, H. M., AND AUBER, L. (1958-1959). The specialized area of skin glands in "Aotes" humboldt (*Simiae plattyrrhini*). *Trans. Roy. Soc. Edinburgh* 63, 535-551.

HORSTMANN, E. (1957). Die Haut. *In* "Handbuch der mikroskopischen Anatomie des Menschen" (W. von Mollendorff, ed.), Vol. 3, Part 3. Berlin, Springer.

KLIGMAN, A. M., AND SHELLEY, W. B. (1958). An investigation of the biology of the human sebaceous gland. *J. Invest. Dermatol.* 30, 99-125.

MOHN, M. P. (1958). The effects of different hormonal states on the growth of hair in rats. *In* "The Biology of Hair Growth" (W. Montagna and R. A. Ellis, eds.) New York, Academic Press.

MONTAGNA, W. (1962). "The Structure and Function of Skin," 2nd ed. New York, Academic Press.

MONTAGNA, W., AND CHASE, H. B. (1956). Histology and cytochemistry of human skin. X. X-irradiation of the scalp. *Am. J. Anat.* 99, 415-446.

MONTAGNA, W., AND ELLIS, R. A. (1959). The skin of primates. 1. The skin of the potto (*Perodicticus potto*). *Am. J. Phys. Anthropol.* 17, 137-162.

MONTAGNA, W., AND ELLIS, R. A. (1960). Sweat glands in the skin of *Ornithorhynchus paradoxus*. *Anat. Record* 137, 271-278.

MONTAGNA, W., AND ELLIS, R. A., eds. (1961). "Advances in Biology of Skin," Vol. II: Blood Vessels and Circulation. New York, Pergamon.

MONTAGNA, W., AND HARRISON, R. J. (1957). Specializations in the skin of the seal (*Phoca vitulina*). *Am. J. Anat.* 100, 81-114.

MONTAGNA, W., AND YUN, J. S. (1962a). The skin of primates. VII. The skin of the great bushbaby (*Galago crassicaudatus*). *Am. J. Phys. Anthropol.* 20, 149-165.

MONTAGNA, W., AND YUN, J. S. (1962b). The skin of primates. VIII. The skin of the Anubis baboon (*Papio doguera*). *Am. J. Phys. Anthropol.* **20**, 131-141.

MONTAGNA, W., YASUDA, K., AND ELLIS, R. A. (1961). The skin of primates. V. The skin of the black lemur (*Lemur macaco*). *Am. J. Phys. Anthropol.* **19** (in press).

ROTHMAN, S. (1954). "Physiology and Biochemistry of the Skin." Chicago, Univ. of Chicago Press.

SCHIEFFERDECKER, P. (1922). Die Hautdrüsen des Menschen und des Säugetieres ihre biologische und rassen-anatomische Bedeutung, sowie die muscularis sexualis. *Zoologica* (*Stuttgart*) **72**, 1-154.

STARICCO, R. G. (1960). The melanocytes and the hair follicle. *J. Invest. Dermatol.* **35**, 185-194.

STRAUS, W. L. S., JR. (1950). The microscopic anatomy of the skin of the gorilla. *In* "The Anatomy of the Gorilla" (W. K. Gregory, ed.) New York, Columbia Univ. Press.

WINKELMANN, R. K. (1960a). Similarities in cutaneous nerve end-organs. *In* "Advances in Biology of Skin," Vol. I: "Cutaneous Innervation" (W. Montagna, ed.) New York, Pergamon.

WINKELMANN, R. K. (1960b). "Nerve Endings in Normal and Pathologic Skin." Springfield, Illinois, Charles C Thomas.

WISLOCKI, G. B. (1930). A study of scent glands in the marmosets, especially *Oedipomidas geoffroyi*. *J. Mammal.* **11**, 475-482.

WISLOCKI, G. B., AND SCHULTZ, A. H. (1925). On the nature of modifications of the skin in the sternal region of certain primates. *J. Mammal.* **6**, 236-243.

YASUDA, K., AOKI, T., AND MONTAGNA, W. (1961). The skin of primates. IV. The skin of the lesser bushbaby (*Galago senegalensis*). *Am. J. Phys. Anthropol.* **19**, 23-34.

Chapter 5

The Sweat Glands of the Lorisidae[1]

RICHARD A. ELLIS AND WILLIAM MONTAGNA

Arnold Biological Laboratory,
Brown University, Providence, Rhode Island

In a comparative investigation of the histophysiology of the skin of primates, we have studied the cytology, histochemistry, and histophysiology of most of the living representatives of the Lorisidae (Montagna and Ellis, 1959, 1960a; Montagna *et al.*, 1961; Yasuda *et al.*, 1961; Montagna and Yun, 1962). Since the publication of these observations we have examined additional material, using the electron microscope to correlate fine structure with our previous information. This chapter reviews our earlier work on the Lorisidae and incorporates new observations.

I. MATERIALS AND METHODS

Pieces of skin were taken from every major part of the body. For general histological studies, the skin was fixed in Helly's fluid and in 10% formalin and embedded in paraffin. Sections of these tissues were stained with Giemsa, with toluidine blue buffered to various pH values

[1] This work was supported by research grants from the United States Public Health Service, RG-8380(CB1) and RG-2125(C11).

(Montagna *et al.*, 1951), and with the periodic acid schiff (PAS) re-action for glycogen and carbohydrates nondigestible by saliva. Phos-phorylase (Takeuchi and Kuriaki, 1955; Ellis and Montagna, 1958), succinic dehydrogenase (Farber and Louvière, 1956), monoamine oxi-dase (Glenner *et al.*, 1957), and cytochrome oxidase (Burstone, 1959, 1960) activity was demonstrated in frozen sections of unfixed tissues. The following enzymes were studied in frozen sections of tissues fixed in chilled 10% formalin for 4 hours: alkaline phosphatase (Gomori, 1952); acid phosphatase (Rutenburg and Seligman, 1955); nonspecific esterases (Pearse, 1960); tween esterases, or lipase (Stowell and Lee, 1950); acetylcholinesterase and butyrylcholinesterase (Montagna and Ellis, 1957).

For electron microscopic study, small biopsy specimens were placed in the cold fixative on a sheet of dental wax. Palade's 2% osmium fixative adjusted to pH 7.4 with veronal-acetate buffer (Pease, 1960) and 1% potassium permanganate dissolved in veronal-acetate buffer at pH 7.4 were the fixatives employed. Segments of glands, surrounded by a minimum of connective tissue, were isolated under the dissecting micro-scope and placed in glass-stoppered bottles of fixative. The tissue was fixed in osmium for 2–4 hours or in permanganate for 15 minutes. The specimens were then rinsed in distilled water, dehydrated through a graded series of ethyl alcohol, infiltrated with monomeric *n*-butyl methac-rylate and embedded in a prepolymerized (45 minutes at 60° C) mix-ture containing 15 cc methyl methacrylate, 85 cc butylmethacrylate, and 2 gm of catalyst (Luperco CDB). After trimming, ultrathin sections, 600–900 Å thick, were cut with glass knives on a Porter-Blum microtome. Sections were mounted on Formvar-coated Electromesh grids (200 mesh). The sections were stained in a saturated aqueous solution of lead acetate or in a 1% aqueous solution of potassium permanganate (Lawn, 1960) and examined in an RCA-EMU-3F electron microscope equipped with a 40µ platinum aperture. Electron micrographs were taken at initial magnifications from 2600 to 18,000 diameters and enlarged photographically as desired.

II. The Apocrine Sweat Glands of the General Body Skin

In the Lorisidae all of the sweat glands of the general body are of the apocrine type. Over most of the body surface these glands are small and inconspicuous. They consist of a dilated, simple, tubular terminal secretory portion and a narrow, short, straight duct that opens directly into a pilosebaceous canal, near the surface epidermis, through a funnel-shaped orifice. The secretory segment of the smaller apocrine sweat glands is nearly straight and runs parallel and close to the neighboring hair follicles; in the larger glands the secretory segment may be twisted or moderately coiled.

Below the orifice of the sweat gland, the duct is composed of two concentric layers of low cuboidal cells. The basal cells have a more basophilic cytoplasm than the luminal cells. There is usually some glycogen present in the duct epithelium; it is especially abundant in the cells near the abrupt junction of the duct with the secretory segment of the gland. The cells of the duct have moderate or low succinic dehydrogenase activity. In the slender loris (*Loris tardigradus*) the duct gives a slight reaction for nonspecific alkaline phosphatase; in the other members of this family the ducts are unreactive for this enzyme. Minimal enzyme levels of esterases, acid phosphatase, and monoamine oxidase are found in the duct, but there is strong reactivity for phosphorylase in all species.

The secretory segments of the apocrine glands of the general body skin are lined with columnar cells and surrounded with myoepithelial cells that rest peripherally upon a thick basement membrane and that are aligned parallel to the long axis of the tubule. Since the secretory cells vary in shape from low to tall columnar, sections of the tubules have a scalloped lumen. The secretory cells characteristically have apical caps or cytoplasmic nipples that protrude into the lumen.

The ground cytoplasm of the secretory cells may be either acidophilic or basophilic. The staining quality of the cytoplasm probably changes with the secretory cycle; it is more basophilic in the early stages of secretion synthesis and tends to become achromic or acidophilic later on. In all species except the galagos, basophile bodies of various sizes are present in the basal and sometimes in the apical cytoplasm. The secretory cells in the glands of *Nycticebus* and *Galago* often contain pigment granules, and the glands of all species except *Nycticebus* contain glycogen. In addition, the apical, and sometimes the basal, cytoplasm is packed with vacuoles that stain with PAS after digestion with saliva. These vacuoles, which in the potto stain metachromatically with toluidine blue at pH 6.0, must contain the principal secretory product of the glands.

The distribution and concentration of specific enzymes in the apocrine glands of the Lorisidae vary considerably (Table I). The secretory cells in the glands of the general body surface of *Nycticebus* and *Loris* react moderately for phosphorylase, but those of the potto and the galagos contain almost none. The apocrine cells of the potto are strongly reactive for the acid phosphatase, while those of the other species are only moderately reactive for this enzyme. All of the Lorisidae have alkaline phosphatase concentrated in the apical cytoplasm of the secretory cells but in the slender loris entire secretory cells are reactive. The apocrine cells are generally intensely reactive for esterases in all the animals examined, except the slow loris (*Nycticebus coucang*) which has almost no α-naphthol esterase activity. All species have strong succinic dehydrogenase activity in the secretory epithelium.

The myoepithelium in all of the species studied is similar in its histochemical properties. Occasional traces of glycogen are present within the myoepithelial cells, but there is no specific granulation that shows up either with the PAS reaction or with buffered toluidine blue. The cells are almost completely unreactive for succinic dehydrogenase, cytochrome oxidase, and monoamine oxidase. The myoepithelial cells have moderate phosphorylase activity. The striped pattern of the alkaline phosphatase reaction suggests that the enzyme is concentrated along the folded plasma membranes of adjacent myoepithelial cells. Myoepithelial cells have only traces of acid phosphatase and give no reaction for α-naphthol esterase, AS-esterase, or tween esterase.

The basement membrane is particularly well developed around the secretory segment of the apocrine glands. It stains with the PAS reaction even after digestion with saliva, and is often scalloped along its inner surface, indicating that extensions of the basement membrane protrude between adjacent myoepithelial cells (see Figs. 5 and 7). Collagenous fibers, connective tissue cells, blood vessels, and unmyelinated nerves are found at the periphery of the glands. The endothelium of blood vessels near the glands is demonstrated with the alkaline phosphatase reaction, but we have not ascertained with injection techniques whether or not these vessels are the only vascular supply to the sweat glands. If the alkaline phosphatase reaction is reliable for showing the capillaries, as it is in man (Ellis *et al.*, 1958), the glands of the Lorisidae are very poorly vascularized.

Only in the slow loris are the glands of the general body skin surrounded by nerves that are demonstrable with cholinesterase technique. These nerves react only with the acetylthiocholine iodide substrate and must contain specific cholinesterase. There are no such nerves around the duct.

III. Specialized Sudoriparous Glands

In contrast to the small sparsely distributed apocrine glands of the general body skin, each of the lorises, except the galagos, has specialized areas of skin where there are aggregates of enlarged apocrine sweat glands. In the potto, the glands are concentrated in the deeply furrowed skin of the scrotum or near the vulva. In the slender loris and in the slow loris large glandular fields are in the skin covering the flexor surface of the arm. Since the glands in each of these areas differ in several respects from the apocrine sweat glands of the general body skin, we will describe each type separately.

A. THE INGUINAL GLANDS OF *Perodicticus potto*

Before describing the glands in this region, let us review the peculiarities of its skin. The surface of the scrotum and of the vulva is broken by deep fissures. The epidermis lining the crevices contains dendritic melanocytes, but that lining the smooth surface facets is non-pigmented. Clusters of fine hairs with large sebaceous glands grow both on the surface facets and in the crevices.

There is a solid bed of large coiled glands in the dermis of this skin. The glands pass through the *tunica dartos* and reach the hypodermis (Figs. 1 and 2). This glandular field is about 2 cm square and 0.5 cm thick; that in the vulva is smaller. These are scent glands, comparable to the brown inguinal glands of the rabbit (Montagna, 1950). The glands in the inguinal region of marmosets (Wislocki, 1930) are mostly sebaceous, and, therefore different.

Each inguinal gland is a simple, coiled, tubular structure the duct of which rises straight up to the surface and opens into a pilary canal at the deepest part of a crevice. The orifices are dilated into eliptical receptacles which usually contain concretions of the secreted material. Adjacent glands are separated by ill-defined connective tissue partitions. The secretory coils measure from 0.25 to 0.5 mm in diameter, and terminate abruptly into a narrow duct about 50μ thick. A thick, hyaline basement membrane surrounds the glands. The glands, clearly of the apocrine type, are lined with tall columnar or cuboidal cells, the free border of which often forms a lingual process that protrudes into the lumen. The epithelium rests upon a layer of large myoepithelial cells. The duct, similar to that of the glands elsewhere on the body, is composed of two layers of flat cuboidal cells.

The secretory epithelial cells are similar to those of the sweat glands over the rest of the body surface. They have a spherical nucleus (often two) with one or more nucleoli. The cytoplasm is replete with delicate, evenly distributed basophile granules and large mitochondria, so closely packed that they are often aligned on the long axis of the cells.

The cells of the duct abound in glycogen, those of the secretory coil contain dust-like glycogen granules, and small, pigmented, barely PAS-reactive saliva-resistant granules. The content of the lumen is PAS-reactive and saliva resistant.

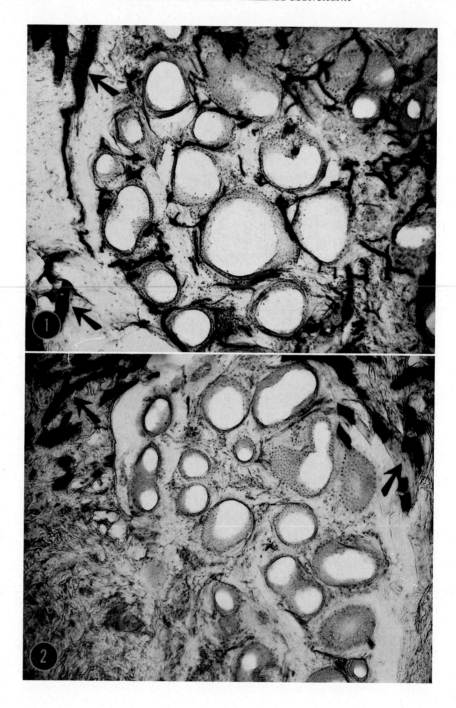

The ducts have strong phosphorylase activity from the pilary canal to the secretory coil, but the secretory coils contain none; the myoepithelial cells have some reactive granules. The entire gland is conspicuously reactive for succinic dehydrogenase. Alkaline phosphatase is present only in the apical part of the secretory cells; the ducts show no reaction. The secretory tubules have an intense acid phosphatase reaction, but the ducts have none. These glands resemble the apocrine glands in the skin of the general body surface in nearly all respects, with the exception that the inguinal glands are surrounded by a rich plexus of nerves that abounds in acetylcholinesterase (Fig. 1). These nerves have no butyrylcholinesterase (Fig. 2).

B. THE BRACHIAL ORGAN OF *Loris tardigradus*

The skin on the medial side of the arm is so rich in large tubular coiled glands that the skin is very thick and the glandular mass is palpable. In shaved, live animals this region becomes covered with a watery, yellowish fluid with an unpleasant smell. This specialized glandular region, which was discovered and described briefly by Hill (1956), is the *brachial organ*.

The short, narrow ducts of the glands of the brachial organ open to the surface independent of hair follicles. The total diameter of the duct is less than the height of the secretory cells. The general structure of the glands is similar to that of the apocrine glands elsewhere on the body. The secretory cells, however, are very tall, and the myoepithelial cells are larger.

The duct contains some glycogen only in the basal cells. The spectacularly tall secretory cells may contain coarse glycogen granules together with faintly PAS-positive saliva digestible granules and plaques. The large secretion droplets inside of, or attached to the apex of the cells, are never PAS-positive. The secretion within the lumen of some tubules is strongly PAS-positive and saliva resistant, with clear, unreactive globules scattered through it; in other tubules the secretion consists entirely of PAS-negative globules. The luminal cytoplasm of the secreting cells is full of secretion fluid, which seems to ooze out of

---

FIG. 1. Acetylcholinesterase activity is present in the nerves surrounding the inguinal glands of the potto. The smooth muscle in the dermis (arrows) is also reactive. (Hematoxylin counterstain; × 90.)

FIG. 2. A field similar to Fig. 1, but this section was incubated with butyrylthiocholine iodide. The nerves demonstrated in Fig. 1 are unreactive with this substrate but the smooth muscle of the dermis (arrows) contains nonspecific cholinesterase. (Hematoxylin counterstain; × 90.)

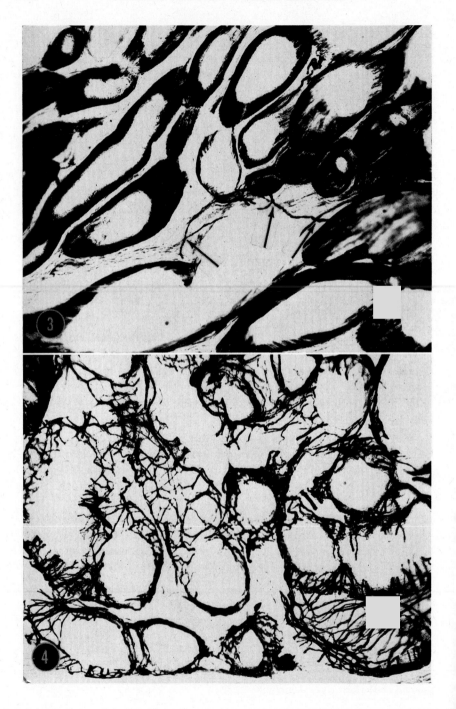

the cell into the lumen. The secretion material in the ducts near the excretory orifice and that encrusted on the surface of the skin is PAS-positive.

Some basophilic granules are clustered at the base of the secretory cells below the nucleus. The upper half of the very tall cells is either achromic or it stains very lightly with toluidine blue. The cytoplasm that bulges into the lumen and the intra- and extracellular droplets are always achromic. In some glands the secretion within the lumen may be composed entirely of achromic or slightly basophilic globules; in other glands it may be homogeneous and intensely basophilic. In some glands the homogeneous, basophilic colloid may contain achromic globules scattered through it. Regardless of the appearance and staining property of the secretion, the luminal border of the secretory cells is always covered with a barrier of achromic globules which look like soap bubbles being released from the cells. The content of the duct and the incrustations on the outer surface of the skin are always intensely basophilic. This corresponds completely to the PAS reactivity of the secretion. The secretion of these glands, then, is first achromic and PAS-negative, but on standing it attains both basophilia and PAS reactivity.

The duct has a low reactivity for succinic dehydrogenase, but the secretory cells are replete with reactive granules; those at the base of the cells are aligned along the axis like basal rodlets or striations. Even the cytoplasmic blebs that protrude into the lumen have a strong succinic dehydrogenase reaction. The myoepithelial cells are practically nonreactive. The glands are rich in phosphorylases and esterases. They differ from the other glands in having a reaction for alkaline phosphatase so strong that after incubation for a few minutes in the substrate the color produced is so deep that all details become masked. With this exception, the histochemical attributes of the glands of the brachial organ are similar to those of the other apocrine glands. There is, however, one profound difference between these and the apocrine glands of the general body skin: the glands of the brachial organ are surrounded by nerves rich in cholinesterases which attack both acetyl-

---

Fig. 3. A field of apocrine sweat glands in the brachial organ of *Nycticebus coucang*. The sites of alkaline phosphatase are restricted primarily to the myoepithelial cells which sheath the secretory epithelium. A few small capillaries (arrows) are also demonstrated. (Azo-dye method for alkaline phosphatase; × 90.)

Fig. 4. Acetylcholinesterase activity in a field of apocrine glands in the brachial organ of *Nycticebus*. The enzyme is restricted to the network of nerves which closely invest the secretory tubules. The nerves are unreactive when incubated with butyrylthiocholine iodide substrate. The structure of these nerves is described in the text. (Modification of the Gomori technique for cholinesterase; × 90.)

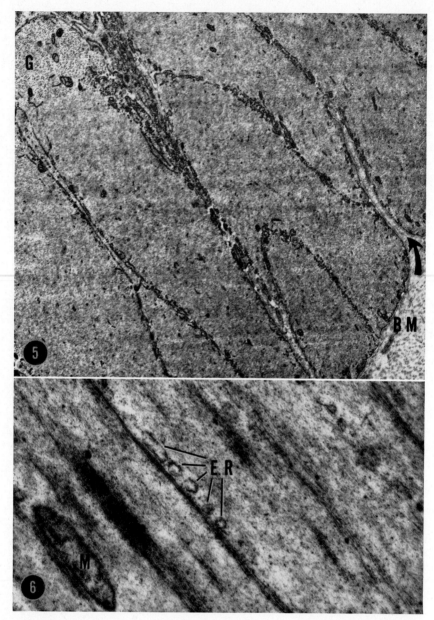

Fig. 5.   A low-power electron micrograph through portions of several myoepithelial cells in the brachial glands of *Nycticebus*. Glycogen (G) is present in the apical cytoplasm of one cell. The endoplasmic reticulum is restricted primarily to the periphery of the cells. The basement membrane (BM) follows closely the outer contours of the myoepithelial cells. The arrow indicates the infolded basement

thiocholine and butyrylthiocholine substrates. The reaction in the nerves is stronger with butyrylthiocholine and the enzyme must be mostly nonspecific cholinesterase.

C. HISTOCHEMISTRY AND ELECTRON MICROSCOPY OF THE BRACHIAL GLANDS OF *Nycticebus coucang*

The large brachial glands of the slow loris are similar in most respects to those of the slender loris. They are separated only by very thin septa of loose, areolar tissue. The thin, long ducts of these glands converge toward and open into the shallow pilary canal at the surface of the skin; some ducts open singly to the surface.

The myoepithelial cells are reactive for alkaline phosphatase (Fig. 3) and show a striped pattern along their bases. This pattern is consistent with the invaginations of the plasma membrane at the base of the secretory cells and the infolding of the basement membrane between adjacent myoepithelial cells (Figs. 5 and 7). Since the main cytoplasmic mass of these cells is unreactive for alkaline phosphatase, the enzyme is probably associated with the plasma membranes and possibly with the endoplasmic reticulum which is restricted to the periphery of the myoepithelial cells. The low level of succinic dehydrogenase, cytochrome oxidase, and monoamine oxidase activity in the myoepithelial cells is consistent with the few small mitochondria in them (Figs. 5, 6, 7). The high phosphorylase activity in the myoepithelium is affirmed by the glycogen (Revel *et al.*, 1960) stores in the peripheral and perinuclear cytoplasm (Figs. 7 and 8). The myoepithelium is completely unreactive for esterases and lipases.

Compared with the fine structure of the myoepithelial cells surrounding the Harderian gland of rats, mice, and rabbits (Chiquoine, 1958), the lacrimal gland of rats (Leeson, 1960), and the eccrine (Hibbs, 1958) and axillary apocrine sweat glands (Kurosumi *et al.*, 1959) of man, these myoepithelial cells are highly developed. The main cytoplasmic mass of the myoepithelial cells in *Nycticebus* is much larger than in any myoepithelial cells described in other species and it consists of a

---

membrane between two adjacent cells, similar to that shown at much higher magnification in Fig. 7. (Potassium permanganate fixation; × 8,500.)

FIG. 6. A high-power electron micrograph of a portion of a myoepithelial cell which has been sectioned through its long axis. The cytoplasm is filled with delicate lines separated from one another by regular spaces. Some fine granules are scattered among the fibrils. A mitochondrion (M) and several profiles of the endoplasmic reticulum (ER) are also shown. (Fixation in 2% osmic acid, stained with potassium permanganate; × 108,000.)

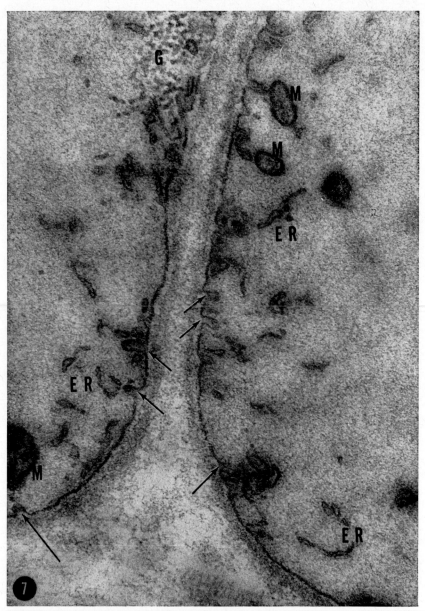

Fig. 7. A high-power electron micrograph showing the basal portions of two myoepithelial cells in cross-section and the cleft separating the adjacent cells. A dense layer, the amorphous basement membrane, follows closely the plasma membranes limiting the cells. Several mitochondria (M) are shown. Profiles of the endoplasmic reticulum (ER) are commonplace in the peripheral cytoplasm and seem to be continuous with inpouchings (arrows) of the plasma membrane. An aggregation of glycogen particles (G) is shown in the upper part of the figure. (KMNO$_4$ fixation; × 108,000.)

fine, highly oriented system of tubules or fibrils (Fig. 6) which are considered to be contractile elements.

The secretory cells of the brachial glands are characteristically in various stages of secretory activity, reflected by their considerable heterogeneity in fine structure. The cells abound in succinic dehydrogenase, monoamine oxidase (Fig. 17), and cytochrome oxidase activity. The mitochondria, which contain these enzymes, are scattered throughout the cytoplasm of the secretory cells. The larger filamentous forms are

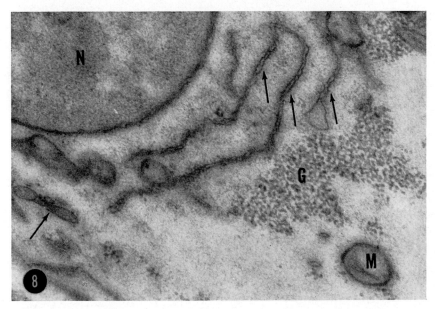

FIG. 8.   Glycogen particles (G), profiles of the endoplasmic reticulum (arrows), and a mitochondrion (M) are present in the apical cytoplasm of a myoepithelial cell from a brachial gland of *Nycticebus*. A segment of the nucleus (N) and its limiting envelope is shown in the upper left. (KMNO$_4$ fixation; × 108,000.)

more numerous near the base of the cells, while the smaller granular types are more frequent near the apex. Both the granular and filamentous types contain only a few internal cristae (Figs. 10 and 11).

The cytoplasm of the secretory cells contains fine, sparse basophile granules, which under the electron microscope appear as clumps of dense granular material with a single external limiting membrane (Fig. 9). Small yellow pigment granules are also present in the basal two-thirds of the cell. These appear to be lipid complexes with a dense granular material when examined with the electron microscope. The pigment granules vary greatly in size and shape and have a delicate

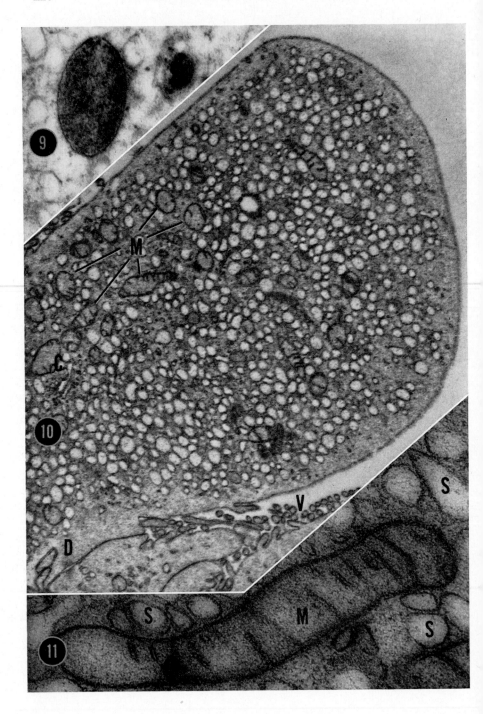

limiting membrane, but are never as large as the pigment granules in the apocrine sweat glands of man (Kurosumi *et al.*, 1959). Much of the esterase activity of the glands of the brachial organ is probably associated with these granules. Numerous achromic vacuoles fill much of the basal and most of the outer part of the secretory cells. With the electron microscope these granules are adielectronic and are bounded by smooth-surfaced membranes (Figs. 9, 10, 11). These comprise the secretory vacuoles of the cell. The relative abundance as well as the form of the endoplasmic reticulum varies with the secretory cycle. In early stages of synthesis it may form large membranous whorls or sheets while later in the cycle the cisternae of the endoplasmic reticulum are dilated, and form clear spaces (Fig. 12). Some ribonucleoprotein particles are associated with the endoplasmic reticulum (Fig. 12) but it is principally smooth-surfaced. The secretory cells contain no glycogen but they have an abundance of phosphorylase. This enzyme is probably associated with the smooth-surfaced endoplasmic reticulum (Porter and Bruni, 1959). Basophilia is slight in the basal cytoplasm of the secretory cells; this is consistent with the low concentration of RNP particles observed with the electron microscope. There is very little acid or alkaline phosphatase in the secretory cells.

The glands are surrounded with myriad nerves of various sizes that contain mostly acetylcholinesterase (Fig. 4). The largest bundles of unmyelinated fibers are surrounded by a connective tissue sheath consisting of an amorphous cement substance, collagen fibers, and a single layer of fibrocytes which form a delicate limiting ring (Figs. 13, 14), which Yamada and Miyake (1960) have identified as the endoneurium in their description of the nerve fibers surrounding the axillary apocrine glands of man. The smaller nerve bundles do not have a continuous

---

FIG. 9.   A dense, membrane-bound vacuole from the basal cytoplasm of a secretory cell in the brachial gland of *Nycticebus*. This has the same size and position in the cell as the pigment granules which are observed with the light microscope. (Fixation in 2% osmium; × 108,000.)

FIG. 10.   The apical portion of a secretory cell in an undilated brachial gland of *Nycticebus*. A rim of cytoplasm at the periphery of the cell is devoid of large, clear secretory vacuoles, while the inner cytoplasm is packed with them. Numerous mitochondria (M) and a Golgi complex (C) appear in the cytoplasm. Microvilli (V), seen in cross- and longitudinal section, are present near the points of juncture of adjacent secretory cells; a desmosome (D), or cell interconnection, appears along the apposed plasma membranes. ($KMNO_4$ fixation; × 23,000.)

FIG. 11.   A typical mitochondrion (M) and clear secretory vacuoles (S) in the basal cytoplasm of a secretory cell. Brachial gland of *Nycticebus*. ($KMNO_4$ fixation; × 126,000.)

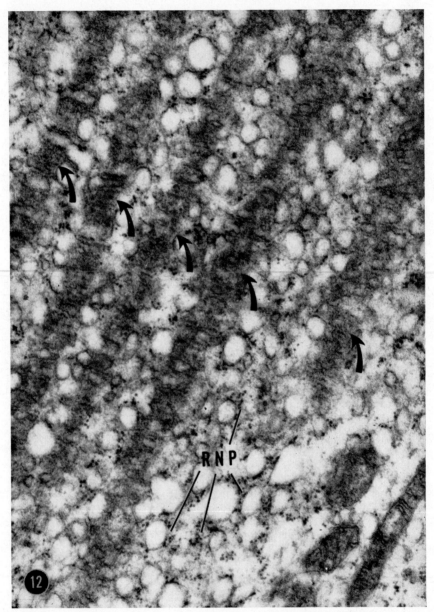

FIG. 12. Basal cytoplasm in a secretory cell from a dilated gland in *Nycticebus*. The plane of sectioning shows bands of clear, membrane-bound secretory vacuoles alternating with profiles of lamellae of the endoplasmic reticulum (arrows). Ribonucleoprotein particles (RNP) are scattered throughout the cytoplasm, and in some areas they are attached to the membranes at the periphery of the secretory vacuoles. (Fixation, 2% osmium; × 108,000.)

sheath of fibrocytes, but they are invested with collagen fibers. These bundles consist of about five to twenty axons of various sizes embedded in the cytoplasm of Schwann cells (Figs. 15 and 16). The larger axons and many of the smaller ones contain small mitochondria and numerous small vesicles (Figs. 15 and 16). The vesicles are equivalent in size and shape to the synaptic vesicles found at synapses of most sensory and motor nerves (De Robertis *et al.*, 1960). Recent biochemical evidence

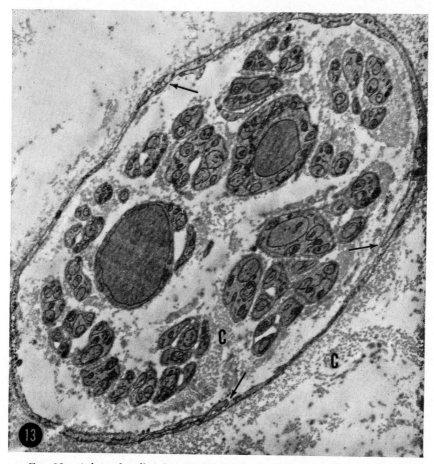

Fig. 13. A large bundle of unmyelinated nerve fibers embedded in the dermis near the brachial glands of *Nycticebus*. The axis cylinders and accompanying Schwann cells (see Fig. 16) are surrounded by collagen fibers (C). The entire bundle is sheathed by a single delicate layer of fibrocytes. The processes of three fibrocytes are dove-tailed (arrows) to form a continuous endoneurial sheath. Collagen fibers (C) are also evident in the dermis outside the endoneurium (KMNO$_4$ fixation; $\times$ 3,600.)

indicates that acetylcholine is contained within the synaptic vesicles (Whittaker, 1959). Close to the basement membrane, individual axons are disengaged from the Schwann cells, but they retain an outer coating of dense amorphous material similar to that surrounding the Schwann cells (Fig. 16). Many of these terminal nerves have small vesicles

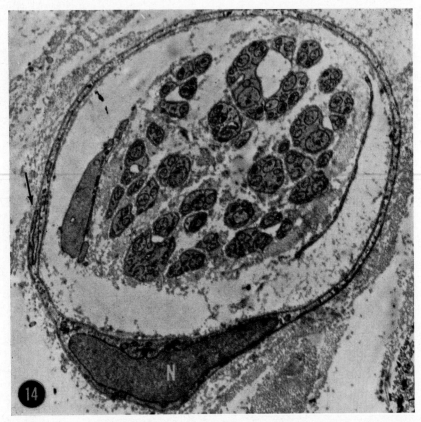

Fig. 14. A smaller bundle of unmyelinated nerves close to the brachial glands of *Nycticebus*. A single fibrocyte sectioned through the nucleus (N) makes up the endoneurium. The fibrocytic processes meet at the arrow to form a perfect ring. (KMNO$_4$ fixation; × 3,600.)

as well as mitochondria in their axoplasm (Fig. 16). None of the nerves surrounding the brachial glands are reactive for monoamine oxidase.

D. The Sweat Glands of the Volar Surface of the Manus and Pes

In the potto and in the galagos the palms, soles, and digital pads contain sweat glands that resemble eccrine glands. The slow loris and

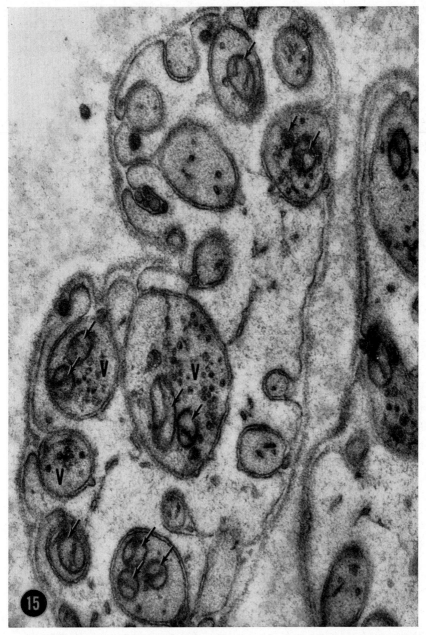

FIG. 15. Portions of two Schwann cells near the base of an apocrine gland in the brachial organ of *Nycticebus*. Numerous axons are burrowed within the peripheral clefts of the two Schwann cells (see Fig. 16). Cross-sections of the larger axons reveal numerous small vesicles (V) as well as many mitochondria (arrows). Each Schwann cell is bounded by a rim of dense granular material, the amorphous basement membrane. (KMNO$_4$ fixation; × 104,000.)

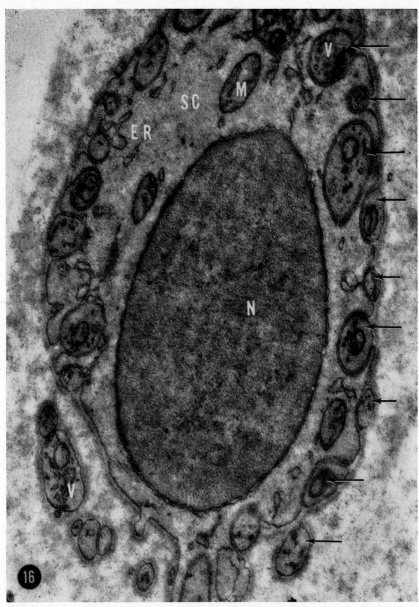

Fɪɢ. 16. A Schwann cell at the periphery of a brachial gland in the skin of *Nycticebus*. The nucleus (N) of the Schwann cell is at the center, with a double membrane surrounding it. The cytoplasm (SC) of the Schwann cell contains profiles of the endoplasmic reticulum as well as mitochondria. Numerous axons (arrows) are embedded within the invaginated plasma membrane of the Schwann cell, but some lie free in the dermis. Small vesicles (V) are present in many axons. The axons which are free in the dermis have an encompassing rim of dense amorphous material similar to that investing the Schwann cell. (KMNO$_4$ fixation; × 96,000.)

the slender loris, however, have sweat glands that have features common to both eccrine and apocrine sweat glands.

1. *Galago senegalensis*

Sweat glands, sparse on the palms and soles, are numerous on the balls of the digits. From the thick, coiled secretory segment deep in the fatty pad, a narrow duct takes a straight path to the epidermis where it forms a slightly coiled intraepidermal segment.

The cells of the secretory segment rest upon a layer of large myoepithelial cells, which are, in turn, surrounded by a thick basement membrane. The smaller secretory cells are shoved toward the lumen, and the larger ones remain at the base. The small cells stain deeply with basic dyes, but the larger ones do not, and the two types correspond to dark and clear cells respectively. Between the clear cells can be seen vestiges of intercellular canaliculi.

The clear cells are rich in glycogen, but the dark cells have little or none. Cytochrome oxidase, succinic dehydrogenase, monoamine oxidase, and phosphorylase are heavily concentrated in the secretory epithelium, but there is practically none in the duct. The secretory segment has small amounts of α-naphthol esterase, naphthol esterase, naphthol AS-esterase, tween esterase, acid phosphatase, and aminopeptidase; the duct has almost none. The basal portions of the secretory cells and the myoepithelial cells have strong alkaline phosphatase activity, but very few arterioles and capillaries with an alkaline phosphatase-rich endothelium surround the glands. Nerve fibers, with strong concentrations of acetylcholinesterase and some butyrylthiocholine esterase, surround the coils of the secretory segment.

2. *Perodicticus potto*

The ducts of these glands open to the surface of the thick epidermis through coiled channels. The straight segment of the duct is about 20 to 25 μ in diameter, like that of apocrine glands, and is composed of two layers of squamous cells. The luminal cells have a barely differentiated cuticular border. Before they penetrate the bottom of the epidermal ridges, the ducts become multilayered and the lumen funnels out in a wider coiled channel. The cuticular border of the intraepidermal part of the duct is composed of two or three cells.

The thick, coiled secretory segment of the glands becomes abruptly constricted at the junction with the narrow duct, as in the apocrine glands; therefore, none of the glomerate portion of the gland is composed of duct. The gland is lined with large pyriform cells differentiated into clear and dark cells. The larger clear cells have a spherical, finely

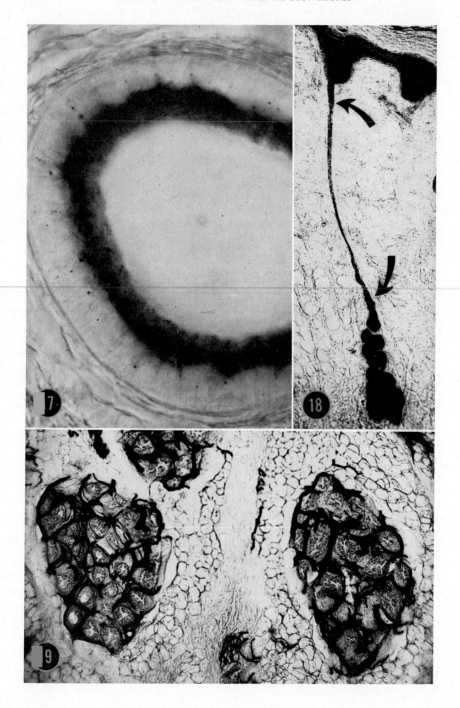

stippled nucleus, and a cytoplasm with sparse, delicate granules barely stainable with basic dyes. The smaller dark cells seem to be piled up toward the lumen, often above the clear cells in such a way that the epithelium appears to have two layers. The cytoplasm of dark cells contains basophile granules and some granules that stain metachromatically with toluidine blue. The nuclei are dense, never spherical, usually oval, and often misshapen. The smaller dark cells are more numerous than the clear cells.

Duct and gland contain abundant glycogen. Small amounts of PAS-positive, saliva-resistant material are found at the tips of the dark cells only. The lumen contains small granules of glycogen and a weakly PAS-positive, saliva-resistant colloid.

Ducts and glands contain so much amylophosphorylase that a strong reaction is obtained by leaving tissues in the incubating medium for only 5 minutes; in contrast, the epidermis, which is also reactive, requires a much longer period of incubation to show a reaction. In the intra-epidermal part of the duct, only the luminal cells have phosphorylase reaction. The entire gland is also intensely reactive for succinic dehydrogenase. The glands contain small amounts of alkaline and acid phosphatases and traces of esterases.

Although the ducts of the glands have no demonstrable nerves around them, the entire glomerate portion of the glands is enveloped by a plexus of large nerve fibers intensely reactive for only acetylcholinesterase (Fig. 19). When eserine is added to the incubation medium all of the reaction in the nerves is inhibited.

3. Loris tardigradus and Nycticebus coucang

The glands are embedded in the thick subcutaneous fat, and their long, straight, and narrow ducts open at spaced intervals along the crests of the epidermal ridges. The path of the duct inside the epidermis

---

FIG. 17. Monoamine oxidase activity in a brachial gland from *Nycticebus*. The myoepithelial cells at the periphery of the gland are unreactive. The secretory cells are reactive throughout, but the reaction is strongest in the basal cytoplasm. (Tryptamine substrate; × 450.)

FIG. 18. Phosphorylase activity in sweat gland from the hallux of *Nycticebus*. The straight duct is very small in diameter. It widens slightly as it approaches the epidermal peg (upper arrow) and where it joins the secretory coil (lower arrow). These glands have no coiled duct. The entire gland is reactive for the enzyme. (× 40.)

FIG. 19. The meshwork of nerves investing the coiled portions of eccrine sweat glands in the palm of the potto contains abundant acetylcholinesterase. (The secretory coils have been counterstained with hematoxylin; × 450.)

is straight or slightly coiled. The duct joins the thick secretory coil abruptly and the gross appearance of the gland is that of an apocrine gland. The wall of the ducts has two layers of flat cuboidal cells, the luminal ones being flatter than the basal ones. The duct is thickest where it joins the secretory coil, proximally, and the epidermal ridges, distally. The secretory tubules are lined with cuboidal or pyramidal cells. A broad layer of myoepithelial cells separates the glandular cells from the thick basement membrane.

The secretory cells are all alike and different from both the dark and the clear cells of the glands of the higher primates. The nucleus is pressed against the base, like that of the mucous cells. The cytoplasm is full of colorless globules between which can be seen small, basophile granules. The globules stain a faint metachromatic color with toluidine blue. No intercellular canaliculi are observed with either the light or the electron microscope.

Most of the cells of these glands contain neither glycogen nor other PAS-reactive material. The cells of the duct at the junction with the secretory cells have some small PAS-positive granules, which are of no consequence. In spite of this, the lumen of the glands often contains moderately PAS-positive, saliva-resistant granules, and the duct always contains a strongly positive colloid. These particular features are like those of the glands of the brachial organ.

The sweat glands of the pes and manus are no more strongly reactive for succinic dehydrogenase activity than the glands elsewhere on the body. The cells of the duct are weakly reactive, and the secretory cells have a moderately strong reaction. The myoepithelial cells are nearly unreactive. The entire gland shows a moderate reaction for phosphoryl-ase activity (Fig. 18); the myoepithelial cells are intensely reactive. The glands have scant reactivity for alkaline phosphatase, and moderate re-activity for acid phosphatase. The secretory coil also shows some non-specific esterase activity, but the ducts are weakly reactive.

The secretory coils are surrounded by nerves which contain both acetylcholinesterase and butyrylcholinesterase, the latter showing the strongest reaction. This means that the nerves contain both specific and nonspecific esterases.

IV. Conclusions

In considering the histology and histochemistry of the sweat glands of the Lorisidae, some similarities are evident (Tables I, II). There are obvious similarities in the apocrine sweat glands of the general body skin within this family (Table I), as well as in the apocrine glands of specialized regions (Table I). Morphologically and histochemically the palmar and plantar sweat glands of the potto and the galagos have striking similarities (Table II). In the same regions the sweat glands of the slender loris and the slow loris resemble each other (Table II), but are vastly different from those of the potto and the galagos. Observations on the morphology and histochemistry of the sweat glands of these animals show striking similarities in the galagos and the potto on one hand and the slow and the slender loris on the other. Many features are common to the family as well as to the primates in general.

The differences among these species are of even more interest than the similarities. In the apocrine sweat glands the differences are frequently quantitative ones, involving higher enzymatic activity in one species than in another (Tables I and II); or there are simply regional differences within the gland. As an example of the latter, the reactivity of the apocrine glands for alkaline phosphatase may be cited. Especially clearly defined is the histochemical reactivity of the nerves innervating the apocrine glands of the specialized regions of the skin. The nerves that surround the inguinal glands of the potto contain acetylcholinesterase. Those surrounding the brachial glands of the slender loris are reactive for acetylcholinesterase but even more strongly reactive for butyrylcholinesterase and thus contain mostly nonspecific cholinesterase. The nerves around the glands of the brachial organ of the slow loris again contain only specific cholinesterase. In this respect, then, the histochemical reactivity of the nerves is similar in the potto and in the slow loris, but different in the slender loris. The sites of the aggregations of apocrine glands are, of course, entirely different in the potto and in the slow loris. On a basis of locus and the cholinesterase reactivity associated with these glands, one could easily make a species identification.

Of special significance is the vast difference in the sweat glands of the palms and soles of the potto and the galagos and those of the slow and slender lorises. The potto and the galagos have sweat glands which, except for the missing coiled duct, are of the typical eccrine type; the secretory coil contains both clear and dark cells. The lorises on the other hand have sweat glands in the volar surfaces of their palms and soles which have many attributes of apocrine glands and consist of only one type of secretory cell. Whereas eccrine glands characteristically contain much glycogen, those of *Nycticebus* contain only traces of it. Other eccrine glands contain little alkaline phosphatase but the glands of the lorisoids are rich in it. Eccrine sweat glands are easily stimulated to secrete with injections of acetylcholine, but in these animals this drug has little effect. The sweat glands of the pes and manus of the lorises

TABLE I

Histochemical Reactions in the Apocrine Sweat Glands in the Skin of Lorisoids

	Perodicticus potto				Loris tardigradus			
	General body skin		Inguinal glands		General body skin		Brachial glands	
	Duct	Secretory coil	Duct	Secretory coil	Duct	Secretory coil	Duct	Secretory coil
Basal basophile granules	−	+	−	+		+	−	+
Apical PAS-positive saliva-resistant granules	−	+	−	+		+	−	−
Metachromasia	−	+	−	+		+	Basal	+
Glycogen	++	+	+++	+	++	+	+	+
Ionic iron	−	−	−	−	−	−	−	−
Pigment	−	−	−	+	−	Eyelid +	−	+
Succinic dehydrogenase	+	++++	+++	++++	±	++++	+	+++
Amylophosphorylase	++++	±	++++	−	+++	++++	++++	++++
Alkaline phosphatase	−	Apex +++	−	Apex +++	+	Apex +++	+++	++++
Acid phosphatase	−	++++	−	++++	−	++	−	++
Tween esterase	−	++++	−	++++	−	++++	−	++
α-Naphthol esterase	±	++++	−	++++	−	++++	+	++++
Naphthol-AS esterase	−	++++	−	+++	−	+++	−	+++
Monoamine oxidase								
Cytochrome oxidase								
Nerves:								
Acetylcholinesterase	−	−	−	++++	−	−	−	+++
Butyrylcholinesterase	−	−	−	++++	−	−	−	++++

TABLE I (Continued)

| | Nycticebus coucang | | | | Galago senegalensis[a] | |
| | General body skin | | Brachial glands | | General body skin | |
	Duct	Secretory coil	Duct	Secretory coil	Duct	Secretory coil
						Cytoplasm
Basal basophile granules	−	+	−	+	−	+
Apical PAS-positive saliva-resistant granules	−	+	−	+	−	+
Metachromasia		Basal		−		−
Glycogen	+	−	+	−	−	+
Ionic iron	−	−	−	−	−	
Pigment	−	+	−	+	−	+
Succinic dehydrogenase	+	++++	+	++++	+	++++
Amylophosphorylase	++++	++++ Base or apex	++++	++++	++++	−
Alkaline phosphatase	−	+++	+	++++	+	+
Acid phosphatase	−	+	−	+	−	++
Tween esterase	−	+++	−	++++	−	+
α-Naphthol esterase	−	+	−	+	−	+++
Naphthol-AS esterase	−	+++	−	++	−	+++
Monoamine oxidase	+	++++	−	++++	−	+++
Cytochrome oxidase	+	++++	+	++++	+	++++
Nerves:						
Acetylcholinesterase	−	++++	−	++++	−	++
Butyrylcholinesterase	−	−	−	−	−	++

[a] The differences between Galago senegalensis (Yasuda et al., 1961) and Galago crassicaudatus (Montagna and Yun, 1962) are minor ones and the latter is not included in this table.

TABLE II

HISTOCHEMICAL REACTIONS IN THE SWEAT GLANDS OF THE PALMS AND SOLES

	Perodicticus potto		Loris tardigradus	
	Duct	Secretory coil	Duct	Secretory coil
Glycogen	+++	+++ In clear cells	—	—
PAS-positive, saliva-resistant granules	—	+ Dark cells only	—	++
Basophilia	—	+ Dark cells only	—	+
Amylophosphorylase	++++	++++	++++	++++
Succinic dehydrogenase	+++	++++	++	++++
Acid phosphatase	++	++	++	++
Alkaline phosphatase	+	++	+	+
α-Naphthol esterase	+	+	+	++
Naphthol AS-esterase	+	+	+	++
Tween esterase	+	+	+	++
Monoamine oxidase				
Nerves: Acetylcholinesterase	—	++++	—	++
Butyrylcholin- esterase	—	—	—	++++

have little resemblance to most eccrine glands we have seen, and may represent a type of sweat gland intermediate between the classic ec- crine and apocrine types. Phylogenetically, the glands on the volar surfaces of the pes and manus are probably the most ancient eccrine sweat glands (Kuno, 1956). At the present time we do not know enough comparative anatomy to ascertain the significance of the "intermediate" type of sweat glands in the lorises. We are currently studying the skin of some insectivores, and it will be interesting to examine the sweat glands in these animals to see if this "intermediate" type of sweat gland is found in that order.

In a comparison of the apocrine sweat glands of these animals with those of man (Montagna, 1956) and the higher primates, the differences far outweigh the similarities. In man, the apocrine glands rarely con- tain glycogen; they are lacking in phosphorylase, are low in succinic

TABLE II (*Continued*)

	Nycticebus coucang		*Galago senegalensis*[a]	
	Duct	Secretory coil	Duct	Secretory coil
Glycogen	+	+	—	+++ In clear cells
PAS-positive, saliva-resistant granules	—	++	—	+
Basophilia	—	++	—	+ Dark cells only
Amylophosphorylase	++++	++++	+	++++
Succinic dehydrogenase	+++	++++	+	++++
Acid phosphatase	++	++	—	+
Alkaline phosphatase	+	+++	—	+++
α-Naphthol esterase	++	++	—	+
Naphthol AS-esterase	++	++	—	+
Tween esterase	++	++	—	+
Monoamine oxidase	+++	+++	+	+++
Nerves: Acetylcholinesterase	—	++++	—	++++
Butyrylcholinesterase	—	+	—	++

[a] The differences between *Galago senegalensis* (Yasuda *et al.*, 1961) and *Galago crassicaudatus* (Montagna and Yun, 1962) are minor ones and the latter is not included in this table.

dehydrogenase, and, except for the glands of Moll and the axillary glands of the Negro (Montagna and Ellis, 1960b), are never surrounded by nerves containing cholinesterase. In the potto, the galagos, and the slender loris the apocrine glands usually contain glycogen; in the slow and slender loris the glands have abundant phosphorylase activity, and the glands in all members of this family are strongly reactive for succinic dehydrogenase activity. In addition, the large, specialized apocrine glands are surrounded by nerves which contain specific or nonspecific cholinesterase.

There are also many differences in fine structure. The apocrine glands of *Nycticebus* have little similarity to those of man. Both the secretory cells and the myoepithelial cells are distinctly different. The mitochondria of the secretory cells are small and unmodified, the cells are filled with clear vacuoles, the pigment granules are relatively small and sparse, and the endoplasmic reticulum is largely of the smooth-surfaced variety. These organelles are quite different in the apocrine sweat glands of man (Kurosumi *et al.*, 1959; Charles, 1959).

Although the structure and the histochemical properties of the apocrine sweat glands of man are vastly different from those of the lorisoids, the nerves around the glands, when present, are similar. The fine structure of the nerves around the brachial glands of *Nycticebus* are identical in every point with those which have been described near the axillary glands of man (Yamada and Miyake, 1960). Also, the nerves contain specific cholinesterase as do those around the axillary glands of Negroes (Montagna and Ellis, 1960b). The nerves are, however, much more numerous around the glands in the brachial organ of *Nycticebus*. Except for numbers, the innervation of the specialized axillary glands of man and that of the brachial glands of *Nycticebus* are similar. This, then, points up the intransient nature of the nervous system as contrasted with the plasticity of the glandular epithelium. The only apparent changes in the nerve terminals are related to enzyme specificity, which is apparently different even within the races of man, as well as among the members of the family Lorisidae.

The massive accumulations of apocrine glands in the inguinal region of the potto and in the brachial skin of *Loris* and *Nycticebus* are probably highly specialized structures with special adaptive significance, related to social and reproductive activities. Nearly all of the primates studied have somewhere on their bodies specialized skin areas in which are concentrated large apocrine glands. The lemurs have arm glands in the flexor side of the arm (Sutton, 1887). Similar specialized glandular areas are also found in the skin at the ventral base of the tail of the Platyrrhini (Hill *et al.*, 1959). Even in man, the axillary organ is comparable to these specialized glandular areas of skin. The glands in these areas all secrete variably fetid substances and are well developed in both sexes.

References

BURSTONE, M. S. (1959). New histochemical techniques for the demonstration of tissue oxidase (cytochrome oxidase). *J. Histochem. and Cytochem.* 7, 112-122.

BURSTONE, M. S. (1960). Histochemical demonstration of cytochrome oxidase with new amine reagents. *J. Histochem. and Cytochem.* 8, 63-70.

CHARLES, A. (1959). An electron microscopic study of the human axillary apocrine gland. *J. Anat.* 93, 226-231.

CHIQUOINE, A. D. (1958). The identification and electron microscopy of myoepithelial cells in the harderian gland. *Anat. Record* 132, 569-583.

DE ROBERTIS, E. D. P., NOWINSKI, W. W., AND SAEZ, F. A. (1960). "General Cytology." Philadelphia, Pennsylvania, Saunders.

ELLIS, R. A., AND MONTAGNA, W. (1958). Histology and cytochemistry of human skin. XV. Sites of phosphorylase and amylo-1,6-glucosidase activity. *J. Histochem. and Cytochem.* 6, 201-207.

ELLIS, R. A., MONTAGNA, W., AND FANGER, H. (1958). Histology and cytochemistry of human skin. XIV. The blood supply of the cutaneous glands. *J. Invest. Dermatol.* 30, 137-145.

FARBER, E., AND LOUVIERE, C. D. (1956). Histochemical localization of specific oxidative enzymes. IV. Soluble oxidation-reduction dyes as aids in the histochemical localization of oxidative enzymes with tetrazolium salts. *J. Histochem. and Cytochem.* 4, 347-356.

GLENNER, G. G., BURTNER, H. J., AND BROWN, G. W., JR. (1957). The histochemical demonstration of monoamine oxidase activity by tetrazolium salts. *J. Histochem. and Cytochem.* 5, 591-600.

GOMORI, G. (1952). "Microscopic Histochemistry. Principles and Practice." Chicago, Univ. of Chicago Press.

HIBBS, R. G. (1958). The fine structure of human eccrine sweat glands. *Am. J. Anat.* 103, 201-218.

HILL, W. C. O. (1956). Body odour in lorises. *Proc. Zool. Soc. London* 127, 580.

HILL, W. C. O., APPLEYARD, H. M., AND AUBER, L. (1959). The specialized area of skin glands in "*Aotes*" Humboldt (Simiae Platyrrhini). *Trans. Roy. Soc. Edinburgh* 63, 535-551.

KUNO, Y. (1956). "Human Perspiration." Springfield, Illinois, Charles C Thomas.

KUROSUMI, K., KITAMURA, T., AND IIJIMA, T. (1959). Electron microscope studies on the human axillary apocrine sweat glands. *Arch. Histol. Japon.* 16, 523-566.

LAWN, A. M. (1960). The use of potassium permanganate as an electron-dense stain for sections of tissue embedded in epoxy resin. *J. Biophys. Biochem. Cytol.* 7, 197.

LEESON, C. R. (1960). The electron microscopy of the myoepithelium in the rat exorbital lacrimal gland. *Anat. Record* 137, 45-56.

MONTAGNA, W. (1950). The brown inguinal glands of the rabbit. *Am. J. Anat.* 87, 213-238.

MONTAGNA, W. (1956). "The Structure and Function of Skin." New York, Academic Press.

MONTAGNA, W., AND ELLIS, R. A. (1957). Histology and cytochemistry of human skin. XII. Cholinesterases in the hair follicles of the scalp. *J. Invest. Dermatol.* 29, 151-157.

MONTAGNA, W., AND ELLIS, R. A. (1959). The skin of primates. I. The skin of the potto (*Perodicticus potto*). *Am. J. Phys. Anthropol.* 17, 137-162.

MONTAGNA, W., AND ELLIS, R. A. (1960a). The skin of primates. II. The skin of the slender loris (*Loris tardigradus*). *Am. J. Phys. Anthropol.* 18, 19-44.

MONTAGNA, W., AND ELLIS, R. A. (1960b). Histology and cytochemistry of human skin. XXI. The nerves around the axillary apocrine glands. *Am. J. Phys. Anthropol.* 18, 69-70.

MONTAGNA, W., AND YUN, J. S. (1962). Skin of primates. VIII. The skin of the greater bushbaby (*Galago crassicaudatus*). *Am. J. Phys. Anthropol.* 20, 149-166.

MONTAGNA, W., CHASE, H. B., AND MELARAGNO, H. P. (1951). Histology and cytochemistry of human skin. I. Metachromasia in the mons pubis. *J. Natl. Cancer Inst.* **12**, 591-597.

MONTAGNA, W., YASUDA, K., AND ELLIS, R. A. (1961). The skin of primates. III. The skin of the slow loris (*Nycticebus coucang*). *Am. J. Phys. Anthropol.* **19**, 1-22.

PEARSE, A. G. E. (1960). "Histochemistry Theoretical and Applied." Boston, Little, Brown.

PEASE, D. C. (1960). "Histological Techniques for Electron Microscopy." New York, Academic Press.

PORTER, K. R., AND BRUNI, C. (1959). An electron microscope study of the early effects of 3-Me-DAB on rat liver cells. *Cancer Research* **19**, 997-1010.

REVEL, J. P., NAPOLITANO, L., AND FAWCETT, D. W. (1960). Identification of glycogen in electron micrographs of thin tissue sections. *J. Biophys. Biochem. Cytol.* **8**, 575-589.

RUTENBURG, A. M., AND SELIGMAN, A. M. (1955). The histochemical demonstration of acid phosphatase by a post-incubation coupling technique. *J. Histochem. and Cytochem.* **3**, 455-470.

STOWELL, R. E., AND LEE, C. S. (1950). Histochemical studies of mouse liver after single feeding of carbon tetrachloride. *Arch. Pathol.* **50**, 519-537.

SUTTON, J. B. (1887). On the arm-glands of the lemurs. *Proc. Zool. Soc. London* pp. 369-372.

TAKEUCHI, T., AND KURIAKI, H. (1955). Histochemical demonstration of phosphorylase in animal tissues. *J. Histochem. and Cytochem.* **3**, 153-160.

WISLOCKI, G. B. (1930). A study of scent glands in the marmosets, especially *Oedipomidas geoffroyi*. *J. Mammal.* **11**, 475-483.

WHITTAKER, V. P. (1959). The isolation and characterization of acetylcholine containing particles from brain. *Biochem. J.* **72**, 694-706.

YAMADA, H., AND MIYAKE, S. (1960). Elektronenmikroskopische Untersuchungen an Nervenfasern in menschlichen Schweissdrüsen. *Z. Zellforsch. mikroskop. Anat.* **52**, 129-139.

YASUDA, K., AOKI, T., AND MONTAGNA, W. (1961). The skin of primates. IV. The skin of the lesser bushbaby (*Galago senegalensis*). *Am. J. Phys. Anthropol.* (in press).

Chapter 6

Nerve Endings in the Skin of Primates[1]

R. K. WINKELMANN

Section of Dermatology, Mayo Clinic and Mayo Foundation, Rochester, Minnesota

All science is descriptive, but the manner of describing primates has changed profoundly in the last two decades. It is now possible to use histological, chemical, and immunological tools to limn the character of the Order Primates. As more modern tools have been developed, the relationship between groups of animals has often become more complex or, sometimes, more simple. The new knowledge about morphology and histochemistry of end organs of nerves in the skin has added to the new field of comparative histochemistry, and it seems possible to describe primates in terms of the sensory-nerve end organs.

[1] This investigation was supported in part by Research Grant B-1755 from the United States Public Health Service.

New technical methods have made it possible to re-evaluate the receptor tissue in the skin. These techniques—frozen section, silver, and methylene blue methods for nerve axoplasm, and histochemical techniques for cholinesterase and alkaline phosphatase—have been described elsewhere (Winkelmann, 1960a). Specific cholinesterase and nonspecific cholinesterase are enzymes with special hydrolytic capacities for choline esters. Specific cholinesterase hydrolyzes acetylcholine. Nonspecific cholinesterase hydrolyzes long-chain aliphatic choline esters and aryl esters. Specific blocking compounds, such as NU 683 [dimethyl-carbamate of (1-hydroxy-2-biphenylylmethyl)-trimethylammonium bromide] and 62C47 [1,5-bis(4-trimethyl-ammoniumphenyl)-n-pentan-3-one diiodide], aid in the specific description of the enzymatic activity.

In assessing histochemical techniques, it is well to recognize that every tissue and every animal will demonstrate minor variations in enzyme content and activity; this by itself represents a difference between animal types. All the usual histochemical controls must be strictly applied. The only useful histochemical reactions are those that may be modified in a specific chemical manner so that they are more than complex ways of coloring tissue components.

I. Nerve Endings in Man

To provide a basis for comparison in the study of the nerves of primate skin, it is easiest to consider man as a prototype. While it certainly is fallacious to consider man as the most developed primate, it is true that his interest in himself remains most fully developed. Because of the detailed knowledge of man, I shall begin this survey with sensory receptors of human skin.

It has been well accepted that most of the nerve tissue in human skin resides in the dermal nerve networks (Weddell and co-workers, 1955). These are complex retia of peripheral nerve fibers formed by the association of many fibers which divide and subdivide to form finer and finer meshworks of nerve fibrils. The diameters of these networks become smaller with proximity to the epidermal surface, and the individual components are noted to have smaller and smaller diameters and less developed myelin sheaths near the surface. Ultimately, these networks become closely applied to the dermal surface of the epidermis; in fact, some of the fine fibrils are found between the epidermal cells. The number of intraepidermal nerve fibers is reported to be highest in fetal skin (Fitzgerald, 1961); my observations confirm this. The dermal nerve networks are the first visible nerve structures in the developing dermis. The dermal nerve network is the most rudimentary nerve organization, for it is found associated with epithelial coverings of vertebrates and of some invertebrates. It is found in all types of skin and it has the capacity for perceiving sensation of all types. It is generally held that touch, pain, and temperature may be perceived through this ending. Figure 1a demonstrates a typical example of such a nerve network. This example obtained in a recent study of tendon sheath represents a new cholinesterase whole-mount technique for demonstrating nerve networks (Lipscomb and Winkelmann, 1961).

The hair follicle in man appears to be principally a cosmetic appurtenance. It is, however, an epidermal appendage which is shared with all mammals. The nerves which form the network about the hair follicle are not clearly associated with dermal nerve networks. These nerves are seen in the dermis as heavily myelinated "A" fibers occurring often singly and in bundles (Winkelmann, 1959b). The fibers divide in the dermis and spread over a broad area to innervate many hairs collectively. Weddell and co-workers (1955) stated that approximately 100,000 hairs are innervated by 6,000 neurons in the rabbit ear and that the nerves are distributed irregularly to the hair follicles. The size and richness of the hair-follicle innervation varies directly with the size of the follicle; large growing hairs have well developed networks, and small resting hairs have small nerve networks. Four to nine nerve trunks form the basic follicular innervation. They are disposed in a rough meshwork about the hair follicle below the level at which the sebaceous gland enters into the follicular canal. The nerve fibers lose their myelin sheaths and divide into an outer, circular, network and an inner, longitudinal, network of nonmyelinated fibers. This is illustrated in Fig. 1b. The nerve fibers appear to terminate along the cells of the external sheath of the hair. Specific cholinesterase is found in the network of some human hair follicles (Montagna and Ellis, 1957); however, this activity is not related to any normal stage of hair growth or to any known structural change. The nerve fibers to the hair follicle perceive tactile sensation.

Organized nerve endings in the volar skin of the hands and feet have been termed Meissner's corpuscles. These end organs are found in almost every connective tissue papilla of the digits and are found with less frequency in the skin of the palms and soles. The nerves extending proximally from these end organs are composed of heavily myelinated nerve fibers which do not participate in the formation of dermal nerve networks. Groups of the end organs are innervated by single nerve trunks, and as many as three to five myelinated fibers from different nerve trunks may supply an individual Meissner corpuscle. The structure of the Meissner corpuscle is characterized by a layering and coiling

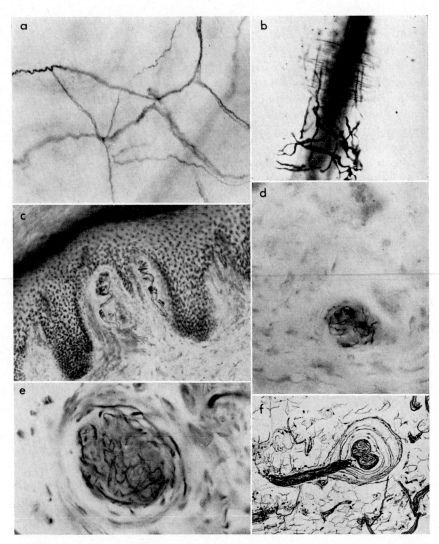

Fig. 1. a. Nerve network in *vinculum tendinum* of human finger. (Acetylthiocholinesterase, whole mount technique; × 78.) b. Hair-follicle nerve network in lip of cat. (Frozen section, silver method; × 186.) [Reprinted from Winkelmann (1960a).] c. Meissner corpuscles in volar surface of human finger pad. (Frozen section, silver method; × 78.) d. Mucocutaneous end organ below the epithelium in human glans penis. (Frozen section, silver method; × 192.) e. Mucocutaneous end organ in human clitoris. (Frozen section, silver method; × 310.) f. Cross-section through stalk of Vater-Pacini corpuscle in human panniculus. (Hematoxylin and eosin; × 93.)

of nerve fibers which ultimately terminate in knoblike or netlike expanded endings (Fig. 1c). It is often multilobulated. Nonspecific cholinesterase seen in these end organs (Winkelmann and Schmit, 1959) is not directly associated with the nerve fibers but probably with the cells or membranous surfaces of the ending (Cauna, 1960). It is agreed that this end organ serves the sensation of light touch. A variation of this end organ found at the dermal-epidermal junction is termed the hederiform ending of Merkel-Ranvier. These expanded tactile-disk endings may be intraepithelial. No enzyme is related directly to them.

Mucocutaneous end organs are the endings common to the glabrous skin of all structures interposed between haired skin and mucous membrane—lip, conjunctiva, palate, tongue, gingiva, prepuce, glans penis, clitoris, and perianal tissue (Winkelmann, 1957; 1959a). These end organs are not related to the dermal papillae, in fact they are usually found in the upper dermis (Fig. 1d). They consist of rolls of nonmyelinated fibrils supplied by several myelinated nerve fibers (Fig. 1e) which innervate them in groups or clusters. Nonspecific cholinesterase is found associated with these end organs. It is thought that they provide for acute perception of light touch.

The largest end organ in human skin is the Vater-Pacini corpuscle. Readily found along nerve trunks in the extremity, in the panniculus of the skin, and more rarely in the dermis, it is composed of an inner bulb containing the nerve fiber and a concentric lamellated capsule containing fluid. The electron microscope has revealed the capsule to be bilaterally symmetrical (Pease and Quilliam, 1957). This is confirmed also by ink-injection preparations indicating that the circulation of the end organ can be demonstrated on either half (Winkelmann and co-workers, 1960). The enzyme cholinesterase is found within the inner bulb about the nerve fiber. On occasion, nerve fibers can be seen coursing through cholinesterase-containing fluid. This end organ is often mistaken for other endings when it is cut through its stalk as shown in Fig. 1f. This is a pressure receptor, and it has been demonstrated that it will give rise to a receptor potential.

Table I indicates the location of the various nerve endings in the skin of man and their probable function. It is interesting that almost all of the attention of investigators has been given to the organized nerve endings which comprise less than 5% of the total nerve tissue in the human skin. The dermal nerve networks are the most important receptor structures for most of the human skin surface. The specialized endings appear to give more acute sensory capacity, and they provide a possibility for masses of nerve tissue to rise closer to the surface. The content of nonspecific cholinesterase in all these organized end organs suggests that the structural differences between the Meissner corpuscle and the mucocutaneous end organs are probably superficial, relating to their development in different types of skin.

TABLE I
NERVE ENDINGS IN HUMAN SKIN

Type of skin	Function		
	Touch	Pain and temperature	Pressure
Mucous membrane	Dermal nerve network	Dermal nerve network	—
Haired skin	Hair-follicle nerve network	Dermal nerve network	—
Glabrous skin			
Mucocutaneous	Mucocutaneous end organ	Dermal nerve network	—
Distal	Meissner corpuscle	Dermal nerve network	—
Subcutaneous tissue	—	—	Vater-Pacini corpuscle

It seems useful to emphasize that one end organ, the nerve network, can subserve all the sensations; and that all the end organs can subserve one sensation, that of touch (Table I). Under these circumstances, it is difficult to ascribe a specific function to a given morphological or histochemical finding. This will be emphasized even more by the discussions of other primates.

II. NERVE ENDINGS IN OTHER PRIMATES

A. GORILLA

Detailed study of gorilla skin (Winkelmann, 1961) led to the finding that the bulk of its cutaneous nerve tissue is disposed in nerve networks about the hair follicles which form its furred surface. These networks comprise the principal receptor tissue of gorilla skin. Dermal nerve networks, on the other hand, are rudimentary and are readily visible only in glabrous skin. Sensory hairs with their surrounding vascular sinuses were found in the brow and lip. Meissnerform corpuscles, simple, monolobular, layered masses of neurofibrils, were seen in distal glabrous skin (Fig. 2a). No expanded nerve terminations were observed in this ending from the gorilla palm. Figure 2b shows the more complex, unorganized nerve ending found in the tongue of the gorilla immediately beneath the epidermis. This represents the mucocutaneous end organ of gorilla skin. Cholinesterase of a nonspecific type was observed in these organized end organs in both distal and mucocutaneous glabrous skin. The Vater-Pacini corpuscle also contained nonspecific cholinesterase within its inner bulb. The mammalian end organ was found in the skin of the perineum of the gorilla. It is illustrated and described more fully in a subsequent section.

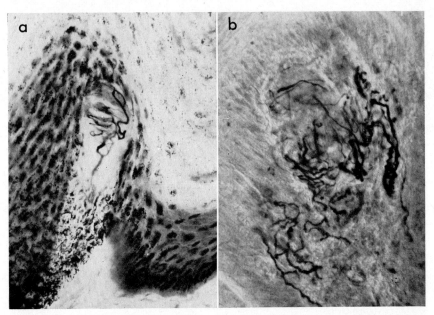

Fig. 2. a. Meissnerform corpuscle in gorilla palm. (Frozen section, silver method; × 287.) b. Large end organ below epithelium of gorilla tongue. (Frozen section, silver method; × 287.)

B. Orangutan

The distributions of dermal nerve networks and hair-follicle nerve networks were essentially the same in the orangutan as in the gorilla. Specialized end organs were comparable also and were found in all glabrous skin. In Fig. 3a, cholinesterase reactivity is seen in Meissnerform corpuscles of the thenar eminence. The light quality of this reaction is due to nonspecific cholinesterase within the end organ slowly hydrolyzing acetylthiocholine, the specific cholinesterase substrate. Figures 3b and 3c illustrate the layered Meissnerform corpuscles from the lip. It should be noted once again that no expanded terminations are present but that the end organs seem to be made up of more than one lobule and to be supplied with many nonmyelinated nerve fibers.

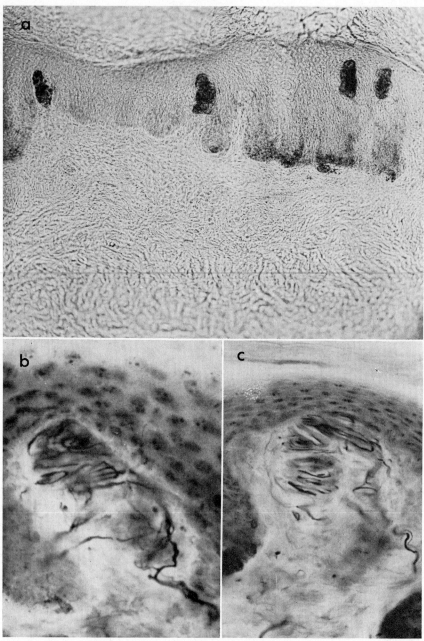

Fig. 3.   a. Meissner corpuscles of thenar eminence in orangutan. (Acetylthiocholine; × 72.) b. Mucocutaneous end organ below epithelium of lip of orangutan. (Frozen section, silver technique; × 450.)   c. End organ of lip of orangutan. (Frozen section, silver technique; × 270.)

C. Chimpanzee

The relationships of dermal nerve networks and hair-follicle networks are the same in all of the great apes (Winkelmann, 1962). Sensory hair was found on the brow, upper lip, and chin of the chimpanzee. Meissner-form corpuscles were seen in the glabrous skin. A general indication of the frequency of their occurrence may be seen in Fig. 4a. Most rete ridges of the toes contained as many Meissnerform corpuscles as did those of the fingers. In Fig. 4b, a closeup of a Meissnerform corpuscle from the nail fold of a chimpanzee indicates its close similarity to that found in man. Once again, no clearly defined expanded terminations are apparent. The rather nonspecific appearance of the nerve ending from the lip of the chimpanzee is typical of the mucocutaneous end organ (Fig. 4c). One would guess that this might be one of the mucocutaneous regions, from the general form of the nerve ending. We see several layered Meissnerform corpuscles with a more typical structure in Fig. 4d for comparison. It is difficult to maintain that a significant difference is present.

The cholinesterase reaction in the chimpanzee paralleled that noted in the other apes. In the lip of the chimpanzee (Fig. 5a) a number of organized nerve endings are found in the dermal papillae below the epidermis. It is interesting that the cholinesterase-positive end organs in the perianal tissue and in the knuckle pads as seen in Fig. 5b and 5c respectively have similar layered Meissnerform corpuscles.

D. Gibbon

Investigation of gibbon tissue provided a good example of the similarity between Meissner corpuscles and mucocutaneous end organs. The specialized endings were smaller and simpler and thus more comparable in all areas. Two of the mucocutaneous regions are demonstrated in Figs. 6a and 6b. Multiple sensory end organs in close relation to the epidermis are demonstrated by the nonspecific cholinesterase technique. It is instructive to compare the nonspecific or butyrylthiocholine-substrate reaction evidenced in these figures with the previous specimens of chimpanzee and orangutan skin incubated with acetylcholine, and to note the greater density of butyrylthiocholine in the same time of incubation.

The demonstration of alkaline phosphatase in Meissner corpuscles of the gibbon is an important finding in comparative histochemistry. This is difficult to observe because of the positive reaction in the capillaries of the skin, but at the peak of almost every papilla of the digit may be found an alkaline-phosphatase-positive end organ. In Fig. 6c such a

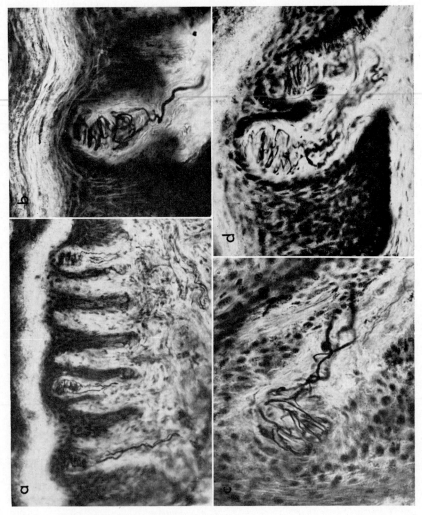

FIG. 4. a. Meissner corpuscles in the dermal papillae of great toe of chimpanzee. (Frozen section, silver technique; × 164.) b. Meissner corpuscle in nail fold of chimpanzee. (Frozen section, silver technique; × 328.) c. Mucocutaneous end organ in lip of chimpanzee. (Frozen section, silver technique; × 328.) d. Meissnerform corpuscles in skin of hypothenar eminence of chimpanzee. (Frozen section, silver technique; × 267.)

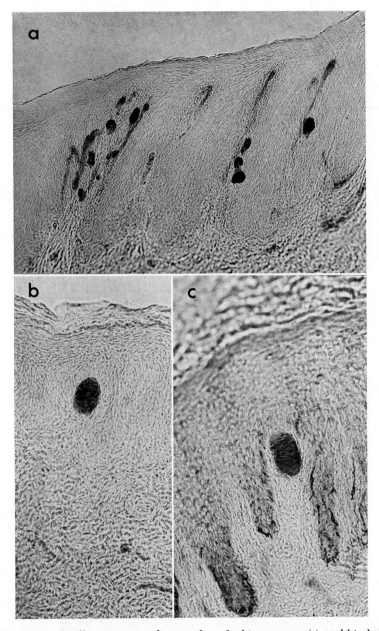

FIG. 5.   a. Papillary nerve ending in lip of chimpanzee. (Acetylthiocholine; × 100.)   b. Meissnerform corpuscle in the perianal skin of chimpanzee. (Acetylthiocholine; × 155.)   c. Meissnerform corpuscle in knuckle pad of chimpanzee. (Acetylthiocholine; × 175.)

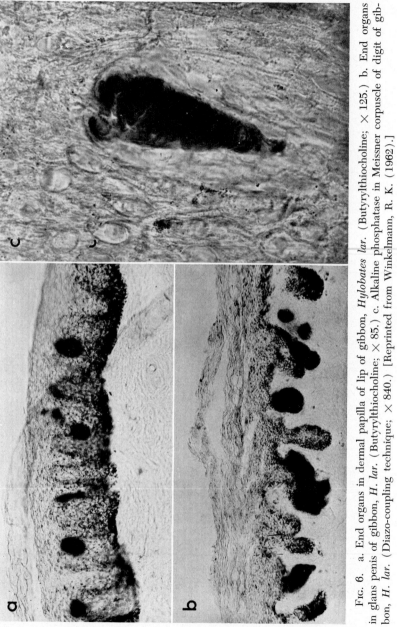

FIG. 6. a. End organs in dermal papilla of lip of gibbon, *Hylobates lar*. (Butyrylthiocholine; × 125.) b. End organs in glans penis of gibbon, *H. lar*. (Butyrylthiocholine; × 85.) c. Alkaline phosphatase in Meissner corpuscle of digit of gibbon, *H. lar*. (Diazo-coupling technique; × 840.) [Reprinted from Winkelmann, R. K. (1962).]

Meissner corpuscle is seen demonstrated by the diazo-coupling technique for alkaline phosphatase. Note that the path of the nerve is clearly demonstrated in negative relief by the activity of the enzyme. This reaction is also found associated with the other specialized end organs of the gibbon.

E. CERCOPITHECIDAE

Silver studies were performed with tissue from a female *Theropithecus gelada* and a female *Papio sphinx* (mandrill), a male *Cercopithecus l'hoesti*, a female *C. mona*, a male *C. neglectus*, a male *C. aethiops*, a male *Macaca mulatta*, and a male *Macaca irus*.

Rudimentary organized nerve endings were seen in glabrous skin. The endings in this group of animals were all monolobular and composed of masses of neurofibrils. The endings had far less formal structure than those of the great apes. A rudimentary papillary ending from the lip of the *Macaca irus* is shown in Fig. 7a. In the glans penis of the *M. mulatta* there is a simple mucocutaneous end organ comparable to those seen in man (Fig. 7b). In the sexual skin of the baboon, *Theropithecus gelada*, one may see a comparable end organ (Fig. 7c). Histochemical studies were done only on *Macaca mulatta*. Nonspecific cholinesterase was seen in the organized end organs. Alkaline phosphatase was seen only in the capillaries. The hair-follicle nerve networks are prominent as in Fig. 7d demonstrating structure comparable to that seen in man and other mammals. The dermal nerve networks are minimally developed as in the anthropoid apes.

F. CEBIDAE

The family Cebidae is represented in this study by male and female capuchin monkeys (*Cebus albifrons*), a female spider monkey (*Ateles geoffroyi*), a male *Ateles fusciceps robustus*, a male Marmoset (*Tamarinus leucogenys*), and a female *Oedipomidas oedipus*. All the studies in these animals were done with frozen-section silver techniques. No histochemical studies were made with this group.

The dermal nerve networks are very primitive. The nerve networks about the small, grouped hair follicles are correspondingly small. Tastscheibe, or tactile epithelial disks of Pinkus, are found near hair follicles in the skin of *Cebus albifrons* and the spider monkey. One of these endings is illustrated in Fig. 8. Heavy myelinated nerve fiber rises to the epithelium and divides into small nonmyelinated fibrils which relate themselves closely to the epithelium.

The organized nerve endings of the glabrous skin of the Cebidae are very much like those of man. The typical mucocutaneous end organs

seen in the lips are prototypes of those found in similar areas in man
(Figs. 9a and 9c). The ending represented in Fig. 9c could be from
any region of glabrous transitional skin in man. Similarly, Meissner
corpuscles seen in the distal glabrous skin are typical of those found

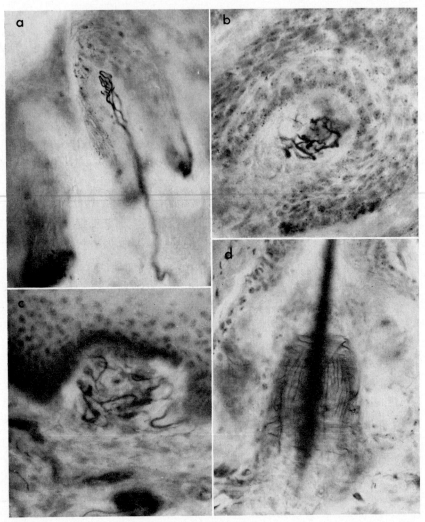

FIG. 7. a. Meissnerform corpuscle in lip of *Macaca irus*. (Frozen section, silver
technique; × 355.) b. End organ in glans penis of rhesus macaque. (Frozen section, silver technique; × 355.) c. End organ in sexual skin of baboon, *Theropithecus gelada*. (Frozen section, silver technique; × 213.) d. Hair-follicle nerve network from perianal skin of rhesus macaque. (Frozen section, silver technique;
× 355.)

in man. They are quite elongated end organs with marked layering and coiling of the component nerves. There is more evidence of expanded disklike formations here (Figs. 9b and 9d) than in most of the rudimentary Meissnerform corpuscles seen in primates. It is interesting to note that in the prehensile tail of the New World monkey, one will find Meissner corpuscles in the glabrous skin equating the sensory innervation of this surface with that of the digital surface.

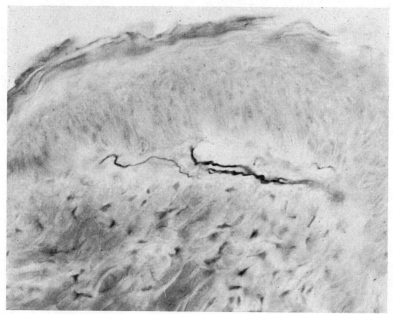

FIG. 8. Tactile hair disk in dorsal skin of *Cebus albifrons.* (Frozen section, silver technique; × 300.)

G. LORISIFORMES

Excellent descriptions of the slender and slow lorises, *Perodicticus potto,* and *Galago senegalensis* have been written by Montagna and his colleagues (1959, 1960, 1961a, 1961b). I will not repeat their findings but will emphasize that these authors have pointed out the rudimentary nature of the skin in these animals. I have studied the greater and lesser bush babies (*Galago crassicaudatus, G. senegalensis*), the slow loris (*Nycticebus coucang*), and *Perodicticus potto.* These animals have been studied with silver and histochemical techniques.

The skin of the Lorisiformes appears to be quite rudimentary. Specific cholinesterase-containing nerve fibrils are found in masses in glabrous skin regions. About the hair follicle, there is a mass of cholin-

esterase-positive nerve tissue. Yasuda and co-workers (1961) referred
to this as the "hair end organ." They also noted alkaline phosphatase
and α-naphthol esterase in the same region in the lesser galago (*G.
senegalensis*).

Coils of nonmyelinated nerve fibrils are found in the specialized skin
of this group of animals. The most rudimentary type of end organ

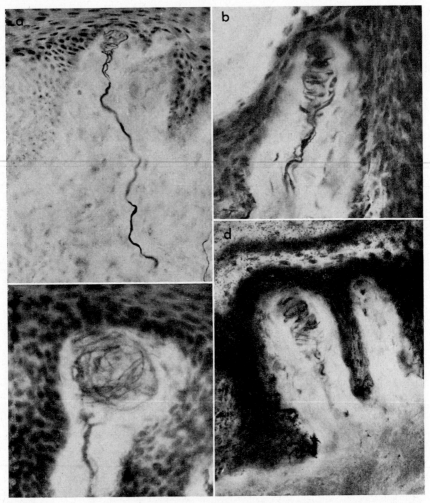

FIG. 9.   a. Meissnerform corpuscle in lip of *Cebus albifrons*. (Frozen section,
silver method; × 350.)   b. Meissnerform corpuscle of palm of *Cebus albifrons*.
(Frozen section, silver method; × 350.)   c. Mucocutaneous end organ of upper
lip of *Cebus albifrons*. (Frozen section, silver method; × 350.)   d. Meissnerform
corpuscle in digit of *Cebus albifrons*. (Frozen section, silver method; × 350.)

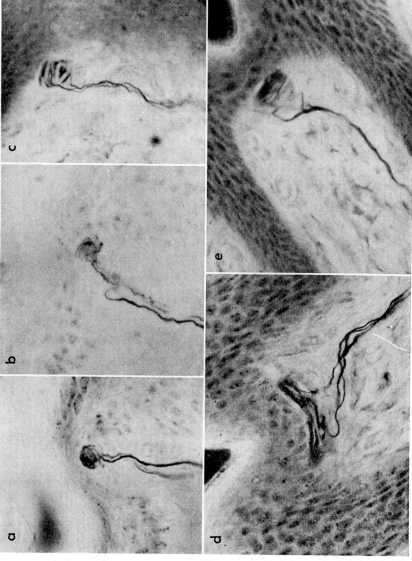

Fig. 10. a. Rudimentary papillary ending in volar skin of finger of *Perodicticus potto*. (Frozen section, silver method; × 360.) b. Rudimentary papillary ending in finger of *P. potto*. (Frozen section, silver method; × 360.) c. Meissnerform corpuscle of digit of slow loris. (Frozen section, silver method; × 360.) d. Flattened Meissnerform ending below epithelium of palm of slow loris. (Frozen section, silver method; × 216.) e. Meissnerform corpuscle in palm of slow loris. (Frozen section, silver method; × 360.)

245

seen in primates, a small ball of nerve fibrils, is shown in Figs. 10a and 10b from the digit of the potto. It should be noted that heavily myelinated nerves supply these end organs, which are found only high in the tips of the papillary body, and are similar to the much larger mucocutaneous end organs of larger primates. In the slow loris the end organ is larger and shows a layered form more like the Meissner corpuscle

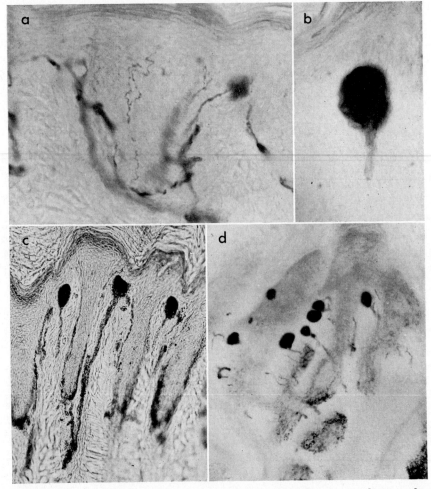

Fig. 11.   a. Subepidermal nerve network and intraepithelial nerve ending in index finger of *Perodicticus potto*. (Acetylthiocholine; × 225.)   b. Papillary end organ in thenar skin of *Galago crassicaudatus*. (Butyrylthiocholine; × 375.)   c. Several papillary nerve end organs in thumb of slow loris. (Acetylthiocholine; × 120.) d. Section parallel to surface of epithelium in thenar skin of *Galago crassicaudatus*. (Butyrylthiocholine; × 94.) Note the multiple end organs.

(Fig. 10c). In the palms of lorises this type of ending may be flattened considerably by the overlying epithelium, demonstrating the effect of growth of epithelium and dermis on the related nerve tissue (Fig. 10d). Simple Meissner corpuscles do occur in the lorises (Fig. 10e). It should be emphasized that these end organs are primitive and lack the size, lobulation, and expanded terminations that characterize them in larger primates.

The rudimentary skin of the potto displays a unique relationship of nerve to epidermis. Below the epidermis of the glabrous skin is a closely applied network of thick fibrils. These resemble meshworks of melanocytes in this position but no dendritic processes can be noted. Figure 11a illustrates this dermoepidermal, cholinesterase-positive nerve network; also it reveals intraepithelial nerve fibers demonstrable in thick glabrous skin of this type.

The Meissnerform corpuscle demonstrates nonspecific cholinesterase, an activity not related to the nerve fibers. The nerve and the cell nuclei of the end organ are often seen in relief in the mass of enzymatic activity (Fig. 11b). This same type of end organ may be seen in a specific-cholinesterase preparation of the loris thumb. Note that there is one end organ for every dermal papilla of the thumb in Fig. 11c. If such an area is cut parallel to the surface of the epithelium, it is possible to look down upon a large number of these endings (Fig. 11d). Here a number of nonspecific cholinesterase-positive end organs are seen from above. The Vater-Pacini corpuscle demonstrates nonspecific-cholinesterase activity in all these species.

H. LEMURIFORMES

Studies of lemur skin are in progress in many laboratories. Some unique features of the black lemur (*Lemur macaco*) have been recorded (Montagna and associates, 1961a). It is apparent at the present time that the end organs are principally papillary nerves similar to those in the lorises, but there also exist—in the lip and nose—complicated endings similar to the mammalian end organ. The histochemistry of these end organs reveals nonspecific cholinesterase. No cholinesterase is found in the dermal or hair-follicle nerve fiber. This data will be reported more completely when more than one species of the lemur family have been studied.

I. TUPAIAFORMES

Silver preparations made from glabrous skin of male and female Philippine tree shrews (*Urogale everetti*) did not reveal papillary endings of the Meissner or mucocutaneous type. Masses of dermal nerves were seen in silver preparations, but none of the end organs character-

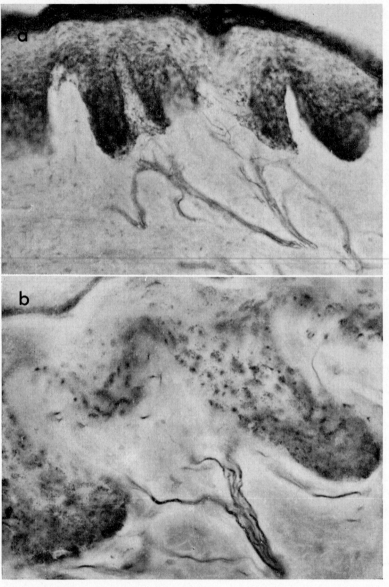

Fig. 12. a. Multiple nerve nets in skin of *Urogale everetti,* Philippine tree shrew. (Frozen section, silver method; × 125.) b. Dermal nerve networks below epithelium in palm of Philippine tree shrew, *Urogale everetti.* (Frozen section, silver method; × 310.)

istic of primates were found. The nose, particularly, had a heavy dermal nerve network (Fig. 12a). No typical mammalian end organs were seen in the specimens collected, but it seems probable that this is the type of innervation possessed by this particular tupaia. Contrasting Fig. 12b with the photomicrographs of the loris emphasizes the distinct lack of organized nerve tissue.

III. The Vater-Pacini Corpuscle

The Vater-Pacini corpuscle in all the animal forms reported herein has essentially the same component parts. These have been adequately described elsewhere (Winkelmann, 1960a), and will be only illustrated here so that it can be seen that animals as diverse as the orangutan and the tree shrew have similar end organs of this type. In the larger animals, such as the orangutan, the end organ can be quite complex and coil on itself many times. This is illustrated in Fig. 13a where three limbs of the same corpuscle have been cut. The inner bulb passes between the two lower limbs, just out of the plane of this section. A similar complex ending with more than one limb, in the gibbon, is seen in Fig. 13b. The more complex Vater-Pacini corpuscle represented in the gibbon and in the orangutan are comparable to those studied in man by Winkelmann and Osment (1956) with wax reconstructions. The simpler, smaller primates have simpler, smaller end organs. This is illustrated by the Vater-Pacini corpuscle, in Fig. 13c, from the slow loris. The inner bulb and its central nerve are clearly demarcated. This is the structure which contains all the enzyme. The tree shrew has this end organ also, as seen in Fig. 13d. The crenations of the border are due to fixation prior to silver staining. In Fig. 13e, there is a cross-section through a Vater-Pacini corpuscle in *Galago crassicaudatus* demonstrating the sharp limitation of nonspecific cholinesterase to the central inner bulb. A similar picture is observed in Fig. 13f in a specimen from the heel of the *Lemur fulvus rufus*. In addition to the cholinesterase, alkaline phosphatase is contained within the inner bulb of the Vater-Pacini corpuscle of the gibbon. These end organs are most numerous in the skin of digits, but they may be found anywhere under the distal glabrous skin and also in preputial, genital, and nipple skin. They have not been seen in the lip or oral tissues of any species studied.

IV. End Organs in Other Animals

A. Other Mammals

It seems useful to illustrate, for purposes of comparison, nerve end organs as they may be seen in animals not considered primates. Such

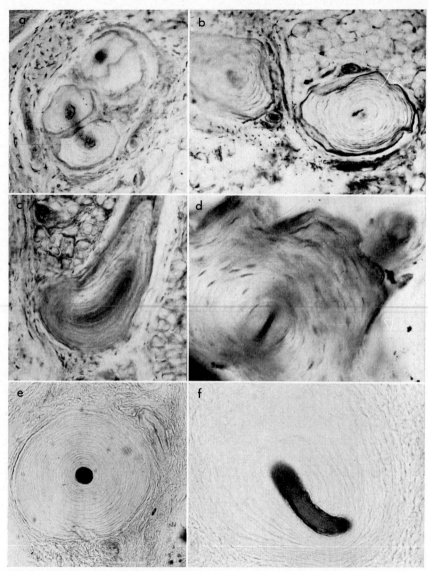

Fig. 13. a. Three limbs of Vater-Pacini corpuscle in panniculus of orangutan. (Frozen section, silver method; × 79.) b. Two limbs of Vater-Pacini corpuscle in panniculus of finger of gibbon, *Hylobates hoolock*. (Frozen section, silver technique; × 195.) c. Vater-Pacini corpuscle in panniculus of palm of slow loris demonstrating prominent inner bulb. (Frozen section, silver method; × 79.) d. Typical Vater-Pacini corpuscle in volar surface of digit of Philippine tree shrew, *Urogale everetti*. (Frozen section, silver technique; × 315.) e. Cross-section of Vater-Pacini corpuscle of *Galago crassicaudatus* demonstrating nonspecific-cholinesterase activity limited to inner bulb. (Butyrylthiocholine; × 79.) f. Nonspecific-cholinesterase activity within inner bulb in oblique section of Vater-Pacini corpuscle of heel of *Lemur fulvus rufus*. (Butyrylthiocholine technique; × 195.)

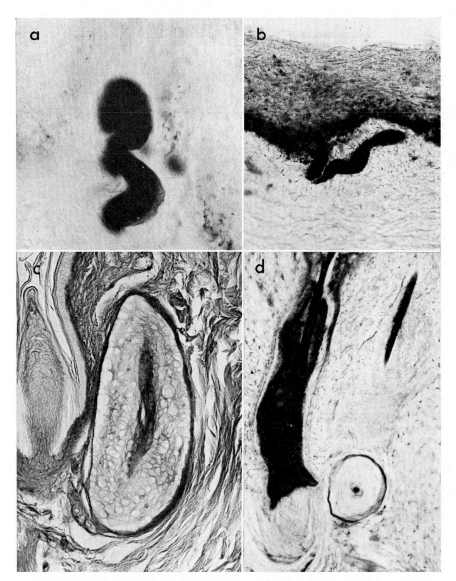

FIG. 14. a. Mammalian end organ below skin in palm of kinkajou demonstrating nonspecific-cholinesterase activity. (Butyrylthiocholine; × 270.) b. Mammalian end organ in lip of puma. (Butyrylthiocholine; × 215.) c. Vater-Pacini corpuscle in feathered skin of chicken demonstrating acid mucopolysaccharide. (Alcian-blue-PAS technique; × 153.) d. Vater-Pacini corpuscle in glabrous skin of base of beak of rooster. (Frozen section, silver technique; × 117.)

an animal is the kinkajou, an arboreal mammal with a grasping extremity. It has the mammalian end organ (Winkelmann, 1960a), an encapsulated end organ, in its fore and hind paws. This is the end organ described in cats and other animals with claws, hoofs, and paws. In Fig. 14a, one of these serpiginous end organs may be seen near the epidermis, outlined by the reaction of its nonspecific cholinesterase. A similar end organ in the lip of a puma (American mountain lion) is seen in Fig. 14b. Such end organs are found in the mucocutaneous regions of all non-primate mammals studied to date. Rarely they are seen in haired skin. This end organ is apparently a duplicate of the inner bulb of the Vater-Pacini corpuscle except for the degree of coiling and turning which it may show. In comparable species, the inner bulbs of Vater-Pacini corpuscles and mammalian end organs will contain the same enzymes. That is, they both contain alkaline phosphatase as well as nonspecific cholinesterase in the felines (Winkelmann, 1960b). The only primate with such an ending is the gorilla in whose genital skin a similar structure was described.

B. Birds

Throughout the glabrous and feathered skin of the chicken is to be found a Vater-Pacini corpuscle which has a close relationship to the feather follicle. This relationship is clearly seen in Figs. 14c and 14d. The large number of these end organs under the skin is unique, for this is not like the glabrous skin of mammals where these bodies are usually found. These end organs contain an acid mucopolysaccharide as illustrated by the alcian blue stain (Fig. 14c). These are the only Vater-Pacini corpuscles studied in any animal which contain such a polysaccharide (Winkelmann and Myers, 1961). A general comparison of the cross-section of one of these end organs to the Vater-Pacini corpuscle may be made from comparing Figs. 13 and 14d; it seems apparent that this is not a unique ending. The usual form of the nerve end organ in the chicken is the Vater-Pacini corpuscle, and this is present in large numbers in glabrous as well as feathered skin. The dermal nerve networks are poorly developed, and feather follicles have minimal innervation. Specific cholinesterase is found within the inner bulb of these end organs in the chicken. Alkaline phosphatase is found in the nerve trunks of the rooster, but it is not found within any organized end organ.

V. Comment

The primate can be characterized by the innervation of its skin just as correctly as by its bipedal gate and its dental formula. A ball of nonmyelinated neurofibrils has been found in the hairless skin of all primates studied to date. While its structure varies from area to area and animal to animal in some degree, basically it appears to represent a common form of innervation of hairless skin in these animals. The haired-skin innervation varies with the density of hair follicles but is quite alike in all the animals of this order. The hair-follicle innervation and the dermal nerve networks comprise almost all of the innervation of the general body surface of these mammals. Under the mucous membrane, one finds only dermal nerve networks or submucosal nerve networks.

One is impressed by the comparable structures for the reception of sensations in all forms of primate skin. The only variations that appear to exist are those of a minor structural nature which seem to be associated with changes in the epidermis, dermis, or deeper tissues. Another major feature which the primates possess in common is the content of enzymes in the organized end organs. Nonspecific cholinesterase is found in association with all the end organs of a specialized nature and provides a recognized chemical similarity.

Some emphasis on the minor distinct differences between the forms of innervation of the various species is necessary for completeness and for comparison. The Meissner corpuscle and mucocutaneous end organ are very definite structures in human skin and, while it is possible to demonstrate some of these differences in other primates, it is not possible to clearly distinguish between the two. A potto has small endings in all its glabrous skin, which are structurally like the mucocutaneous end organs of man. Meissnerform corpuscles were observed in the mucocutaneous region in most of the primates studied. Monolobular Meissner nerve endings were seen in almost all groups, but the expanded nerve terminations in the Meissner corpuscle are only typical of man. The common aspect of the endings of the glabrous skin of primates is emphasized by the lack of clear identifying structural features.

Human glabrous skin differs in several ways from that of the primates studied. The Meissner corpuscle is well developed in man and usually shows several lobules and terminates in expanded disklike endings. Just as this typical development of the end organ is not seen in other primates, the hederiform ending of Merkel-Ranvier does not occur in primates other than man. Tactile disks of Merkel-Ranvier have been seen in other animals, notably the mole, cat, and pig; but no such structures were seen in any of the primates except man. The dermal nerve networks are more prominent in human skin principally because the hair-follicle innervation is not as well developed and does not preempt the dermis. In the primitive primates such as the lorises and potto there is grouping of the hair and this grouping of hair provides a pattern of innervation which has been called the "hair end organ." The hairs are innervated in common by a number of nonmyelinated fibrils which possess a unique cholinesterase activity. In the human hair, only an occasional follicle will be found to have cholinesterase-positive nerves in relation to it. The primate hair organ will contain nonspecific cholinesterase as well as specific cholinesterase-positive fibers. The tactile hair disk (Tastscheibe) of Pinkus has been seen in all primate skin. It is interesting that man does not possess sensory hair and that all other primates do. This is apparently as characteristic of human skin as any other morphological feature.

Man is unique in the small number of hair follicles in a given area of skin surface. The other furred primates are more closely related to one another and to the other furred mammals than they are to man in this respect. The innervation of furred skin is related to hair-follicle density. It appears that man is a unique animal and is unlike other primates in some small structural details relative to innervation of skin. Other primates are much more like other furred animals in the general organization of their skin nerves.

Encapsulated end organs are found in primates, other mammals, and reptiles, and they are the common cutaneous end organs of chickens. These appear in the most ancient and most recent forms of vertebrates. As illustrated, the basic shape is the same in the Vater-Pacini corpuscle of all animal types. A greater complexity of external form is all that distinguishes the Vater-Pacini corpuscle of the smallest primate from that of man or the orangutan.

All encapsulated end organs of primates are similar with regard to their content of nonspecific cholinesterase. It should be noted that the demonstration of mammalian end organs in the perineal skin of gorillas is unique, a finding that merits special consideration. One might not be quite so surprised to find this end organ common to many mammals in the skin of the lorises or lemurs, but to find it only in the skin of the gorilla is of great interest. It may be that despite its size this animal is not one of the more developed primates in this respect. Probably this is simply a vestigial sensory ending.

One morphological principle appears to hold fast for primates—the larger the part innervated, the more complex the innervation. Nerve networks about large hair follicles in large primates are more complex and are supplied by more nerve fibers than are those about small hair follicles in smaller primates. In the rudimentary primates the hair follicles are grouped, thus increasing the mass of innervation in a given area and forming what has been called a "hair end organ." In the resting stage of the hair growth cycle, the innervation is simple and rudimentary; in the growing phase the hair nerve network is large, complex, and well developed. Specialized end organs are larger and more complex in larger primates. The Meissnerform corpuscles are best developed in the great apes and man and are smallest and simplest in the little lorises. The simple balls of nerve fibrils present in all the glabrous skin of *P. potto* are much different from the lobulated complex Meissner end organs seen only in the distal glabrous skin of man. Cauna (1956) tried to relate the complexity of the Meissner end organ to the occupation of the man and indicated that the complex Meissner end organs were seen principally in manual laborers. It seems that man is the only animal that has truly complex Meissner corpuscles. This emphasizes that some developmental changes have occurred in the specialization of the primates, and also emphasizes that these are not fundamental. It is significant that the Cebidae demonstrate more organization in their nerve endings than do the Cercopithecidae. This is one exception to the rule: the larger the animal the more complex the nerve ending. The Cebidae (New World monkeys) also show a fifth-hand innervation in their prehensile tails. This gives an unusual degree of specialization to the peripheral sensory nerve endings in the skin of these monkeys.

Lemurs and lorises displayed "hair end organs," or complexes of nerve networks about groups of hair, and small rudimentary end organs as their principal cutaneous nerve endings. The Meissner form quality of the organized nerve endings is as well developed in them as in the Cercopithecidae. No unique findings set the lemurs and lorises apart from other primates which are termed more developed, and it may be stated that these are small primates in respect to the nerve supply of the skin. This is not true for the *Tupaia* tissue available. The complete lack of nerve organization similar to the primate casts some doubt on the kinship of the Philippine tree shrew, *Urogale everetti*, to the other animals studied. It would hardly be a surprise to find the mammalian type end organ in this animal when more opportunities for study present themselves.

It is important to emphasize that the existence of a grasping extremity does not necessarily imply a sensory function comparable to that of the primates. Special gross anatomical features of the primate extremity are well known but the fact that the sensory capacity of this extremity is unique also has not been emphasized. The grasping hand of such mammals as the raccoon and kinkajou possesses the long convoluted end organ termed the mammalian end organ, and masses of papillary nerve tissue are notably absent. The end organs in these extremities are much closer to those in animals with hoofs and paws than to those in primates, despite the capacity of the animals to grasp objects for climbing or for eating.

Comparison of primates with other animals provides the clearest evidence of differences in sensory receptors. The endings in animals of the feline, canine, and rodent groups are so unlike the end organs of primates that the difference should not have been overlooked. Only Krause (1860) noted that man and some monkeys had similar end organs with characteristics quite unlike those of nonprimates. Now that the mammalian end organ has been rediscovered and described, it is apparent that it has a universal distribution in the glabrous skin of nonprimate mammals. It has been observed in the rat, mouse, gopher, mole, cat, dog, rabbit, guinea pig, sheep, goat, cow, raccoon, and kinkajou. It functions as both the Meissner corpuscle and the mucocutaneous end organ of these animals. In common with the primates, these mammals have a Vater-Pacini corpuscle in their deeper tissues. The structural relationship between the Vater-Pacini corpuscle and the mammalian end organ is readily apparent, and in all species studied, the histochemical relationship is similar also. The enzyme content is a common unifying feature of all the nerve end organs.

The organization for the perception of sensation of the peripheral and central nervous systems of the raccoon and the kinkajou must be different from that of the primate. This implies some conceptual differences also. Relying principally on nerve networks and on encapsulated end organs, it is interesting that these animals perform manual feats fundamentally similar to those performed by primates with their more elaborate end organs. One would suppose that the principal difference is in the fine discriminatory sensory capacity that the primate possesses.

This definite division between the primates studied and the other mammals suggests that the morphology of the endings may have phylogenetic or anthropological significance as measured in living examples. If the primates are considered to be mammals which developed later than the nonprimates, then one would suppose their end organs would not be represented in animals known to have evolved earlier. Possibly some unstudied primates or unstudied mammals have a transitional form of innervation. These are questions which require answers.

The cholinesterase reactions provide an interesting method of studying and locating sensory end organs of the skin. However, these techniques should be controlled, for nonspecific cholinesterase may slowly hydrolyze acetylthiocholine, producing false-positive reactions with this specific choline substrate when incubation is prolonged. In human tissue the division between specific cholinesterase in the autonomic nervous system of the skin and nonspecific cholinesterase in the sensory end organs is quite definite after 1 to 2 hours of incubation. Montagna *et al.* (1961a, b) have stated that some of the more primitive primates have a mixture of cholinesterases in their end organs. It is possible that this represents principally nonspecific cholinesterase activity which is capable of hydrolyzing the specific substrate too, if sufficient time is allowed. In the lemur no such mixture appears to occur and no mixture of cholinesterases was found in the gorilla, orangutan, chimpanzee, or gibbon. Unusual localization for cholinesterase is sometimes observed as in the glands of the dog paw where the cholinesterase is located within the cells of the gland. In skin of the rooster specific cholinesterase is found within encapsulated end organs. It should be remembered, too, that human plasma contains nonspecific cholinesterase and that human red blood cells contain specific cholinesterase. Determinations of similar tissue cholinesterases have not been made for the other primates, but this might affect the results of histochemical studies.

Nonspecific cholinesterase is a great chemical link that bypasses structural variation in providing a basis for the thesis that all the organized end organs may have a common functional capacity. Only a few studies have been done to relate function of the end organs to their histochemistry. Hurley and Koelle (1958) have shown that inhibiting the enzyme with dispropyl fluorophosphate does not inhibit the function of touch in human skin. I have shown (unpublished observations) that nerve section which interrupts axoplasmic continuity does not cause the loss of cholinesterase activity. Therefore, the direct relationship of the cholinesterase to the function of the end organ has no experimental support at the present time.

Montagna and Ellis (1959) have stated that the primates are characterized by having phosphorylase in the epidermis. The organized nervous tissue in primate skin is characterized principally by the cholinesterase content described herein. α-Naphthol acetate esterase and naphthol AS-esterase have been found in human Meissner corpuscles. Montagna and Yun (1961) found cytochrome oxidase in human Meissner corpuscles by means of the newer technique of Burstone. Monamine oxidase and β-glucuronidase, found in peripheral nerve fibers, are not found in end organs. Alkaline phosphatase in the specialized endings of the gibbon is a unique finding for the primates studied. Does the siamang have a similar alkaline phosphatase content in its end organs? If this is characteristic of the gibbon, can a relation to other unstudied primates be foretold?

It has been shown in the past that certain animal skins possess characteristic chemical signatures (Scheen and Winkelmann, 1961). This has been demonstrated particularly by using alkaline phosphatase techniques. Man and the other primates, except the gibbon, have alkaline phosphatase within capillaries but not within their end organs. The cat has alkaline phosphatase in the mammalian end organ but not within the capillaries. The cow has alkaline phosphatase within end organs and capillaries. It has been possible to characterize all of the feline family from all continents by means of histochemical techniques. The cheetah definitely has the histochemical signature of a feline within its skin; the genet (*Genetta genetta*) does not. It is anticipated that histochemistry will add other evidences of variation in chemical content of primate tissues and provide a new means of comparative study and a means of demonstrating new relationships between existing forms of life.

REFERENCES

CAUNA, N. (1956). Nerve supply and nerve endings in Meissner's corpuscles. *Am. J. Anat.* 99, 315-350.

CAUNA, N. (1960). The distribution of cholinesterase in the cutaneous receptor organs, especially touch corpuscles of the human finger. *J. Histochem. and Cytochem.* 8, 367-375.

FITZGERALD, M. J. T. (1961). Developmental changes in epidermal innervation. *J. Anat.* 95, 495-514.

HURLEY, H. J., AND KOELLE, G. B. (1958). The effect of inhibition of nonspecific cholinesterase on perception of tactile sensation in human volar skin. *J. Invest. Dermatol.* 31, 243-245.

KRAUSE, W. (1860). "Die terminalen Körperchen der einfach sensiblen Nerven," 271 pp. Hanover, Germany, Hahn.

LIPSCOMB, P. R., AND WINKELMANN, R. K. (1961). A whole-mount technic for study of innervation of the deep structures of the limbs. *J. Invest. Dermatol.* 37, 481-483.

MONTAGNA, W., AND ELLIS, R. A. (1957). Histology and cytochemistry of the human skin. XII. Cholinesterases in the hair follicle of the scalp. *J. Invest. Dermatol.* 29, 151-157.

MONTAGNA, W., AND ELLIS, R. A. (1959). The skin of Primates. I. The skin of the potto (*Perodicticus potto*). *Am. J. Phys. Anthropol.* 17, 137-161.

MONTAGNA, W., AND ELLIS, R. A. (1960). The skin of Primates. II. The skin of the slender loris (*Loris tardigradus*). *Am. J. Phys. Anthropol.* 18, 19-43.

MONTAGNA, W., AND YUN, J. S. (1961). Histology and cytochemistry of the human skin. XXIII. The distribution of cytochrome oxidase. *J. Histochem. and Cytochem.* 9, 694-698.

MONTAGNA, W., YASUDA, K., AND ELLIS, R. A. (1961a). The skin of Primates. III. The skin of the slow loris (*Nycticebus coucang*). *Am. J. Phys. Anthropol.* 19, 1-21.

MONTAGNA, W., YASUDA, K., AND ELLIS, R. A. (1961b). The skin of Primates. V. The skin of the black lemur (*Lemur macaco*). *Am. J. Phys. Anthropol.* 19, 115-129.

PEASE, D. C., AND QUILLIAM, T. A. (1957). Electron microscopy of the pacinian corpuscle. *J. Biophys. Biochem. Cytol.* **3**, 331-342.

SCHEEN, S. R., JR., AND WINKELMANN, R. D. (1961). Alkaline phosphatase in skin of certain animals. *Arch. Dermatol.* **83**, 439-446.

WEDDELL, G., PALMER, E., AND PALLIE, W. (1955). Nerve endings in mammalian skin. *Cambridge Phil. Soc., Biol. Revs.* **30**, 159-195.

WINKELMANN, R. K. (1957). The mucocutaneous end-organ: The primary organized sensory ending in human skin. *A.M.A. Arch. Dermatol.* **76**, 225-235.

WINKELMANN, R. K. (1959a). The erogenous zones: Their innervation and its significance. *Proc. Staff Meetings Mayo Clinic* **34**, 39-47.

WINKELMANN, R. K. (1959b). The innervation of a hair follicle. *Ann. N.Y. Acad. Sci.* **83**, 400-407.

WINKELMANN, R. K. (1960a). "Nerve Endings in Normal and Pathologic Skin: Contributions to the Anatomy of Sensation," 195 pp. Springfield, Illinois, Charles C Thomas.

WINKELMANN, R. K. (1960b). The end-organ of feline skin: A morphologic and histochemical study. *Am. J. Anat.* **107**, 281-290.

WINKELMANN, R. K. (1961). The nerve endings in the skin of the gorilla. *J. Comp. Neurol.* **116**, 145-155.

WINKELMANN, R. K. (1962). Cutaneous sensory end-organs of some anthropoid apes. *Science* **136**, 384-386.

WINKELMANN, R. K., AND MYERS, T. T. (1961). The histochemistry and morphology of the cutaneous sensory end-organs of the chicken. *J. Comp. Neurol.* **117**, 27-35.

WINKELMANN, R. K., AND OSMENT, L. S. (1956). The Vater-Pacinian corpuscle in the skin of the human finger tip. *A.M.A. Arch. Dermatol.* **73**, 116-122.

WINKELMANN, R. K., AND SCHMIT, R. W. (1959). Cholinesterases in human skin. *A.M.A. Arch. Dermatol.* **80**, 543-548.

WINKELMANN, R. K., SCHEEN, S. R., JR., PYKA, R. A., AND COVENTRY, M. B. (1960). Cutaneous vascular patterns in studies with injection preparation and alkaline phosphatase reaction. *In* "Advances in Biology of the Skin," Vol. 2, pp. 1-19. New York, Pergamon.

YASUDA, K., AOKI, T., AND MONTAGNA, W. (1961). The skin of primates. IV. The skin of the lesser bushbaby (*Galago senegalensis*). *Am. J. Phys. Anthropol.* **19**, 23-33.

Chapter 7

The Chromosomes of Primates

M. A BENDER AND E. H. Y. CHU

Biology Division, Oak Ridge National Laboratory,[1]
Oak Ridge, Tennessee

I. INTRODUCTION

Of all morphological characteristics, the karyotype, or number and form of the chromosomes, is the most intimately associated with the genetic make-up of an organism. Any change in the karyotype, with its consequent rearrangement of genetic material, is very likely to result in a change in its possessor. Such changes are frequently lethal. Also, most nonlethal changes are in one way or another detrimental. Changes which produce as a genetic consequence a deviation from the norm will, especially in highly adapted species, be rapidly selected against and eliminated from the population. Thus, selection confers an enormous degree of stability on the karyotype, and successful changes are rare. It is not surprising, then, that with very few exceptions there is only one karyotype that is characteristic of each species. The converse,

[1] Operated by Union Carbide Corporation for the United States Atomic Energy Commission.

unfortunately, is not always true. Species, and even genera, frequently have indistinguishable karyotypes. Even so, however, there is enough variation between members of different species to make the karyotype a character of particular interest to the taxonomist.

Karyotypes do, of course, change. Frequently, in the evolution of a species, i.e., in the course of alteration of the genetic structure of the

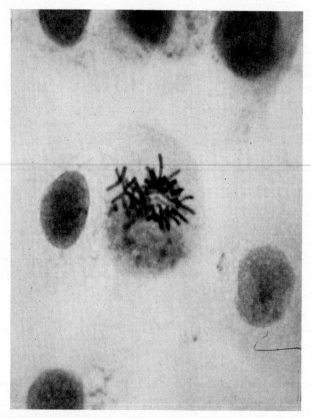

FIG. 1.   Mitosis in a cell from a human female, fixed and stained in the classic manner. Magnified 1350 times.

population, there is a coincident alteration of the karyotype. When advantageous mutations associated with some visible alteration in the chromosomes are fixed in a population, then the karyotype of the population will also be altered. Since such karyotypic changes must proceed in an orderly fashion, according to the rules of chromosome mechanics, it is often possible to deduce the course of evolution in a group from the karyotypes of the existing species.

Since the publication of "The Origin of Species," the primates and their evolution have been of prime interest to biologists. It would seem surprising, then, that karyotypic analysis has not been used more often to study primate taxonomy and evolution. The reason is quite simple. We learned only recently how to make cytological preparations that allowed us to count accurately and to study the form of mammalian chromosomes. Primate chromosomes are numerous and small. They tend to crowd on the metaphase plate, a situation that makes even counting impossible (Fig. 1).

A brief history of the study of human chromosomes will illustrate the difficulty [cf. Stern (1959) for an excellent review]. The first positive statement of the human chromosome number was made by von Winiwarter in 1912. He stated that the human female has 48 chromosomes, and the human male 47. He concluded that man has an XX-XO sex-determining mechanism. In 1923 Painter re-examined this question, and found that there was a small Y chromosome in the male. He stated that the correct diploid number for both male and female was 48 and that there was an XX-XY sex-determining mechanism. For many years, sporadic conflicting reports notwithstanding, the human chromosome number was accepted as 48. It was not until 1956 that Tjio and Levan, using modern techniques, reported that the somatic chromosome number is really 46. This report was rapidly confirmed by Ford and Hamerton (1956a) for human meiotic chromosomes, and then by many other authors for somatic chromosomes, firmly establishing that the number is, indeed, 46 (Fig. 2). If the chromosomes of the most studied primate were correctly counted only as recently as 1956, it is not surprising that the chromosomes of most other primates were, and in many cases remain, completely unknown.

There are, of course, two sorts of chromosome material that can be analyzed: the somatic mitotic chromosomes and the germinal meiotic chromosomes. Each type has its advantages.

The meiotic chromosomes have the enormous advantage of reduced number. In the first prophase and metaphase of meiosis the homologous chromosomes are paired, and only the haploid number (n) of these bivalents need be counted. In the second metaphase of meiosis, the total number of chromosomes in each cell has actually been reduced to the haploid number. This reduction should make analysis far easier. Unfortunately, meiotic chromosomes are quite small, and it is very difficult to determine their morphology (Fig. 3). Furthermore, they are difficult to fix properly.

Mitotic figures, on the other hand, have the diploid number ($2n$) of chromosomes. And analysis becomes much more than twice as difficult when the number of chromosomes is doubled. Somatic chromosomes do, however, have certain advantages. They are larger, and it is much easier to determine their morphology (Fig. 2).

Most of the earlier work on primate chromosomes was done on meiotic material because of the reduced number. Recent developments

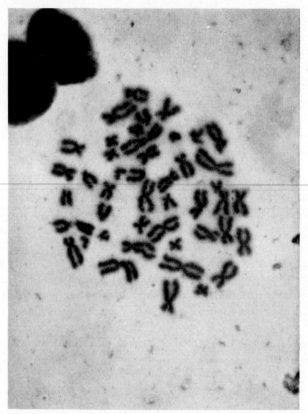

FIG. 2. Mitosis in a tissue-cultured human leukocyte prepared by the colchicine, hypotonic saline pretreatment method. Magnified 1350 times.

in mammalian cytology have made it very easy to study somatic material, and thus recent work has been done on mitotic chromosomes.

Figure 4 illustrates some of the features of chromosome morphology that are important in karyotypic analysis. Each chromosome is composed of two parallel chromatids attached at a relatively unstained (primary) constriction, the centromere. The centromere divides at the start of anaphase, separating the two chromatids into daughter chromosomes, which move to opposite poles of the spindle. Sometimes, one or more pairs of chromosomes in a set may have a lightly stained secondary

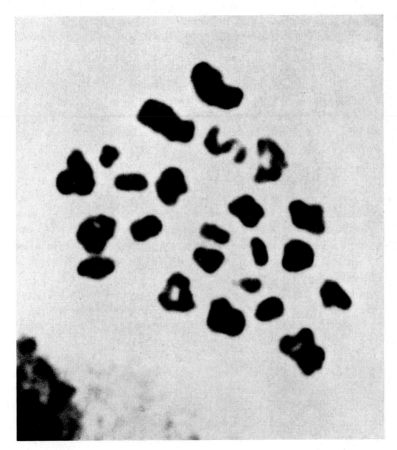

FIG. 3. Meiotic chromosomes of a human male. (From Ford and Hamerton, 1956a.) Magnified 5040 times.

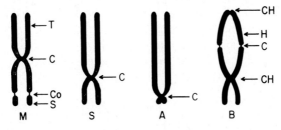

FIG. 4. Diagrams of the various chromosome types. KEY: M, metacentric; S, subterminal; A, acrocentric; B, meiotic bivalent; Co, secondary constriction; CH, chiasmata; H, homologous chromosome; C, centromere; S, satellite; T, chromatid.

constriction. The region distal to a secondary constriction is sometimes referred to as a satellite. If present at all, this is a constant morphological feature of the karyotype. The relative lengths of each chromosome and the position of the centromere are also constant. According to convention (Tjio and Levan, 1956), if the centromere is located near the middle of the chromosome, so that the ratio between the lengths of the two arms is 1.0 to 1.9, the chromosome is referred to as metacentric (M). If the centromere is much nearer one end, so that the interarm ratio is 2.0 to 4.9, the chromosome is called subterminal (S). If the centromere is at or very near one end (interarm ratio of more than 5.0), then the chromosome is telocentric or acrocentric (A). In the first division of meiosis, these features are somewhat obscure. The chromatids are usually not visible, but the paired homologues resemble chromatids, sometimes making the bivalent look rather like an overcontracted mitotic chromosome. Usually, the homologues are associated at one or more points called chiasmata. The centromeres, of course, are separate, and frequently not visible.

Several advances in cytological technique are responsible for our present ability to make accurate karyotypic analyses of primates. Some of these, as Stern (1959) pointed out, are actually rediscoveries of old methods. One is the use of unsectioned material. Another is the use of tissue cultures from various tissues that can provide actively dividing cells that are already spread out and attached to a cover glass or a slide. These cultures can also provide free mitotic cells, which can be flattened by drying onto a slide, in much the same way that a blood film is made. A helpful method is the use of the drug colchicine, which prevents spindle development, arrests the cells in metaphase, and results in spreading and contraction of the chromosomes. The use of prefixation treatments with hypotonic solutions (Hughes, 1952; Hsu, 1952; Makino and Nishimura, 1952) is particularly valuable, because it swells the dividing cells and results in much better spreading of the chromosomes.

Although a comprehensive treatment of methods for preparing mammalian chromosomes for study is out of place here, we do feel that a description of a few of the methods useful for primate chromosomes might be of value.

II. METHODS FOR PRIMATE CHROMOSOMES

A. TISSUE CULTURES

The tissue culture methods used are based on techniques developed by many workers over a long period. Cultures may be made from a variety of tissues. Two that are commonly used in our laboratory are kidney and skin. Although both grow well, they require somewhat different culture methods. One method for each type of culture will be described in this section. Whatever method is used, all of the media and solutions required may be purchased, already sterile and ready to use, from commercial suppliers. There is one very important matter of technique that applies to all tissue culture methods. In almost every case, the media and balanced salt solutions (BSS) used are buffered with sodium bicarbonate. Such systems are useful only when the *gas phase* above the liquid contains CO_2 in equilibrium with the buffer. If the container is open to the atmosphere, CO_2 will escape and the medium will become progressively more and more alkaline. Although tissue cultures can tolerate brief periods of high or low pH, they must be maintained near pH 7. There are two ways to do this: (1) the incubator may be provided at all times with an artificial atmosphere of about 5% CO_2 in air (*not oxygen!*), and the culture containers left open to allow diffusion; or (2) the proper amount of CO_2 may be placed in the sealed containers, either by adjusting with 5% CO_2 or by making the medium in the container somewhat too acid to begin with, so that when equilibrium is reached the pH is correct.

Tissue specimens may be shipped from one place to another in sterile screw-cap vials containing nutrient medium of the same type used for culture (see below). The vials are wrapped and placed in a plastic bag, which is then sealed. The bag is put in ice (*not dry ice!*) in a Thermos container, preferably one of all stainless steel construction, and shipped via Air Express. In this way we have successfully shipped specimens from Madagascar to Oak Ridge.

1. *Kidney*

Kidney cells are grown in much the same way as they are in poliovirus research. A kidney is removed sterilely either by surgery or at necropsy. Provided the corpse is refrigerated promptly, successful cultures may be made up to several days after death. The surgical technique, while relatively uncomplicated, is tedious, and is used where it is especially desirable to save the animal for display or further research. Veterinary sodium pentobarbital (60 mg/ml) is a convenient anesthetic. It is given intraperitoneally at a rate of 1 ml per 5 pounds of body weight. Mikedimide (Parlam Corp., Englewood, New Jersey) is extremely useful as an antagonist to this anesthetic, and is used both when an unusually sensitive animal is anesthetized too deeply and to bring about rapid postoperative recovery.

The kidney is stripped of its capsule, and as much of the pelvis as possible is removed. The rest is minced with Number 11 scalpel blades into 1- to 2-mm cubes. After being washed once or twice with BSS, the pieces are placed in a continuous-flow trypsinizing flask. Our flasks, of about 100-ml capacity, are miniaturized versions of the commercially available type. Figure 5 shows the trypsinizing flask set up for use, as well as a schematic diagram of the whole process. One hundred milli-liters of 0.25% 1:250 or 1:300 trypsin dissolved in BSS are allowed to

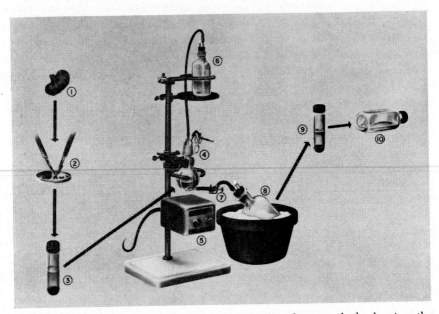

Fig. 5. Schematic diagram of the kidney cell culture method, showing the continuous-flow trypsinizing flask set up. Sterile kidney (1) is cut into small cubes (2), rinsed with sterile BSS (3), and placed in a continuous-flow trypsinizing flask (4) suspended over a magnetic stirrer (5). Trypsin solution runs into the flask from a reservoir bottle (6) at a rate controlled by a screw clamp on the outlet (7). The cells suspended in trypsin solution are run into a sterile flask in an ice bath (8). When enough cells are collected, they are spun out of the trypsin solution (9) and suspended in medium in culture flask (10).

run through during 1 to 2 hours. As a magnetic stirrer agitates the tissue fragments, the trypsin frees single cells. The cells are then spun out of the trypsin solution at about half-speed in a clinical centrifuge and resuspended in tissue culture medium. While any one of a number of media can be used, we have settled on a mixture of 80% Mixture 199 (Morgan et al., 1950) and 20% inactivated type AB+ human serum, containing 50 I.U. of penicillin G and 0.05 mg of streptomycin per milli-liter. Usually, all of the cells obtained from 100 ml of trypsin solution are suspended in 100 ml of medium, and this is used to make up four milk dilution bottle cultures (about 20 ml each) and 10–12 Leighton tube cover slip cultures. After 1 week, the old medium is replaced with fresh. Thereafter the cells are "fed" twice a week.

2. Skin

Skin is handled somewhat differently. The plasma clot culture method used for skin may, however, be used for other tissues, including kidney. Skin biopsies or necropsies may be made from any area of the body, but the softer regions, where the epidermis is thinnest, are generally the best. The skin at the site is washed, dried, and sterilized with 70% alcohol. Iodine or antiseptics containing heavy metal ions must not be used because they will poison the culture. A fold of skin is picked up with forceps and nipped off with scissors or scalpel. The biopsy need be only a few square millimeters in area. The tissue is cut up as previously described except that pieces about 0.5 mm in diameter are made. With a capillary pipette, chick plasma is streaked either on the floor of a Carrel flask (D 3.5), T flask (T-9), or on a cover slip in a Leighton tube. Pieces of tissue are placed in the neck of the container with forceps and pushed down and spaced evenly in the plasma with another pipette. Eight to ten pieces of tissue are usually put in each flask, and about four on a cover slip. A drop of chick embryo extract or thrombin solution is then added, and the resulting clot is allowed to harden for an hour or two before the medium is added. A suitable medium is that developed by Puck et al. (1958), containing fetal calf serum. About 1 ml of medium is used per flask or tube. The medium on the cultures is renewed two or three times weekly. Figure 6 is a schematic diagram of this culture method.

All cultures are, of course, incubated at 37°C, with special attention to the pH, as previously outlined. When a good, but not confluent, sheet of cells has grown (cf. Fig. 7; the amount of growth shown usually takes 1 to 2 weeks for kidney and 2 to 3 weeks for skin cultures), the cover slips are prepared for cytological examination, as described below. At the same time, one or more of the stock cultures are treated with trypsin solution and replanted for a "second generation" of stock and cover slip cultures. A 0.05% trypsin solution is used for kidney cells, while a 0.25% solution is suitable for skin cultures. The old medium is poured off and the trypsin solution added. Kidney cultures are incubated for 10–15 minutes with 5–10 ml of trypsin. After this treatment most of the cells are in suspension. Skin cultures are allowed to incubate for the same time with about 0.5 ml of trypsin. In this case, not all of the cells come free from the glass. In either case, the cell suspension is vigorously pipetted a few times to break up clumps, and then diluted with sufficient new medium to make fresh cultures. New medium may be added to the old skin culture, and it may be reharvested later. Usually, serial cultures will begin to play out after five or ten passages. If they do not, they should be viewed with suspicion, since they may contain cells of altered karyotype or even a contaminant cell of quite different origin.

From 4 to 6 hours before the cells are to be fixed, colchicine is added to the medium to a final concentration of 10^{-7} to 10^{-8} M. We

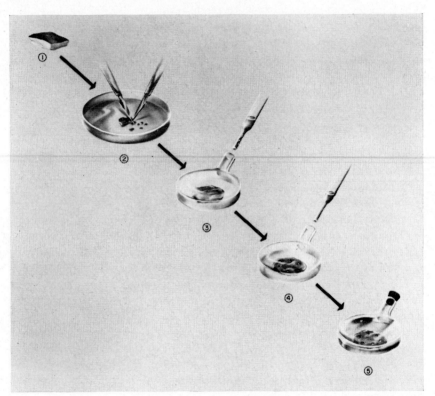

Fig. 6. Schematic diagram of the plasma clot culture technique. Skin biopsy or other tissue sample (1) is cut into small pieces in a sterile dish (2). With a pipette, a few pieces are placed in a Carrel flask or other container containing a ring of plasma (3). Embryo extract or thrombin is added to clot the plasma (4), and after the clot has set, medium is added and the flask stoppered (5).

find a 20–100 × stock solution made up in BSS convenient for this purpose. Just before fixation, the medium is poured off and a hypotonic solution is added to the cultures. Either 0.7% sodium citrate or a mixture of 20% BSS in water may be used. The fixative most commonly used is Carnoy's fluid (3 parts absolute ethanol:1 part glacial acetic acid). It should be freshly made and, preferably, cold. Cover slips are usually handled in a Chen staining rack. The rack is immersed in a dilute fixative (or just plain acetic acid) mixture (0.1 ml in 100 ml of hypotonic saline) for a few seconds and then immediately immersed in full-strength fixative. After three 5- to 10-minute changes of fixative, the cover slips are placed, cell side up, on a paper towel and allowed to dry.

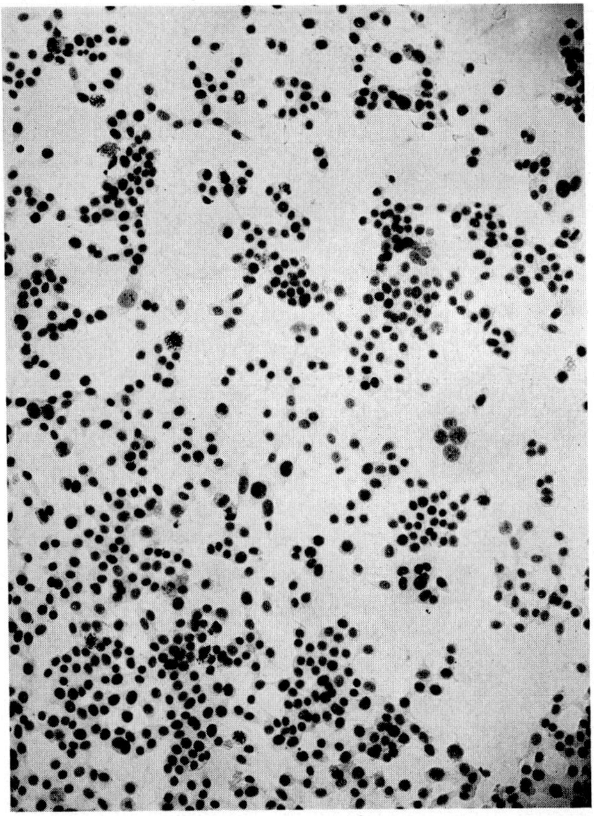

FIG. 7.   A nearly confluent sheet of cultured cells ready for harvesting.

The cover slips, when thoroughly dry, are stained in 1 to 2% orcein in 45% acetic acid for 10–20 minutes. It is important to use freshly filtered aceto-orcein, because it crystallizes rapidly from solution. The stained cover slips are dehydrated in two half-minute changes of absolute alcohol (tertiary butyl alcohol may be used to prevent destaining) and mounted in Euparal. If the cover slips are left too long in the alcohol they will destain to an objectionable degree. If one prefers, the cover slips may be cleared in xylene or toluene, and mounted in balsam or Permount.

3. *Leukocytes*

Leukocytes from peripheral blood may be cultured for short periods of time, and yield good chromosome preparations. While this method has been used for only a few species of primates, there is no reason to suppose that it will not work for others. The method was described by Moorhead *et al.* (1960). We use it with very little modification. A sample of peripheral blood is drawn aseptically and placed in a sterile, screw cap, 10 ml centrifuge tube containing 0.1 ml of 1000 unit per ml heparin solution. The sample is then treated with Phytohemagglutinin (Difco) to remove the red cells. One-tenth of a milliliter of the solution (made up as recommended by the manufacturer) is used for each 5 ml of blood. After the tube is inverted a few times to mix the sample, it is placed in an ice bath for $\frac{1}{2}$ hour. The sample is centrifuged at *very low speed* in a clinical centrifuge for 5 minutes. With a sterile Pasteur pipette, the plasma and the top 1–2 mm of the red cell layer (usually about 1.5 ml in all) are drawn off and added to the culture medium in a milk dilution bottle. The medium is composed of 10 ml of Mixture 199 and 4 ml of inactivated AB$^+$ human serum, with 50 I.U. of penicillin G and 0.05 mg of streptomycin. The cultures are incubated for 3 days at 37°C.

On the morning of the third day, colchicine is added to the culture to a concentration of about 10^{-7} M; 6 hours later, the cultures are fixed. The medium and all of the cells from the bottle are placed in a centrifuge tube and spun down for 5 minutes at half-speed in a clinical centrifuge. The culture medium is drawn off and the cells resuspended in 6 ml of BSS. They are then spun down again and all but 1 ml of the BSS is removed. After resuspending the cells in the remaining BSS, 3 ml of distilled water are added, and the tube is incubated at 37°C for 10 minutes. Then the cells are again spun down for 5 minutes, and the supernatant fluid is removed. The cells are thus in hypotonic saline for 15 minutes. Fixation is accomplished by slowly adding 4–5 ml of 3:1 methanol-glacial acetic acid *without* disturbing the button of cells. The fixative is allowed to act for at least $\frac{1}{2}$ hour, after which the cells are resuspended in the fixative, centrifuged, and rinsed once or twice in fresh fixative. After the final rinse, all but about 0.5 ml of the fixative is removed, and the cells are mounted by an air-drying technique. Single drops of cell suspension are dropped on the surface of wet slides and the excess water is wiped off. The slides are allowed to dry thoroughly. (The secret of good chromosome spreading is to have the slide really wet. If the water film breaks before the cells are dropped on, they will not spread out. Therefore, the slides must be well cleaned. If they cannot be gotten really wettable, one solution is to leave a small amount of some wetting agent in the final rinse. The detergent used to wash the slides is usually quite satisfactory.) The cells may be stained with aceto-orcein, as previously outlined for cover slip cultures.

B. NONCULTURE TECHNIQUES

1. *Bone Marrow*

Bone marrow is a good source of rapidly dividing cells. Acceptable cytological preparations may be made by a modification of the method of Ford and Hamerton (1956b). In this method colchicine is injected into the animal and allowed to act *in vivo* for several hours before the marrow is taken. Colchicine is quite toxic, and only a few milligrams may be given to an average-size monkey without killing it. Although there is no great advantage if the animal is to be destroyed anyway, in cases where the animal must be saved, Colcemid (CIBA) should be used, because it is much less toxic. For a 2–3 kg animal, 2 ml of 0.1% Colcemid may be given intraperitoneally with no obvious aftereffects.

If the animal is to be killed, we use ether or an overdose of sodium pentobarbital. The femurs are excised immediately and the marrow is flushed out of the shafts with a few milliliters of 0.7% sodium citrate. The lumps of marrow should be broken up by vigorous pipetting. If the animal is large enough, and one desires to save it, it is lightly anesthetized with sodium pentobarbital ½ hour before the cells are to be fixed. Fifteen minutes before the cells are to be fixed, the marrow is aspirated from the iliac crest of the pelvis or, as we have found particularly convenient, from the distal end of the femur. From 2 to 5 ml of blood and marrow are aspirated from a single puncture made with a Turkel trephine of the infant infusion size. The blood-marrow mixture is added to 25–50 ml of 5% BSS in water containing 0.5–1.0 ml of heparin (1000 I.U./ml) solution. The heparin solution prevents both clot formation and clumping of the marrow cells. The difference in hypotonic solution used in the two methods is largely because of the large amount of blood in samples drawn from living animals.

After incubation for about 10 minutes in the hypotonic solution, the cells are spun down in the centrifuge and all but a few drops of the supernatant fluid is removed. The cells are resuspended in the remaining fluid, and cold Carnoy's fixative is slowly added to a volume of 4–5 ml. After ½ hour, the cells are washed several times in fresh fixative and mounted by the air-drying technique previously described for leukocyte cultures and stained with aceto-orcein.

In cases where it is impossible to give either colchicine or Colcemid before the marrow is taken, it is possible to get some degree of colchicine effect by incubating the marrow cells in a medium, such as that described for leukocytes, that contains 10^{-6} to 10^{-7} M colchicine. A few hours suffice to get some effect, although longer times have been used. The cells may be spun down out of the medium, and handled as just discussed. Unfortunately, in our hands this method does not give as good a result as does the method of using colchicine *in vivo*.

2. *Testis*

Testis may be fixed and stained by the method of Welshons *et al.* (1962). The testis may be removed either by unilateral orchiectomy or *directly* after the animal is killed. In either case, the testicular sheath is removed and the mass of tubules is placed in 0.7% citrate solution. After about 15 minutes, an equal volume of glacial acetic acid is added to fix the cells. Segments of tubule are then taken out and placed on slides, each in a drop of lactic-orcein. This stain is made by dissolving 2% orcein in a mixture of 42.5 ml lactic acid, 42.5 ml glacial acetic acid, and 15 ml distilled water. The slides are covered with watch glasses and set aside as made. After 10–20 minutes, a cover slip is added and the preparations are squashed *very hard* in a bibulous book. The resulting preparations may be sealed with wax to make temporary mounts, or they may be made permanent by freezing the slides in liquid nitrogen (dry ice will not do, because its temperature is not low enough to adequately freeze the lactic-orcein). The frozen preparation is taken from the nitrogen and the cover slip immediately "popped" off with a scalpel blade. The cells will remain on the slide if this is correctly done. The slide is immersed in absolute alcohol as soon as the cover slip is off, rapidly passed through several changes of alcohol, and mounted in Euparal. As with somatic material, the dehydration must be rapid in order to prevent destaining. Since not all of the tubule sections will have the divisions in which one is interested, it is practical to examine the slides before they are frozen and discard those that will not be useful.

C. CYTOLOGICAL METHODS

Ordinary high-quality microscopy is all that is required to examine primate chromosomes. Although more contrast is available with phase microscopy, we find that the increased resolution possible with good bright-field equipment is more important. In any case, apochromatic or fluorite lenses, with the proper condenser and eyepieces, are very valuable, as is adequate, properly centered illumination. For orcein-stained material, a light-green filter, such as a Wratten No. 58 should be used. We routinely scan for good figures under low power (100–

150 ×). After deciding that a figure is good enough to score, we always finish scoring it in order to avoid any bias in the counts. The counts are usually made from freehand sketches of the figure. It is easy to

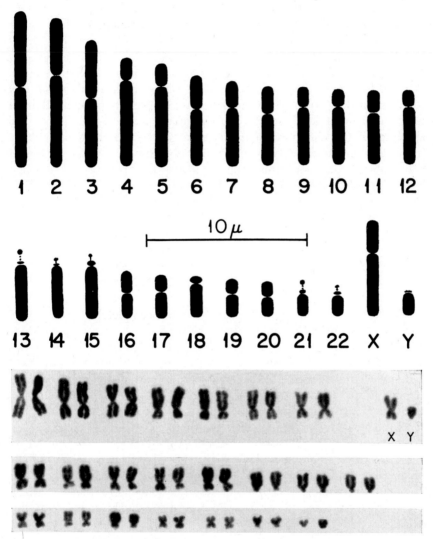

Fig. 8.   Karyotype and ideogram of a human male.

mark off the chromosomes counted in this manner, especially when the chromosome number is high.

For detailed analysis, either karyotypes or ideograms may be constructed. Ideograms are schematic diagrams, one for each chromosome pair, made from measurements of the chromosomes. The measurements may be made directly from the material with a filar micrometer, or from enlarged photographs. Usually, the measurements from at least ten cells are averaged to get the values used to construct the ideogram.

Karyotypes are constructed by selecting and photographing figures of suitable quality. The chromosomes are cut out from enlarged prints and used for the familiar "paste up." Although the technique has now been largely abandoned, karyotypes may also be made from *camera lucida* drawings of good figures. Figure 8 shows both an ideogram and a "paste up" karyotype of the human chromosome complement. It must be pointed out that there is variation in the sizes, both relative and absolute, of the chromosomes in different cells from the same culture from the same animal. Thus, one pair may only sometimes be longer than another, and sometimes the members of a pair are of unequal length in particular figures. Pairing of chromosomes in a karyotype does not mean that the chromosomes are always necessarily homologous. In the human karyotype (Fig. 8), for instance, it is impossible to be absolutely certain about chromosomes in the group of pairs numbered six through twelve, and the pairing is arbitrary.

III. Primate Chromosomes

While the chromosomes of primates are incompletely known, there is quite a lot of information about some groups, and at least some information about most of them. In order to simplify a review of this information, we will use the classification proposed by Fiedler (1956). Although we are aware that recent work on particular groups dictates taxonomic revisions, we feel that less confusion will result if we follow one classification throughout.

Our knowledge of primate chromosomes has been reviewed several times recently (Tobias, 1956; Chiarelli, 1958), but because of recent work both reviews are now incomplete. The subject has also been briefly reviewed recently by ourselves (Chu and Bender, 1961), but even this is already incomplete. The present chapter will doubtless need expansion very soon, since many workers are now actively engaged in this field.

A. The Prosimii

Table I summarizes the chromosome number and karyotype information available for the Prosimii. In the Tupaiidae, only one species, *Urogale everetti*, has been examined. Dodson (personal communication) made tentative counts using both testicular material and corneal epithelium. He found a diploid number of $2n = 26$. More recently, we have examined skin and kidney cultures from another specimen, and found a diploid number of $2n = 44$. No information is available on the karyotype.

In the Lemuriformes, a number of species have recently been examined (Chu and Bender, 1961; Chu and Swomley, 1961a, b; Buettner-Janusch et al., 1962). All counts were made from mitotic cells from cultures of skin biopsies. A wide variation in chromosome number was found. Even in the single genus, Lemur, counts for different species range from $2n = 44$ up to $2n = 60$ (Table I). There is even variation within a single recognized species (Lemur fulvus). One of the animals reported, although resembling L. fulvus fulvus, which has 48 chromosomes, turned out to have $2n = 52$ instead, leading Buettner-Janusch et al. (1962) to propose that it be regarded as a new species. Also, Chiarelli (1961a) has made a tentative count of $2n = 58$ for a specimen identified as L. fulvus.

In the genus Hapalemur, two subspecies of Hapalemur griseus have been investigated. Here again there is a variation in number (Table I).

Accompanying the intrageneric variation in the Lemurinae, there is also a wide variation in the morphology of their chromosomes. Figure 9 gives the karyotypes for some of the species of Lemuriformes investigated. It can be seen that there is an extremely wide variation in the lengths of the chromosomes. They vary all the way from 14 down to about 0.3μ. In many species, L. macaco for instance, the chromosomes fall into two distinct categories. There are very small or microchromosomes, and longer macrochromosomes. In other species, such as L. fulvus albifrons, there is no discontinuity in chromosome lengths. The Y chromosome in the Lemurinae is acrocentric and is always the smallest in the complement. The X chromosome is medium-sized and acrocentric except in L. variegatus and Lemur sp., in which it is metacentric. On the basis of karyotypic analysis, Chu and Swomley (1961a) suggested that the lemurine lemurs fall naturally into three categories: Hapalemur; a second group including Lemur catta, L. mongoz, and L. fulvus rufus and albifrons; and a third group including L. fulvus fulvus, L. variegatus, L. macaco, and the new subspecies. Since the groupings cut across a species (L. fulvus), they suggest that a revision of the genus Lemur is in order.

The chromosomes of one species in the subfamily Cheirogaleinae have been studied. Mitotic cells from cultured skin biopsies from a female Microcebus murinus have a chromosome number of $2n = 66$ (Chu and Swomley, 1961b). All chromosomes but two are acrocentric.

TABLE I

CHROMOSOME NUMBERS AND TYPES IN THE PROSIMII

Species	Common name	Number of specimens examined		Chromosomes[a]							Authority
		Male	Fe-male	2n	M	S	A	X	Y		
Tupaiiformes											
Tupaiidae											
Urogale everetti	Philippine tree shrew	1		[26][b]							Dodson (1960)
U. everetti			1	44							This report
Lemuriformes											
Lemuridae											
Lemur catta	Ring-tail lemur	2	2	56	6	4	44	A	A	⎫	Chu and Swomley (1961a, b)
L. mongoz	Mongoose lemur	2	3	60	0	4	54	A	A	⎬	
L. fulvus	Brown lemur	.....[c]		[58][b]							Chiarelli (1961a)
L. fulvus rufus	Red-fronted lemur		2	60	0	4	54	A	A	⎫	
L. fulvus albifrons	White-fronted lemur		1	60	0	4	54	A	A	⎬	
L. fulvus fulvus	Brown lemur	1	1	48	10	6	30	A	A	⎭	Chu and Swomley (1961a, b)
Lemur sp.[d]	—	1		52	8	4	38	M	A		
L. variegatus	Ruffed lemur	1		46	14	4	26	M	A		
L. macaco	Black lemur	1	1	44	12	8	22	A	A		Chu and Bender (1961)
Hapalemur griseus											
griseus	Gray gentle lemur	1	1	54	4	6	42	A	A		
H. griseus olivaceus	—	1		58	2	4	52	—	—	⎫	Chu and Swomley (1961a, b)
Microcebus murinus	Miller's mouse lemur	1		66	0	2	64	—	—	⎭	

TABLE I (*Continued*)

Species	Common name	Number of specimens examined		Chromosomes[a]						Authority
		Male	Female	2n	M	S	A	X	Y	
Lorisiformes										
Lorisinae										
Nycticebus coucang	Slow loris		1	50						Bender and Mettler (1958)
Perodicticus potto	Potto		1	62						Chu and Bender (1961)
P. potto		1	3	62	12	12	36	S	A	This report
Galaginae										
Galago senegalensis	Lesser bush baby	1		38	20	10		S	S	Matthey (1955a)
G. senegalensis		2	2	38	20	10	6	S	A	⎫ Chu and Bender (1961)
G. crassicaudatus	Thick-tailed bush baby	2	2	62	0	6	54	S	A	⎭

[a] M, metacentric; S, subterminal; A, acrocentric.
[b] Data in brackets are tentative.
[c] The number and sex of the animals was not stated.
[d] This animal, similar to *L. fulvus fulvus*, is probably a new species. See text.

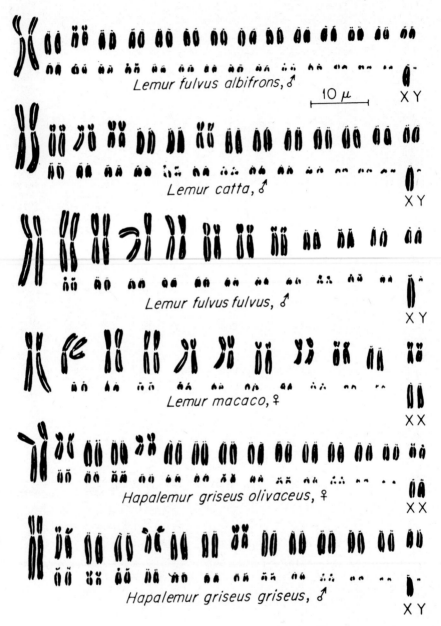

FIG. 9. Representative karyotypes of Lemuriformes.

No species in the families Indriidae or Daubentoniidae have been investigated.

In the Lorisiformes, a few species from both families have been studied. In the Lorisinae, a single count of $2n = 50$ was made from cultured kidney cells of a female slow loris, *Nycticebus coucang* (Bender and Mettler, 1958). Unfortunately, no information about the karyotype

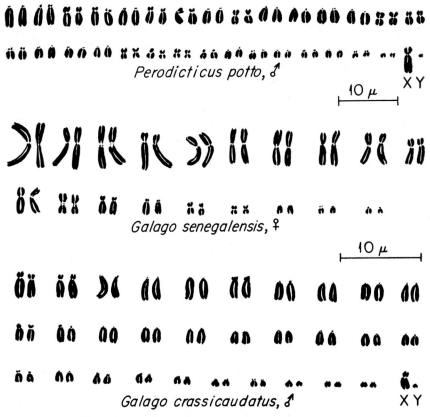

Perodicticus potto, ♂

10 μ   X Y

Galago senegalensis, ♀

10 μ

Galago crassicaudatus, ♂   X Y

FIG. 10. Representative karyotypes of Lorisiformes.

is available. More is known about the potto. Mitotic cells from skin biopsy cultures of five specimens of *Perodicticus potto* have been examined (Chu and Bender, 1961; this report). The diploid number is 62. A karyotype appears in Fig. 10. It can be seen that most of the chromosomes are acrocentric. The X is the longest chromosome of the complement and is subterminal; the Y is acrocentric and one of the smallest.

The first count in the family Galaginae was made by Matthey

(1955a), who studied the chromosomes of *Galago senegalensis*. In testicular material from one animal, both spermatogonial mitoses and meiotic stages were studied. The diploid number was found to be 38, with 24 large metacentrics, 4 small acrocentrics, and 8 very small microchromosomes. The X chromosome was large and submetacentric and the small Y was subterminal. During meiosis, pairing occurred between the short arms of the X and the Y. Four more specimens of this species were recently investigated, using the skin culture method (Chu and Bender, 1961). All had 38 chromosomes. The karyotype found agrees with the original description of Matthey (Fig. 10), except that we have classified the Y chromosome as acrocentric. Such a conflict is not at all surprising, because the sex chromosomes of many species are known to have large heterochromatic regions that contract differently in meiosis and in mitosis. Skin cultures from four specimens of the species *G. crassicaudatus* were also examined (Chu and Bender, 1961). In this species the chromosome number is much higher—$2n = 62$. As shown in Fig. 10, the karyotype is also markedly different. The chromosomes of *G. crassicaudatus* are in general shorter than those of *G. senegalensis*, and there is no discontinuity in their lengths. There are no microchromosomes in *G. crassicaudatus*, and most of the chromosomes are acrocentric, including the Y. The X is subterminal, as in *G. senegalensis*.

Unfortunately, no studies have been made of the Tarsiiformes.[2]

B. The Platyrrhini

The chromosomes of most of the genera of Platyrrhini have been studied. No intrageneric variation has been found in this group. Table II summarizes all available information on their chromosome numbers and morphologies. Within the family Cebidae, there is wide variation in diploid chromosome number. In the genus *Aotes*, one specimen of *Aotes trivirgatus* has been examined by the kidney culture method (Bender and Mettler, unpublished). The diploid number is 54. No information is as yet available on the karyotype.

Kidney cells in culture were used to examine the karyotype of a male

---

[2] The authors have recently published chromosome data for several additional species of Prosimii. Karyotype analyses of these species, together with those published previously, have led us to propose a tentative scheme of phylogenetic relationships in the Lemuridae, Indriidae, and Galiginae [see Chu, E. H. Y., and Bender, M. A (1962) Cytogenetics and evolution of primates. Ann. N.Y. Acad. Sci. **102**, 253-266]. The new chromosome counts include: *Tupaia glis* ($2n = 60$), *Lemur fulvus collaris* ($2n = 48$), *Cheirogaleus major* ($2n = 66$), *Propithecus verreauxi verreauxi* ($2n = 48$), *P. v. coquereli* ($2n = 48$), *Nycticebus coucang bengalensis* ($2n = 50$), and *N. pygmaeus* ($2n = 50$).

Callicebus cupreus (Bender and Mettler, 1958). The chromosome number is 46. There are 12 pairs of acrocentric chromosomes, as may be seen from Fig. 11, which shows all of the karyotypes known for the Platyrrhini. The X chromosome of *C. cupreus* is subterminal, and one of the longest chromosomes, while the Y is acrocentric, and the smallest in the complement.

Only tentative counts are available for the genera *Pithecia* and *Cacajao*. Kidney cultures from single specimens of both *Pithecia pithecia* and *Cacajao rubicundus* had 46 chromosomes (Bender and Mettler, unpublished).

Two specimens of *Alouatta seniculus* were examined, using cultures of kidney cells. A tentative count of $2n = 44$ was made on one animal (Bender and Mettler, unpublished). This count recently was confirmed by study of the cultures from a second specimen. The karyotype is illustrated in Fig. 11. This species is peculiar, in that the X chromosome appears to be small and acrocentric, whereas the Y is an even smaller metacentric. Also, there are two pairs of very small microchromosomes, which do not occur in any of the other platyrrhine genera studied.

Kidney cultures from three specimens of *Saimiri sciurea* have been examined (Bender and Mettler, 1958). The diploid number is 44. There are only six pairs of acrocentric chromosomes (Fig. 11). The X is a fairly long subterminal, while the Y is the smallest and is acrocentric. One of the medium-sized metacentrics has a prominent constriction, probably secondary.

The chromosomes of a species of *Cebus* were first counted by Painter (1922, 1924). He found that cells from testis of an animal referred to only as "Brown cebus" had a diploid number of 54. The X chromosome was subterminal and the Y was acrocentric and small. This count has been confirmed for several species in the genus. In kidney cultures from two animals (Bender and Mettler, 1958), and in skin cultures from another two (Chu and Bender, 1961) of *Cebus capucinus*, the diploid number is 54. Chiarelli (1961a) has also confirmed this number. Kidney cultures from one (Bender and Mettler, 1958) and skin cultures from two (Chu and Bender, 1961) specimens of *C. apella* also had $2n = 54$, as did material studied by Chiarelli (1961a). Both species have the same karyotype (Fig. 11), with 13 pairs of acrocentrics. Both the X and the Y chromosomes are acrocentric; the X is large and the Y is the smallest in the complement. There is probably no disagreement between the subterminal X described by Painter and the more recent description, as discussed under *Galago senegalensis*.

A large number of specimens from three species of the genus *Ateles* have been investigated (Bender and Mettler, 1958; Chu and Bender,

TABLE II

CHROMOSOME NUMBERS AND TYPES IN THE PLATYRRHINI

Species	Common name	Number of specimens examined		Chromosomes						Authority
		Male	Female	2n	M	S	A	X	Y	
Cebidae										
Aotes trivirgatus	Owl monkey	1		54						Bender and Mettler (unpublished)
Callicebus cupreus	Red titi	1	1	46	10	10	24	[S	A]a	Bender and Mettler (1958)
Pithecia pithecia	Saki			46						Bender and Mettler (unpublished)
Cacajao rubicundus	Red uakari	1		46						
Alouatta seniculus	Red howler	1		44						
A. seniculus		1		44	6	6	30	[A	M]a	This report
Saimiri sciurea	Squirrel monkey	1	2	44	16	14	12	S	A	Bender and Mettler (1958)
Cebus sp.	"Brown cebus"	1		54	6	20	26	S	A	Painter (1922, 1924)
C. capucinus	Capuchin ringtail		1	54	6	20	26	[A	–]a	Bender and Mettler (1958)
C. capucinus		2		54						Chu and Bender (1961)
C. capucinus		.....b		54						Chiarelli (1961a)
C. apella	Cinnamon ringtail	2		54	6	20	26	A	A	Bender and Mettler (1958)
C. apella		2		54						Chu and Bender (1961)
C. apella		.....b		54						Chiarelli (1961a)

TABLE II (Continued)

Species	Common name	Number of specimens examined Male	Fe-male	Chromosomes 2n	M	S	A	X	Y	Authority
Cebidae (con't.)										
Ateles paniscus chamek	Black-faced spider monkey	1	1	34	12	18	2	M	A	Bender and Mettler (1958)
A. belzebuth	Golden spider monkey	5	6	34	12	18	2c	M	A	Chu and Bender (1961)
A. geoffroyi	Hooded spider monkey	1		34	12	18	2	M	A	Bender and Mettler (1958)
A. arachnoides	Woolly spider monkey	.....b		[34]a						Chiarelli (1961a)
Lagothrix ubericola	Brown woolly monkey	1		62						This report
Callimico goeldii	Goeldi's marmoset		1	48	2	30	16	—	—	Bender and Mettler (1960)
Callithricidae										
Callithrix chrysoleucos	Silkey marmoset	1	2	46	4	30	10	S	M	Bender and Mettler (1960)
C. jacchus	Common marmoset	.....b	2	[46]a						Chiarelli (1961a)
Leontocebus illigeri	Red-mantled tamarin	2	2	46	4	30	10	S	M	Bender and Mettler (1960)

a Data in brackets are tentative.

b The number and sex of the animals is not stated.

c In one animal there was one metacentric and one acrocentric (cf. Bender, 1960).

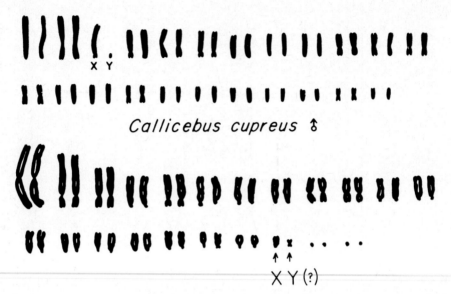

Callicebus cupreus ♂

X Y (?)

Alouatta seniculus ♂

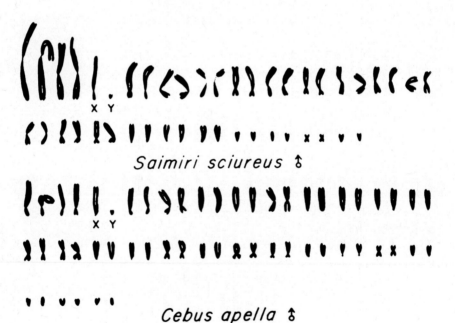

Saimiri sciureus ♂

Cebus apella ♂

FIG. 11. Representative karyotypes of Platyrrhini.

X Y

Ateles geoffroyi cucullatus ♂

Callimico goeldii ♀

X Y

Callithrix chrysoleucos ♂

X Y

Leontocebus illigeri ♂

FIG. 11. (*Continued*)

1961). *Ateles paniscus chamek, A. belzebuth,* and *A. geoffroyi* all have the same karyotype (Fig. 11), with a diploid number of 34. Except for the tentative count for *Urogale,* this is the lowest number recorded for a primate. The karyotype is interesting because there is only one pair of acrocentrics, excluding the Y chromosome, which is also acrocentric. The X is a medium-sized metacentric. Another of the medium-sized metacentric pairs has a secondary constriction. One specimen of *A. belzebuth* differed slightly from the others in karyotype (Bender, 1960). This animal had a small subterminal and an acrocentric instead of the usual pair of acrocentrics. Analysis of bone marrow cells showed that this abnormality did not arise in culture. It is assumed that this animal was heterozygous for a pericentric inversion of one of its small acrocentrics.

Chiarelli (1961a) recently made a tentative count of $2n = 34$ on material from a specimen of *A. arachnoides,* the woolly spider monkey, formerly placed in a separate genus, *Brachyteles.* It will be most interesting to learn how closely the karyotype of this species resembles that of the other species in the genus.

We recently examined the genus *Lagothrix* cytologically. A tentative count of $2n = 62$ was made from cultured kidney cells from a single specimen of *L. ubericola.*[3] No karyotype was constructed. If the tentative count is confirmed, it will be the highest diploid number in the Platyrrhina.

Only one female of the rather peculiar species *Callimico goeldii* has been investigated (Bender and Mettler, 1960). Tissue cultures of both kidney and spleen revealed a diploid number of 48. The karyotype appears in Fig. 11. Since the animal was female, no information about the sex chromosomes is available. The first pair of chromosomes in the karyotype is slightly mismatched as to length. This is apparently not a case of differential contraction, which is often obvious in long chromosomes, but a real difference in length. It occurred in all cells seen in the kidney cultures, and also in cells from cultured spleen. More specimens must be obtained before the position of this "pair" is established with certainty. In the meantime, we have placed it first, as though one member of the pair had a small deletion.

Species of both genera of Callithricidae have been examined. Three specimens of *Callithrix chrysoleucos* and four specimens of *Leontocebus illigeri* were used to establish kidney cultures (Bender and Mettler, 1960). Both species have a diploid number of 46. In addition, Chiarelli (1961a) has made a tentative count of $2n = 46$ for *C. jacchus.* Both *C. chrysoleucos* and *L. illigeri* have identical karyotypes (Fig. 11). The X

---

[3] This name has been superseded by *L. Cana poeppigi.*

chromosome is a medium-sized subterminal; the Y is metacentric and quite small.[4]

C. THE CATARRHINI

Table III is a summary of information available about catarrhine chromosomes. The family Cercopithecidae has been extensively studied. In all cases where the karyotypes are known, they are characterized by a moderate-sized submetacentric X chromosome and a small Y chromosome. There is also a single, rather small pair bearing a marked secondary constriction.

Macaca mulatta is the most extensively studied species in the group, possibly because of its importance as a research animal. Painter (1924) studied the testis of one animal and also tissue from three embryos. Using sectioned material, he described 48 chromosomes for this species, although he commented on the poor quality of the figures examined. From the testicular material, he described the sex chromosomes as a large, rod-shaped X and a small, ball-shaped Y. Painter's findings later led Shiwago (1939), who counted only 42 chromosomes in cells from two animals, to ascribe the difference to possible subspecific differences in diploid number. Since then, however, only 42 have been found by a number of workers. Darlington and Haque (1955) found this number in testicular mitoses from one male. Chu and Giles (1957) exam-

---

[4] Since this chapter was written, Benirschke and his collaborators [Benirschke, K., Anderson, J. M., and Brownhill, L. E. (1962) Marrow chimerism in marmosets. *Science* **138**, 513-515, and personal communication] have studied the chromosomes of five additional species of marmosets by means of the bone marrow technique. *Callithrix jacchus, Leontocebus rosalia, L. nigricollis,* and *L. oedipus* were all found to have a diploid number (2n) of 46. The karyotypes appear very similar to those of *Callithrix chrysoleucos* and *Leontocebus illigeri* shown in Fig. 11, with 10-12 acrocentric, four small metacentric, and 28-30 subterminal chromosomes, and with a fairly large subterminal X chromosome. The Y chromosome, however, is reported to be quite different in these species. *Callithrix jacchus* has an extremely tiny acrocentric Y, while *Leontocebus nigricollis* has a small acrocentric Y; *L. rosalia* and *L. oedipus* have small metacentric Y chromosomes like those of *Callithrix chrysoleucos* and *Leontocebus illigeri*. It would thus appear that a metacentric Y chromosome is not a distinguishing feature of the Callithricidae. The karyotype of *Callithrix pygmaea* is of particular interest. The diploid number for this species appears to be 44, and the difference in number can be accounted for by assuming that two pairs of acrocentric chromosomes have been converted into one pair of metacentrics by the mechanism of centric fusion. The karyotype, which shows a small acrocentric Y and a moderately large subterminal X chromosome, is otherwise very similar to the other marmoset karyotypes. The obvious close relationship between the karyotypes of the various species of marmosets studied, together with the apparent example of centric fusion make the marmosets appear a particularly favorable group for the study of chromosome evolution in primates.

TABLE III

CHROMOSOME NUMBERS AND TYPES IN THE CATARRHINI

Species	Common name	Number of specimens examined		Chromosomes						Authority
		Male	Female	2n	M	S	A	X	Y	
Cercopithecidae										
Macaca mulatta	Rhesus monkey	2	2	48				A	A	Painter (1924)
M. mulatta		2	2	42						Shiwago (1939)
M. mulatta		1		42						Darlington and Haque (1955)
M. mulatta		3	1	42	[18	22][a]	0	M	M	Chu and Giles (1957)
M. mulatta		....[b]		42	18	22	0	M	A	Rothfels and Siminovitch (1958)
M. mulatta		....[b]		42						Chiarelli (1961a)
M. irus	Cynomolgus macaque	1		42	[18	22][a]	0	[M	M][a]	Chu and Bender (1961)
M. irus		....[b]		42						Chiarelli (1961a)
M. nemestrina	Pig-tailed macaque	1		42						Darlington and Haque (1955)
M. cyclopis	Formosan macaque	1		42						Makino (1952)
M. sylvana	Barbary ape	....[b]		42						Chiarelli (1961a)
M. assamensis	Assamese macaque	....[b]		42						
M. fuscata	Japanese macaque	....[b]		[42][a]						
M. silenus	Lion-tailed macaque	....[b]		42						
Papio sphinx	Mandrill	1		42			0			Bender and Mettler (1958)
P. sphinx		....[b]		42						Chiarelli (1961a)
P. leucophaeus	Drill		1	42			0			This report
P. leucophaeus		....[b]		42						Chiarelli (1961a)
P. doguera	Olive baboon	2		42						Chu and Giles (1957)

TABLE III (Continued)

Species	Common name	Number of specimens examined		Chromosomes						Authority
		Male	Fe-male	2n	M	S	A	X	Y	
Cercopithecidae (con't.)										
P. doguera		1	1	42	20	20	0	M	M	This report
P. papio	Guinea baboon	1	1	42	20	20	0	M	M	Darlington and Haque (1955)
P. papio		1		42	[20	20][a]	0	M	M	Chu and Giles (1957)
P. cynocephalus			......[b]	42						Chiarelli (1961a)
P. hamadryas	Hamadryas baboon		......[b]	42						
Theropithecus gelada	Gelada baboon		......[b]	42						Chiarelli (1961a)
Cercocebus albigena	Gray-cheeked mangabey	1		[42][a]						Tappen (1960)
C. aterrimus	Black mangabey		......[b]	[42][a]						Chiarelli (1961a)
C. galeritus	Crested mangabey	1		[42][a]						Tappen (1960)
C. galeritus			......[b]	42						Chiarelli (1961a)
C. torquatus	—		......[b]	42						
C. torquatus torquatus	Sooty mangabey	1		42			0			Bender and Mettler (1958)
C. torquatus lunulatus	White-crowned mangabey	2		42				S	M	Chu and Giles (1957)
Cercopithecus aethiops	—	2		60	18	34	6	S	M	This report
C. aethiops			......[b]	60						Chiarelli (1961a)

TABLE III (*Continued*)

Species	Common name	Number of specimens examined Male	Fe- male	Chromosomes 2n	M	S	A	X	Y	Authority
Cercopithecidae (*con't.*)										
C. aethiops sabaeus	Green monkey	1		60				S	M	Chu and Giles (1957)
C. tantalus	White monkey	2	1	60				S	M	Chu and Giles (1957)
C. diana roloway	Diana monkey	1	1	60						
C. l'hoesti	l'Hoest's guenon	1		72	[28	24	18]a	M	M	Chu and Bender (1961)
C. nigroviridis	—	.....b		60						Chiarelli (1961a)
C. mitis	Diadem guenon	1	2	72	28	24	18	M	M	This report
C. mitis		.....b		66						Chiarelli (1961a)
C. mona mona	Mona guenon	1	1	66						Bender and Mettler (1958)
C. mona mona		1	4	66	28	24	12	M	M	This report
C. mona campbelli	Campbell's guenon		2	66				–	–	Chu and Giles (1957)
C. mona denti				[66]a						
C. neglectus	De Brassa's guenon	1		[60]a						Tappen (1960)
C. nictitans buttikoferi	White- or spot-nosed guenon	1	3	66	[28	24]a	12	M	M	Chu and Giles (1957)
C. cephus	Moustached guenon	.....b		[54]a						Chiarelli (1961a)
Erythrocebus patas	Patas monkey	1	3	54	[18	24]a	10	S	M	Chu and Giles (1957)
E. patas		.....b		54						Chiarelli (1961a)
Presbytis entellus	Langur	1		50		14		M	A	Makino (1952)
Colobus [polykomos]	Colobus monkey	1		44	28	14	0	M	A	This report
Hylobatinae										
Symphalangus syndactylus	Siamang	.....b		[38]a						Chiarelli (1961a)
S. syndactylus		1		50						This report

TABLE III (Continued)

Species	Common name	Number of specimens examined		Chromosomes						Authority
		Male	Female	2n	M	S	A	X	Y	
Hylobatinae (con't.)										
Hylobates lar	White-handed gibbon	1		44	38	6	0	–	–	This report
H. lar		.....b		44	38	6	0			Chiarelli (1961a)
H. hoolock	Hoolock gibbon	1		44	38	6	0	–	–	Chu and Bender (1961)
H. hoolock		.....b		44						} Chiarelli (1961a)
H. agilis	—	.....b		44						
Ponginae										
Pongo pygmaeus	Orangutan	1	1	48	10	18	18	M	A	Chiarelli (1961b)
Pan troglodytes	Northern chimpanzee	1	1	48					M]a	Yeager et al. (1940)
P. troglodytes		7	2	48				[M		Young et al. (1960)
P. troglodytes			5	48	38	10	0	–	–	Chu and Bender (1961)
P. troglodytes		2		48	36	10	0	M	M	This report
Gorilla gorilla	Gorilla	1	1	48	30	[8	8]a	M	M	Hamerton et al. (1961)
Hominidae										
Homo sapiens	Man	Several hundred		46	16	18	10	M [S]	A	See Human Chromosomes Study Group (1960)

a Data in brackets are tentative.
b The number of animals examined is not stated.

ined kidney cultures from four more animals. They found that there were no acrocentric chromosomes in the complement, and that there was a small pair of chromosomes with a prominent secondary constriction, now seen to be characteristic of at least the cercopithecine members of the family. The X was found to be a fairly long metacentric chromosome, while the Y was very small, and also metacentric. Rothfels and Siminovitch (1958) made an extensive and detailed analysis of the karyotype of M. mulatta. Kidney cultures from both male and female animals were examined. The karyotype is similar to that found by Chu and Giles except that the Y chromosome was found to be an acrocentric. Rothfels and Siminovitch also found polymorphism for two pairs of chromosomes, the X and a very short metacentric. In both cases, the lengths of the alternative chromosomes were the same, but the interarm ratios were different. These authors also noted that a small secondary constriction was consistently present in the long arm of the longest chromosome.

The chromosomes of several other species of Macaca have been examined. All had 42 chromosomes. The karyotype of a male Macaca irus is probably the same as that of M. mulatta (Chu and Bender, 1961). A count of $2n = 42$ was made on spermatogonial metaphases from M. nemestrina by Darlington and Haque (1955). Makino (1952) counted 42 chromosomes in spermatogonia from a specimen of M. cyclopis. Chiarelli (1961a) has found 42 chromosomes in specimens of M. sylvana, M. assamensis, M. fuscata, and M. silenus.

The chromosomes of four species in the genus Papio have been studied by means of skin and kidney cultures and, in one case, spermatogonial mitoses. The mandrill, Papio sphinx, and the drill, P. leucophaeus, both have a diploid number of 42 [Bender and Mettler, unpublished; the present report; and Chiarelli (1961a)]. No karyotype information is available. Papio doguera and P. papio also have 42 chromosomes (Darlington and Haque, 1955; Chu and Giles, 1957; and the present report). Both species appear to have the same karyotype, which differs from that of Macaca in that more of the chromosomes are metacentric, and the X is subterminal in the baboons (Chu and Giles, 1957). The Y is metacentric and ranks fourth smallest in the complement. A karyotype is shown in Fig. 12. Both P. cynocephalus and P. hamadryas also have 42 chromosomes (Chiarelli, 1961a). No karyotype information is available.

The Gelada baboon, Theropithecus gelada, has also been studied by Chiarelli (1961a), and found to have a chromosome number of $2n = 42$.

A number of species and subspecies of mangabeys have been studied.

Tappen (1960) made tentative counts of $2n = 42$ for both *Cercocebus albigena* and *C. galeritus*, while Chiarelli (1961a) has made a count of $2n = 42$ for *C. galeritus* and a tentative count of $2n = 42$ for *C. aterrimus*. Tissue cultures of both skin and kidney from *C. torquatus torquatus* and *C. torquatus lunulatus* also show 42 chromosomes (Bender and Mettler, 1958; Chu and Giles, 1957; Chiarelli, 1961a) of which none are acrocentric. The X is a medium-sized subterminal and the Y is a small metacentric.

A number of species in the genus *Cercopithecus* have been investigated from skin and kidney cultures. The genus is particularly interesting because at least three different numbers and karyotypes occur (Chu and Giles, 1957; Chu and Bender, 1961). One group, including *C. aethiops, C. diana*, and *C. neglectus* has a diploid number of 60. *Cercopithecus mona*, including its subspecies *mona, campbelli*, and one tentatively identified as *denti* (Tappen, 1960), and the species *Cercopithecus nictitans buttikoferi* have 66 chromosomes. *Cercopithecus l'hoesti* and *C. mitis* both have 72 chromosomes, the highest diploid number recorded for a primate. In addition, *C. cephus* may have a number as low as $2n = 54$ (Chiarelli, 1961a). The groups differ markedly in karyotype. Although complete karyotype information is not available for the genus, it is clear that there is a regular difference between the three groups. The 60-chromosome species have 6 acrocentrics, the 66-chromosome species have 12 acrocentrics, and the 72-chromosome species have 18 acrocentrics, so far as is known. Typical karyotypes appear in Fig. 12.

Erythrocebus patas was studied by Chu and Giles (1957) and more recently by Chiarelli (1961a). They found that kidney cultures have a diploid number of 54, and that the karyotype included 10 acrocentrics. The X is a subterminal of moderate length, and the Y is the usual small metacentric.

Only two animals in the subfamily Colobinae have been studied. Makino (1952) reported that spermatogonial metaphases of the langur, *Presbytis entellus*, had a diploid number of 50. Recently we studied skin cultures from a specimen of *Colobus*, probably *C. polykomos*, and found that the diploid number is 44. The karyotype of this animal appears in Fig. 12.

A number of species of Hylobatinae have been investigated. *Symphalangus syndactylus* has been examined by Chiarelli (1961a) who made a tentative count of $2n = 38$. More recently, we have examined another specimen and found that $2n = 50$. Cultures of *Hylobates agilis, H. lar*, and *H. hoolock* all have a diploid number of $2n = 44$ (Chu and Bender, 1961; Chiarelli, 1961a; and this report). The karyotypes of *H. lar* and

H. hoolock are identical, with no acrocentric chromosomes. One small pair of metacentrics bears a secondary constriction reminiscent of that typical of the Cercopithecidae. A karyotype appears in Fig. 12. Unfortunately, since all of our specimens were females, we still know nothing about the sex chromosomes.

Papio doguera, ♀   10 μ   [X X]

Cercopithecus aethiops, ♂   X Y

Cercopithecus mona, ♂   X Y

Cercopithecus mitis, ♂   X Y

Colobus [*polykomos*] ♂   X Y

Fig. 12. Representative karyotypes of Catarrhini.

The chromosomes of all the great apes have been studied, and at least the diploid number has been determined. The chimpanzee was first studied by Yeager *et al.* (1940), who obtained counts of $2n = 48$ from spermatogonial metaphases from one specimen of *Pan troglodytes.* Using the bone marrow technique, Young *et al.* (1960) studied nine animals and confirmed this number. They tentatively identified the X as a moderately large metacentric and the Y as a small metacentric. We have studied material from five females using kidney cultures (Chu and Bender, 1961), and two males, using skin cultures. Again the number $2n = 48$ was found; the X and Y were both metacentric. A karyotype is shown in Fig. 12.

The orangutan, *Pongo pygmaeus,* recently was studied by Chiarelli (1961b). A diploid number of $2n = 48$ was found. From one male and one female specimen, this species was found to have a medium-sized, metacentric X chromosome and a very small acrocentric Y chromosome. The Y appears to have a large achromatic zone.

Hamerton *et al.* (1961) have examined the chromosomes of the gorilla, and again the number $2n = 48$ was found. Peripheral blood cells from a male and cultured skin cells from a female were used. The X chromosome is metacentric and is the largest in the complement. The Y chromosome is also metacentric but one of the smallest in the complement.

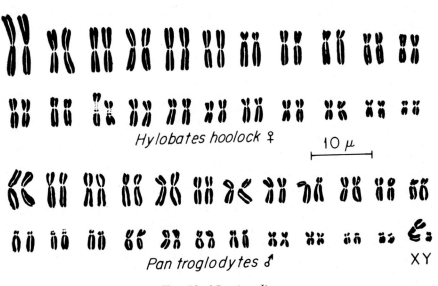

Hylobates hoolock ♀ 10 μ

Pan troglodytes ♂ XY

Fig. 12. (*Continued*)

The chromosomes of many hundreds of humans have been examined since Tjio and Levan (1956) first showed that the diploid number was 46 and not 48, as had been supposed. Although Kodani (1958) found 47 and 48 chromosomes in testicular material from a number of Japanese and one Caucasian, the fundamental diploid number of man is firmly established as 46. Human karyotypes were published by Tjio and Puck (1958) and by Chu and Giles (1959), and a recent conference established a proposed standard nomenclature for the human chromosomes (Human Chromosomes Study Group, 1960). A normal human karyotype is presented in Fig. 8. The X is a fairly large chromosome on the borderline between metacentric and subterminal, and the Y is a small acrocentric. There are five pairs of acrocentric chromosomes, two very small and three somewhat larger. All these acrocentrics bear small satellites on their short arms (Ferguson-Smith and Handmaker, 1961; cf. Fig. 8). A great number of abnormal human karyotypes have been described; since these usually accompany some clinical disorder, they will not be discussed here.

IV. PRIMATE CHROMOSOME EVOLUTION

A. MECHANICS OF CHROMOSOME EVOLUTION

There are a number of ways in which a karyotype can change. The chromosomes may change in form, their number may change, or both events may happen simultaneously. The last is, in fact, quite frequent, because changes in number are usually the direct result of changes in form. A chromosome may change in form in a number of ways. All involve at least one break in the continuity of the chromosome. Such breaks are known to occur spontaneously with a very low, but measurable, frequency. Many of the rearrangements that are important in chromosome evolution require at least two breaks in the same cell at the same time. This is an extremely infrequent occurrence, since the probability of getting two breaks is the square of the probability, already low, of getting one break. Infrequent as these breakage events are, however, their probability in a population over a period of many generations is high enough to account for the chromosome evolution that is observed. Chromosome breakage, of course, is only part of the story. Rearrangement of the broken pieces is also necessary. Frequently, the breaks in chromosomes "heal," returning the chromosome to its original configuration, and leading to no change in the karyotype. Sometimes, however, the broken ends reunite in new configurations to produce new chromosome types. In spite of their infrequent occurrence, these rearrangements are the raw material for karyotype evolution.

Because karyotype evolution must occur in a regular, predictable way, according to the mechanics of chromosome rearrangement, we shall consider chromosome aberrations in a little more detail.

If a chromosome is broken in only one place, the broken ends may reunite with breaks in the same or another chromosome. If they do not, a deletion of a portion of the chromosome may result, because the portion not attached to the centromere does not move to the pole at anaphase, and is thus not included in the daughter nucleus. Figure 13a shows this process. Such a deletion of a portion of a chromosome, if it persisted in the population, could become homozygous and thus represent a change in the karyotype. This must be a rare occurrence, however, for if the deleted portion were of any length, it would probably carry genes without which the animal could not survive.

If more than one chromosome break is present, an exchange of portions of chromosomes can take place. If the breaks are in different chromosomes, this exchange is known as reciprocal translocation. If the exchange is asymmetrical, as shown in Fig. 13b, a dicentric chromosome results. Since dicentric chromosomes can form bridges at anaphase they are unlikely to persist for long, and apparently never become fixed in the karyotype of a population. If the exchange is symmetrical, however, as shown in Fig. 13c, the resulting new chromosomes segregate normally at anaphase, and can persist in the population. The new chromosomes will not be detectable, however, unless the chromosome pieces exchanged are of unequal length. An extreme form of unequal exchange, known as "fusion," can also result in a change in chromosome number. This type will be discussed in the following paragraphs.

If more than one break is present in the same chromosome, the breaks can reunite to change its form. If the ends adjacent to the centromere rejoin, a ring chromosome and one or more fragments are produced (Fig. 13d). A twist in the chromatids before reunion could lead to interlocking of the two ring-shaped chromatids, and failure of the rings to separate at anaphase. A single somatic crossover within a ring would also lead to failure to separate, because a long dicentric ring would result. In any case, ring chromosomes have never been found as part of a normal karyotype. If the broken ends adjacent to the centromere reunite, not with each other, but with the broken-off ends of the chromosome, a stable configuration known as an inversion results. If the inversion includes the centromere (pericentric inversion) the centromere position will be shifted by an amount governed by the relative lengths of the arms between the breaks and the centromere. Figure 13e shows this process converting an acrocentric into a metacentric.

As previously mentioned, there is a class of symmetrical translocation that can lead to a reduction in chromosome number by what is termed "fusion." In this case, the translocation involves an acrocentric chromosome, which is broken very close to the centromere. The other

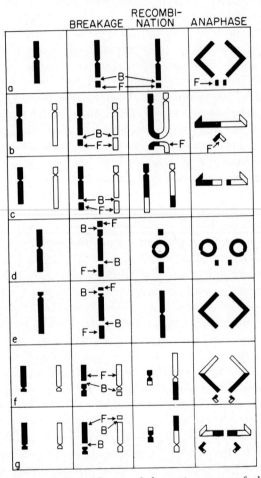

FIG. 13. Diagrams of the mechanics of the various types of chromosome aberrations discussed in the text, and how they contribute to chromosome evolution. a, simple deletion; b, asymmetrical translocation; c, symmetrical translocation; d, ring formation; e, pericentric inversion; f, centric fusion; g, tandem fusion. B, break; F, fragment.

chromosome may or may not be acrocentric. When reunion takes place (Figs. 13f and 13g) a longer chromosome and a very much smaller chromosome result. If the small chromosome has practically no genetic material on its new short arm, it can be lost with no ill effect on the species. If, as shown in Fig. 13f, the translocation takes place between two acrocentrics, with the breaks near the centromere, and one of the breaks is either in the centromere region or in the short arm of one acrocentric and the other break is in the long arm of the other, the type of symmetrical translocation known as "centric fusion" results. Centric fusion leads to the production of a metacentric or subterminal chromosome and a very small chromosome. If the latter is lost, the chromosome number is reduced by one. If, as shown in Fig. 13g, only one of the breaks occurs near the centromere, and the other near the tip of the chromosome, the process known as tandem fusion can result. The second chromosome in this case may be any type, and the new chromosome may be any type.

There are several ways in which a chromosome complement can increase in number. One mechanism is polyploidy, in which one or more whole haploid sets of chromosomes is gained, possibly through failure of reduction at meiosis or failure of mitotic cytokinesis. In higher animals, where a chromosomal sex-determining mechanism is well established, polyploidy would probably lead to infertility and would thus be lost from the population. Single chromosomes can be gained through nondisjunction. This phenomenon, known as trisomy, has been demonstrated for several different chromosomes in the human complement. While the known trisomic conditions are deleterious in man, there is no reason to suppose that they must always be so. Indeed, the clinical symptoms are just what has led to the discovery of the known trisomic conditions in man. Other cases without clinical symptoms doubtless remain undetected. At least in one instance trisomy for chromosome 19 in man shows no detectable phenotypic effect (Fraccaro *et al.*, 1960). Both polyploidy and trisomy lead to an increase in the total amount of genetic material in the karyotype. Another mechanism exists which can lead to an increase in chromosome number without any gain in genetic material. In this mechanism, called centromeric misdivision, a centromere splits crosswise in relation to the chromosome at meiosis instead of splitting lengthwise. The chromosome thus is broken into two new ones, each having a functional centromere. Both of the new chromosomes will, of course, be metacentric.

Invoking the mechanisms just discussed, we can account for all of the differences in karyotypes we observe in the Primates. Since the mechanisms are regular and follow certain mechanical laws, we can frequently trace the probable course of chromosome evolution in the Primates.

It must be remembered, however, that although the mechanisms we have described can provide the raw material for karyotype evolution, they will not account for changes in the karyotype of a species. Karyotypic alterations, occurring in individuals, can only affect the individual, and in order to affect the species, selection must operate to perpetuate and fix the alteration in the population. If the newly created karyotype is advantageous of itself, or is closely associated with some advantageous mutation, it will quite possibly become the karyotype of a group of animals, and perhaps eventually of a new species. If, on the other hand, the new karyotype is disadvantageous, it is likely to be lost from the population. New karyotypes unassociated with any selective advantage or disadvantage may be either lost or preserved depending on chance. Thus, as with other morphological characters, karyotype evolution is merely the visible evidence of the selection of advantageous genotypes.

B. Evidence of Chromosome Evolution

We have seen that a very large variety of chromosome numbers has already been found in the Primates. We have also seen that even in cases where different groups have the same chromosome number, there are striking differences in the form of the chromosomes. Thus no one, seeing the chromosomes of man and of the ruffed lemur, which both have 46 chromosomes, would be tempted to come to the conclusion that they were very closely related. On the other hand, one cannot help but be struck by the similarity of the karyotypes of animals within certain groups of primates.

The definitely established primate chromosome numbers vary from a low of $2n = 34$ to a high of $2n = 72$. The distribution of numbers is such that the only common denominator is two. This fact would seem to rule out polyploidy as a mechanism of chromosome evolution in primates. In the family Cercopithecidae, however, the fact that all five numbers are multiples of six (42, 54, 60, 66, and 72) has led to a consideration of polyploidy as a mechanism in this family. There are several arguments against this interpretation. In the first place, as previously mentioned, it is hard to understand how the sex-determining mechanism of a polyploid primate would operate. In the second place, each of the species of Cercopithecidae studied has one pair of chromosomes marked with a secondary constriction. If any of the species had arisen as a polyploid, different numbers of constricted chromosomes would be expected. Finally, spectrophotometric measurements have been made of the deoxyribonucleic acid (DNA) content of cells from *Macaca mulatta* ($2n = 42$), *Erythrocebus patas* ($2n = 54$), and *Cercopithecus aethiops* ($2n = 60$) (Kleinfeld and Chu, 1958). If polyploidy were responsible for the differences in chromosome number, species with higher chromosome numbers would be expected to show increased DNA contents. The measurements show, however, that despite the differences in chromosome number all species have essentially the same DNA content.

It seems likely, then, that the differences in the numbers of chromosomes among primates have been caused by alterations in the chromosomes of a basic set. Either larger, or more probably, smaller chromosome numbers could have arisen with very little gain or loss of chromosomal material. There are a number of reasons to suppose that chromosome numbers in the Primates have evolved from the higher to the lower. As we mentioned earlier, there are a number of ways in which chromosome numbers can be reduced, but only a few in which they can be increased. Further, there is some evidence from other groups of animals that this reduction is the usual course of evolution. Patterson and Stone (1952), who discussed chromosome evolution in the fruit fly, *Drosophila*, found that the most primitive species have a high number of acrocentric chromosomes, while the more specialized species have fewer chromosomes, most of which are metacentric or subterminal. Centric fusions can account for most of the differences in chromosome number in the genus. Such a fusion mechanism has been seen in a number of other groups of animals. Among the invertebrates, centric fusion has been studied in grasshoppers by White (1954) and in snails by Staiger (1954). Among the vertebrates, Makino (1943) has found that the domestic sheep has 54 chromosomes, while the goat has 60 chromosomes. In the goat all of the chromosomes are acrocentric, while in the sheep 6 are metacentric. Makino suggested that 12 of the acrocentrics of the goat correspond to the 6 metacentrics of the sheep. A similar pattern has also been observed in a number of rodents. Matthey (1957) has studied the subfamily Microtinae extensively. Similar studies have been made on shrews by Ford *et al.* (1957) and on gerbils by Wahrman and Zahavi (1958).

The karyotypes of many groups of primates studied show a remarkable correlation between low chromosome numbers and low numbers of acrocentric chromosomes and between high chromosome numbers and high numbers of acrocentrics. As has been pointed out before (Matthey, 1955b; Bender and Mettler, 1958), these correlations suggest that centric fusion has played an important role in the chromosome evolution of the Primates. In considering the importance of this mechanism, we must remember that it is only in particularly favorable circumstances that the evidence for fusion is preserved. In many cases fusion of the tandem type can be expected to yield new acrocentrics from the ancestral acrocentrics. Also, processes such as pericentric inversion or symmetrical translocation can be expected to obscure the record of fusion by changing the form of the newly produced chromosomes. If there is any particular advantage in a certain chromosome form, such processes can be expected to quickly convert the new chromosome type back into the old one. The evidence for a fusion is thus lost. In view of these mechanisms, which may operate to obscure the pattern of fusion, it is surprising that as much evidence as we can now see has persisted.

In the Lemuriformes, the highest chromosome number is 66 for *Microcebus murinus*, and all of the chromosomes are acrocentric. Three species with 60 chromosomes, *Lemur mongoz, L. fulvus rufus,* and *L. fulvus albifrons,* all have 4 nonacrocentric chromosomes. As the chromosome number drops, fewer and fewer acrocentrics, relative to the total number of chromosomes, are found. Thus, *Hapalemur griseus olivaceous* has 6 nonacrocentrics out of 58 chromosomes, *Lemur catta* has 10 out of 56, *Hapalemur griseus griseus* has 10 out of 54, *Lemur fulvus fulvus* has 16 out of 48, and *L. macaco* has 20 out of 44. The new subspecies of *L. fulvus* has 52 chromosomes, of which 12 are nonacrocentric. *Lemur variegatus* has 18 nonacrocentrics out of a total of 46 chromosomes. The last two species, both with low numbers for the group, are also distinguished by the fact that their X chromosomes are metacentric while the sex chromosomes of all of the other lemurs are acrocentric.

In the Galaginae, where only two numbers have been seen, *Galago crassicaudatus* has only 7 nonacrocentrics (counting the X chromosome) out of a total of 62 chromosomes. *Galago senegalensis,* on the other hand, has only 38 chromosomes of which all but 7 are either metacentric or subterminal. A striking feature of the karyotype of *G. senegalensis* and also of some of the lemurs is the presence of microchromosomes in the complement. One is led to wonder if some of them might not be the small chromosomes resulting from recent fusions, and if they might not be in the process of being lost from the species.

In the Platyrrhini a similar relation between chromosome number and the number of acrocentrics has been observed. Thus, in *Cebus,* with 54 chromosomes, all but 26 are acrocentric, including the X and the Y chromosomes. At the other extreme is *Ateles* with only 34 chromosomes, of which only one pair plus the Y chromosome are acrocentric. In between, *Callimico* has 48 chromosomes, of which 16 are acrocentric; and of a number of genera with 46 chromosomes, *Alouatta* has 15 acrocentrics, *Callicebus* has 25, and *Callithrix* and *Leontocebus* both have 30. *Saimiri* with 44 chromosomes has only 13 acrocentrics. The marmosets *Callithrix* and *Leontocebus* both have metacentric Y chromosomes. If *Alouatta* also has a metacentric Y chromosome, as it seems

to, then one of the most striking differences pointed out between Callithricidae and the Cebidae (Bender and Mettler, 1960) will no longer
exist. This point, as well as whether or not *Callimico* has a metacentric
Y chromosome, can only be settled by the examination of more animals.

There are very few acrocentrics in the Catarrhini. In the genus
Cercopithecus, the species *Cercopithecus aethiops* and *C. diana*, which
have 60 chromosomes, have 6 acrocentrics. The 66-chromosome species
C. mona has 12 acrocentrics, and the 72-chromosome species *C. l'hoesti*
and *C. mitis* have 18 acrocentrics. It is tempting to speculate that 6
of the acrocentrics in the 66-chromosome species and 12 of the acrocentrics in the 72-chromosome species are represented by metacentrics
in the 60-chromosome species. Only one other genus in the Cercopithecidae is known to have acrocentric chromosomes. Of the 54 chromosomes of *Erythrocebus*, 10 are acrocentric. It should be noted, however,
that although Chu and Giles (1957) found no acrocentrics in *Macaca
mulatta*, Rothfels and Siminovitch (1958) found that this species had
an acrocentric Y chromosome.

Of the Hominoidea studied so far, all have some acrocentric chromosomes. In the human karyotype there are three medium-sized and
two small pairs of acrocentric chromosomes, not counting the Y. The
chimpanzee, however, has only three moderate-sized pairs, while the
gorilla has six pairs of medium length and two small pairs, and, according to Chiarelli (1961b), the orangutan has one long pair and eight pairs
of medium-sized acrocentric chromosomes. The Y chromosome is acrocentric in the orangutan, as it is in man, but the chimpanzee and the
gorilla appear to have a metacentric Y. Thus in these respects, as well
as others, there are no striking similarities between the karyotypes of
man and those of the anthropoid apes, although the greatest over-all
similarity appears between man and the gorilla. In man, the discovery
of an example of centric fusion with no abnormal phenotypic expression
(Moorhead *et al.*, 1961) lends weight to the centric fusion hypothesis
of chromosome evolution.

As pointed out by Matthey (1955b), the "nombre fondamental" or
N.F. is a valuable parameter for the study of chromosome evolution.
This value, which is simply the number of major chromosome arms
in the karyotype of a species, is more significant than chromosome number alone. The N.F. for the three major groups of the Primates is
surprisingly uniform. For example, those species of Prosimii whose
karyotypes have been determined range from 62 to 70. The range of
N.F. for the Platyrrhini is 66 to 82, and that of the Catarrhini is 84
to 132. The higher range for the Catarrhini is probably just a reflection
of the rarity of acrocentric chromosomes in the group, and our conse-

quent inability to correctly determine "major" arms. If allowance is made for this factor, the N.F. values are remarkably similar. This uniformity further supports the suggestion that centric fusion has played a major role in primate chromosome evolution.

In the Cebidae, and perhaps in other groups as well, the animals with higher chromosome numbers seem to be those which are the least specialized, such as the genus *Cebus*. Conversely, animals with lower chromosome numbers, *Ateles*, for example, are highly specialized. Although the correlation is by no means perfect, it suggests that a low chromosome number might be an advantage to a highly specialized animal. Such an animal is restricted to a very narrow ecological niche, and even a small deviation from the norm of form or behavior, which might be tolerated in a less specialized animal, could be lethal in a specialized species. A low chromosome number would create blocks of genes that would tend to segregate together at meiosis, and thus reduce the chance of serious deviation in the offspring. If the species' adaptation were strict enough, this factor could lead to a significant increase in the number of offspring that survived and contributed to the next generation.

As a general rule, more specialized forms have probably evolved from more generalized ancestral forms. Although it is obvious that none of the existing primates can be ancestral to any of the others, it is also true that some of the existing forms are much nearer to the ancestral forms in all of their characteristics, including their karyotypes, than others. The evidence gained from analyses of primate chromosomes suggests that the chromosome numbers of these forms tend to be higher than those that are more highly specialized. Conversely, species with a lower number of chromosomes have departed further from the ancestral type. Further, it seems entirely plausible that the more recently evolved species tend to have more acrocentrics left, regardless of chromosome number, than those that evolved first, because the older forms have had more time for inversions and translocations to convert the acrocentrics into other types.

Additional work on primate karyotypes will probably help us to understand more of the details of primate chromosome evolution. For a detailed analysis of the step-by-step changes that have occurred (and are doubtless still occurring), however, the karyotypic method has serious limitations. The main drawback is our inability to tell whether or not a particular chromosome or chromosome arm is homologous with that of another species. In order to determine homology, it is necessary to observe whether the chromosomes or chromosome arms pair with each other during meiosis. For such a study, it will be necessary to cross different species or subspecies, or at least to make use of the accidental hybridizations occurring from time to time in zoos.

Chromosome analysis, even in its present state, can be of great assistance in the classification of primates. In the Prosimii, for example, we have seen that revision of the genus *Lemur* is indicated because of our recently acquired knowledge of the karyotypes of its species and subspecies (Chu and Swomley, 1961a). Similarly, even a limited study of the marmosets and *Callimico* (Bender and Mettler, 1960) has helped to clarify their taxonomy. Fiedler (1956) places the marmosets and tamarins in just two genera. Other taxonomists, such as Hill (1957), have divided the Callithricidae into many genera. The absence of detectable karyotypic difference between *Leontocebus* and *Callithrix* supports Fiedler's view, although more species certainly must be examined before a final conclusion can be drawn. Similarly, the karyotypes of the Callithricidae and of *Callimico* support the view of Hill (1959) that the Callithricidae are a specialized group, and not primitive as has been stated in the past, and that *Callimico* is more primitive and is thus probably much closer to the ancestral ceboid stem.

In conclusion, a considerable amount of knowledge of primate chromosomes has been acquired in the few years during which adequate methods for their study have been available. Although our knowledge of primate chromosome numbers is far from complete, we do have at least some counts from most of the subgroups of primates, and the existing gaps will doubtless be closed in the near future. Our karyotypic knowledge is less complete, but it has already made valuable contributions, both by increasing our understanding of the process of chromosome evolution and by adding to the number of criteria available to the taxonomist for classification. In view of the importance of this subject to the study of evolution in general and human evolution in particular, and also because many of the rarer, unstudied species are in danger of extinction, we can only urge that anthropologists and primatologists will take every opportunity to use the simplified cytological techniques now available, and that progress in that field will be at least as rapid during the next few years as it has been in the past few.

ACKNOWLEDGMENTS

Much of the work described in this chapter was done by the authors under the sponsorship of, or in collaboration with, others. We are particularly indebted to Dr. N. H. Giles, Dr. J. Buettner-Janusch, and Dr. B. A. Swomley of Yale University, Dr. H. B. Glass and Dr. W. L. Straus, Jr., of The Johns Hopkins University, and Dr. L. E. Mettler of North Carolina State College. We are also indebted to the following agencies which supported various parts of the work: The National Science Foundation (Grants G-1760, G-3272, and G-12331), the

United States Atomic Energy Commission [contracts AT(30-1)1908 and AT(30-1)1939] and the United States Public Health Service (for a postdoctoral fellowship). In addition, we gratefully acknowledge the help of a number of animal dealers and zoo directors who either obtained or donated specimens for our studies.

REFERENCES

BENDER, M. A (1960). X-ray-induced chromosome aberrations in mammalian cells *in vivo* and *in vitro*. *In* "Immediate and Low Level Effects of Ionizing Radiation" (A. A. Buzzati-Traverso, ed.), International Journal of Radiation Biology, Supplement, pp. 103-118. London, Taylor and Francis.

BENDER, M. A, AND METTLER, L. E. (1958). Chromosome studies of primates. *Science* 128, 186-190.

BENDER, M. A, AND METTLER, L. E. (1960). Chromosome studies of primates. II. *Callithrix, Leontocebus,* and *Callimico. Cytologia (Tokyo)* 25, 400-404.

BUETTNER-JANUSCH, J., SWOMLEY, B. A., AND CHU, E. H. Y. (1962). Les nombres chromosomiques de certains Lemuriens de Madagascar et les problèmes d'éspeciation. (In preparation.)

CHIARELLI, B. (1958). Tavole chromosomiche dei Primati. *Caryologia* 11, 99-104.

CHIARELLI, B. (1961a). Personal communication.

CHIARELLI, B. (1961b). Chromosomes of the Orang-utan (*Pongo pygmaeus*). *Nature* 192, 285.

CHU, E. H. Y., AND BENDER, M. A (1961). Chromosome cytology and evolution in primates. *Science* 133, 1399-1405.

CHU, E. H. Y., AND GILES, N. H. (1957). A study of primate chromosome complements. *Am. Naturalist* 91, 273-282.

CHU, E. H. Y., AND GILES, N. H. (1959). Human chromosome complements in normal somatic cells in culture. *Am. J. Human Genet.* 11, 63-79.

CHU, E. H. Y., AND SWOMLEY, B. A. (1961a). Chromosomes of lemurine lemurs. *Science* 133, 1925-1926.

CHU, E. H. Y., AND SWOMLEY, B. A. (1961b). Chromosome evolution in the family Lemuridae. (In preparation.)

DARLINGTON, C. D., AND HAQUE, A. (1955). Chromosomes of monkeys and men. *Nature* 175, 32.

DODSON, E. O. (1960). Personal communication.

FERGUSON-SMITH, M. A., AND HANDMAKER, S. D. (1961). Observations on the satellited human chromosomes. *Lancet* i, 638-640.

FIEDLER, W. (1956). Übersicht über das System der Primates. *Primatologia* 1, 1-266.

FORD, C. E., AND HAMERTON, J. L. (1956a). The chromosomes of man. *Nature* 178, 1020-1023.

FORD, C. E., AND HAMERTON, J. L. (1956b). A colchicine, hypotonic citrate, squash sequence for mammalian chromosomes. *Stain Technol.* 31, 247-251.

FORD, C. E., HAMERTON, J. L., AND SHARMAN, G. B. (1957). Chromosome polymorphism in the common shrew. *Nature* 180, 392-393.

FRACCARO, M., KAIJSEN, K., AND LINSTEN, J. (1960). Chromosomal abnormalities in father and mongol child. *Lancet* i, 724-727.

HAMERTON, J. L., FRACCARO, M., DECARLI, L., NUZZO, F., KLINGER, H. P., HULLIGER, L., TAYLOR, A., AND LANG, E. M. (1961). Somatic chromosomes of *Gorilla. Nature* 192, 225-228.

HILL, W. C. O. (1957). "Primates. Comparative Anatomy and Taxonomy," Vol.

III: Pithecoidea, Platyrrhini (families Hapalidae and Callimiconidae). New York, Wiley (Interscience).

HILL, W. C. O. (1959). The anatomy of *Callimico goeldii* (Thomas). *Trans. Am. Phil. Soc.* **49**(5), 1-116.

Hsu, T. C. (1952). Mammalian chromosomes *in vitro*. I. The karyotype of man. *J. Heredity* **43**, 167-172.

HUGHES, A. (1952). Some effects of abnormal tonicity on dividing cells in chick tissue cultures. *Quart. J. Microscop. Sci.* **93**, 207-220.

HUMAN CHROMOSOMES STUDY GROUP (1960). A proposed standard system of nomenclature of human mitotic chromosomes. *Lancet* **i**, 1063-1065.

KLEINFELD, R., AND CHU, E. H. Y. (1958). DNA determinations of kidney cell cultures of three species of monkeys. *Cytologia (Tokyo)* **23**, 452-459.

KODANI, M. (1958). The supernumerary chromosome of man. *Am. J. Human Genet.* **10**, 125-140.

MAKINO, S. (1943). The chromosome complexes in goat (*Capra hircus*) and sheep (*Ovis aries*) and their relationship (chromosome studies in domestic mammals, II). *Cytologia (Tokyo)* **13**, 39-54.

MAKINO, S. (1952). A contribution to the study of the chromosomes in some Asiatic mammals. *Cytologia (Tokyo)* **16**, 288-301.

MAKINO, S., AND NISHIMURA, I. (1952). Water-pretreatment squash technic. *Stain Technol.* **27**, 1-7.

MATTHEY, R. (1955a). Les chromosomes de *Galago senegalensis* Geoffroy (Prosimii-Lorisidae-Galaginae). *Rev. suisse zool.* **62**, Suppl., 190-197.

MATTHEY, R. (1955b). Nouveaux documents sur les chromosomes des Muridae, Problèmes de cytologie comparée et da taxonomie chez les Microtinae. *Rev. suisse zool.* **62**, 163-206.

MATTHEY, R. (1957). Cytologie comparée, systématique et phylogénie des Microtinae (Rodentia-Muridae). *Rev. suisse zool.* **64**, 39-71.

MOORHEAD, P. S., MELLMAN, W. J., AND WENAR, C. (1961). A familial chromosomal translocation associated with speech and mental retardation. *Am. J. Human Genetics* **13**, 32-46.

MOORHEAD, P. S., NOWELL, P. C., MELLMAN, W. J., BATTIPS, D. M., AND HUNGERFORD, D. A. (1960). Chromosome preparations of leukocytes cultured from human peripheral blood. *Exptl. Cell Research* **20**, 613-616.

MORGAN, J. F., MORTON, H. J., AND PARKER, R. C. (1950). Nutrition of animal cells in tissue culture. I. Initial studies on a synthetic medium. *Proc. Soc. Exptl. Biol. Med.* **73**, 1-8.

PAINTER, T. S. (1922). The sex chromosomes of the monkey. *Science* **56**, 286-287.

PAINTER, T. S. (1923). Studies in mammalian spermatogenesis. II. The spermatogenesis of man. *J. Exptl. Zool.* **37**, 291-321.

PAINTER, T. S. (1924). Studies on mammalian spermatogenesis. IV. The sex chromosomes of monkeys. *J. Exptl. Zool.* **39**, 433-464.

PATTERSON, J. T., AND STONE, W. S. (1952). "Evolution in the Genus Drosophila." New York, Macmillan.

PUCK, T. T., CIECIURA, S. J., AND ROBINSON, A. (1958). Genetics of somatic mammalian cells. III. Long-term cultivation of euploid cells from human and animal subjects. *J. Exptl. Med.* **108**, 945-956.

ROTHFELS, K. H., AND SIMINOVITCH, L. (1958). The chromosome complement of the rhesus monkey (*Macaca mulatta*) determined in kidney cells cultured *in vitro*. *Chromosoma* **9**, 163-175.

SHIWAGO, P. I. (1939). Recherches sur le caryotype du *Rhesus macacus*. *Bull. biol. mèd. exptl. U.R.S.S.* **8**, 3-8.

STAIGER, H. (1954). Der Chromosomendimorphismus beim Prosobranchier *Purpura lapillus* in Beziehung zur Ökologie der Art. *Chromosoma* **6**, 419-478.

STERN, C. (1959). The chromosomes of man. *J. Med. Educ.* **34**, 301-314.

TAPPEN, N. (1960). Personal communication.

TJIO, J. H., AND LEVAN, A. (1956). The chromosome number of man. *Hereditas* **42**, 1-6.

TJIO, J. H., AND PUCK, T. T. (1958). The somatic chromosomes of man. *Proc. Natl. Acad. Sci. U.S.* **44**, 1229-1237.

TOBIAS, P. V. (1956). "Chromosomes, Sex Cells, and Evolution in a Mammal; Based Mainly on Studies of the Reproductive Glands of the Gerbil, and a New List of Chromosomes of Mammals." London, Lund, Humphries.

VON WINIWARTER, H. (1912). Etudes sur la spermatogenése humain. I. Cellule de Sertoli. II. Hétérochromosome et mitose de l'épithelium séminale. *Arch. biol. (Liège)* **27**, 91-189.

WAHRMAN, J., AND ZAHAVI, A. (1958). Cytogenetic analysis of mammalian sibling species by means of hybridization. *Proc. 10th Intern. Cong. Genet., Montreal, 1958*, Vol. 2, 304-305 (abstract).

WELSHONS, W. J., GIBSON, B. H., AND SCANDLYN, B. J. (1962). Slide processing for the examination of male mammalian meiotic chromosomes. *Stain Technol.* **37**, 1-5.

WHITE, M. J. D. (1954). "Animal Cytology and Evolution," 2nd ed. London and New York, Cambridge Univ. Press.

YEAGER, C. H., PAINTER, T. S., AND YERKES, R. M. (1940). The chromosomes of the chimpanzee. *Science* **91**, 74-75.

YOUNG, W. J., MERZ, T., FERGUSON-SMITH, M. A., AND JOHNSTON, A. W. (1960). Chromosome number of the chimpanzee, *Pan troglodytes*. *Science* **131**, 1672-1673.

Author Index

Numbers in italics indicate pages on which the complete references are given.

A

Abel, O., 72, 73, 79, 102, *126*
Adey, A., 160, *177*
Allen, G. M., 36, *62*
Anderson, J. M., *289*
Andrew, R. J., 25, *62*
Aoki, T., 184, *196*, 197, 223, 225, 228, 244, *259*
Appleyard, H. M., 190, *195*, 226, *227*
Arey, L. B., 161, *173*
Auber, L., 190, *195*, 226, *227*

B

Bailey, P., 155, *173*
Battips, D. M., 305, *309*
Beadnell, H. J. L., 105, *126*
Bender, M. A., 10, 25, 31, *62*, 276, 277, 278, 279, 281, 282, 283, 284, 285, 288, 290, 291, 292, 293, 294, 295, 297, 303, 305, 307, *308*
Benirschke, K., *289*
Benjamin, R., 156, 159, *173*, *177*
Berman, A., 160, *176*
Bishop, G., 139, *174*
Bohlin, B., 97, *126*
Bolwig, N., 11, 26, *62*
Booth, A. H., 36, *62*
Brindley, G. S., 164, *173*
Brown, G. W., Jr., 198, *227*
Brownhill, L. E., *289*
Bruesch, S. R., 161, *173*
Brunet, P., 188, *195*
Bruni, C., 211, *228*
Buettner-Janusch, J., 8, 9, 30, *62*, 277, *308*
Burstone, M. S., 198, *226*
Burtner, H. J., 198, *227*
Butler, P. M., 123, *126*

C

Carpenter, M. B., 143, *174*
Cauna, N., 233, 255, *258*
Chacko, L. W., 164, 165, 166, 167, 168, 169, *173*

Charles, A., *226*
Chase, H. B., 188, *195*, 198, *227*
Chiarelli, B., 276, 277, 278, 283, 284, 285, 288, 290, 291, 292, 293, 294, 295, 297, 305, *308*
Chiquoine, A. D., 207, *226*
Chow, K. L., 172, *173*
Chow, M., 95, 96, *126*, *129*
Chu, E. H. Y., 10, 25, *62*, 276, 277, 278, 279, 281, 282, 283, 284, 285, 288, 289, 290, 291, 292, 293, 294, 295, 297, 298, 302, 305, 307, *308*, *309*
Cieciura, S. J., 269, *309*
Clark, W. E. LeGros, 3, 4, 12, *62*, 69, 72, 102, 112, 113, 116, *126*, 132, 140, 147, 150, 154, 161, 163, 164, 165, 166, 169, 170, 171, *174*
Coghill, G. E., 144, *174*
Colbert, E. H., 96, 106, *126*
Conel, J. L., 160, *174*
Connolly, C. J., 132, 154, *174*
Cooper, E. R. A., 166, *174*
Count, E. W., 133, 153, *174*
Coventrey, M. B., 233, *259*
Crescitelli, F., 163, *174*
Crosby, E. C., 132, 137, 141, 167, 170, *174*, *175*
Crusafont, M., 116, *129*

D

Darlington, C. D., 289, 290, 291, 294, *308*
Dart, R., 133, 153, *174*
Davis, P. R., 114, *127*
de Beaux, O., 187, *195*
Decarli, L., 293, 297, *308*
De Robertis, E. D. P., 213, *227*
Dodson, E. O., 278, *308*
Dow, R. S., 147, *174*
Dunn, H. L., 149, *174*

E

Edinger, T., 119, *126*, 154, *174*
Ellerman, J. R., 36, *62*

311

Subject Index

A

Aminopeptidase in epidermis, 184
Amphipithecus, status as Primates, 71
Amylophosphorylase in skin, 184, 188, 191, 193, 219
  epidermis, 184
  hair follicles, 188
  sebaceous glands, 191
  sweat glands, 193
  of hands and feet, 219
Antebrachial organs, 11
Apidium, status as Primates, 71
Apocrine sweat glands of Lorisidae, 198-200, 205, 207, 220-226
  compared with brachial glands, 205, 207
    with other species, 224-226
  distribution and concentration of enzymes, 222-223
  similarities and differences within family, 220-221
  structure, 198-200
  vascularity, 200

B

Baldness, 181, 189
  and androgenic hormones, 181, 189
Basal ganglia, composition of, 143
  volume of, 143
Biochemical genetics, 8-9
  hemoglobin, 8-9
  phylogenetic significance, 9
  transferrins, 8
Biochemical traits, 8-9
  relevant to taxonomy and classification, 8-9
Brachial glands, 11, 226
Brachial glands of *Loris tardigradus,* 203-207
  brachial organ, 203
  compared with apocrine sweat glands, 205, 207
  structure, 203
Brachial glands of *Nycticebus coucang,* 207-214

compared with glands of other species, 207-209
  nerves surrounding, 211-214
  structure, 207, 209, 211
Brachiation, 5, 114
  multiple occurrences, 5
  partial brachiator, 114
Brachium conjunctivum, 145
Brachium pontis, 145
Brain size in Eocene Primates, 84

C

Carbohydrates in skin, 199, 200, 201, 203, 205
  brachial glands, 203, 205
  inguinal glands, 201
  sweat glands, 199, 200
Caudate nucleus, 143
Central cortex, 171
  thickness, 171
Cerebellum, 147, 150
  expansion of, 147
  growth, 150
Cerebral cortex, 150-161
  association cortex, 156
  commissure, 156
  corpus callosum, 156
  evolution, 154-155
  expansion of, 155-156
  expansion of volume, 152
  fissuration, 150, 152, 154, 155
  increase in size and weight, 152
  lateral geniculate bodies, 161
  optic chiasma, 161
  optic pathways, 161
  optic radiations, 161
  optic tracts, 161
  pattern of organization, 159
  primary sensory areas, 156
  retinas, 161
Cholinesterases in skin, 186-188, 193, 203, 204, 207, 211, 217, 219-221, 231, 233-234, 235, 237, 241, 243-244, 247, 252, 256-257
  brachial glands, 205, 207, 211

Taxonomic Index

In addition to this taxonomic index, the reader can find a comprehensive taxonomic list of the Primates on pp. 38-57; he can also find a synoptic list, including fossil forms, on pp. 57-62.

A

Absarokius, 74, 81, 87, 89
Adapidae, 86, 88-89, 91
Adapinae, 86
Adapis, 86, 88, 89
Allenopithecus, see *Cercopithecus nigro-*
viridis
Alouatta, 283, 304
Alouatta seniculus, 283
Alsaticopithecus, 87, 91
Alsaticopithecus leemanni, 91
Amphipithecus, 70, 71, 87, 96, 97, 106, 107
Amphipithecus mogaungensis, 96, 106
Anagale, 97, 98
Anagalopsis, 97
Anaptomorphidae, 83, 87, 89-91
Anaptomorphus, 74, 87
Anchomomys, 86, 88
Anemorhysis, 74, 87
Ankarapithecus meteai, 121
Anthropoidea, 25, 31-36, 73, 77, 83, 91, 92, 98, 99, 100, 104, 105, 106, 107, 108, 109
Aotes (= *Nyctipithecus*), 164, 168, 169, 282
Aotes trivirgatus, 282
Apidium, 71, 96, 100, 101, 102, 105, 123
Apidium moustafi, 101
Apidium phiomense, 100, 101
Arctocebus, 26, 27
Artiodactyla, 154
Ateles, 143, 168, 169, 171, 190, 194, 241, 283, 288, 304, 306
Ateles arachnoides (= *Brachyteles*), 288
Ateles ater, 143, 171
Ateles belzebuth, 288
Ateles fusciceps robustus, 241
Ateles geoffroyi, 168, 169, 190, 241, 288
Ateles paniscus chamek, 288
Atelinae, 137

Australopithecus africanus, 124
Austriacopithecus, 115
Avahi, see *Lichanotus*

B

Bettongia, 78
Brachyteles, see *Ateles arachnoides*
Bramapithecus, 116

C

Caenopithecus, 86, 89
Cacajao, 189, 283
Cacajao rubicundus, 189, 283
Callicebus, 283, 304
Callicebus cupreus, 283
Callimico, 288, 304, 305, 307
Callimico goeldii, 288
Callithricidae, 288, 289, 305, 307
Callithrix, 288, 289, 304, 307
Callithrix chrysoleucos, 288, 289
Callithrix jacchus, 288, 289
Callithrix pygmaea, 289
Cantius, 87, 94, 95
Cantius eppsi, 94, 95
Carnivora, 154
Carpodaptes, 77, 78
Carpolestes, 77, 78
Carpolestidae, 77, 78-79
Catarrhini, 106, 289-297, 305
Cebidae, 92, 241-243, 255, 305, 306
Ceboidea, 3, 6, 31, 36, 81, 106, 118
Cebupithecia, 106, 109
Cebupithecia sarmientoi, 109
Cebus, 132, 137, 143, 168, 169, 171, 241, 283, 304, 306
Cebus albifrons, 241
Cebus apella, 283
Cebus capucinus, 283
Cebus fatuellus, 137, 143, 168, 169, 171
Cercocebus albigena, 295
Cercocebus aterimus, 295
Cercocebus galeritus, 295

323